The **Association**
for **Science Educa**

Teaching Secondary
Physics
Third Edition

Series Editor: Chris Harrison
Editors: James de Winter and Mark Hardman

HODDER
EDUCATION
AN HACHETTE UK COMPANY

Titles in this series

Teaching Secondary Biology 978 1 5104 6256 4
Teaching Secondary Chemistry 978 1 5104 6257 1
Teaching Secondary Physics 978 1 5104 6258 8

Photo credits

Figure 2.1 © James de Winter, Figure 3.1 © Rachel Hartley, Figure 3.2 © Peter Fairhurst, Figure 3.9 © Rachel Hartley, Figure 3.13 © Tom Hartley, Figure 3.15 © Rachel Hartley, Figure 3.16 © Peter Fairhurst, Figure 3.19 © Peter Fairhurst, Figure 5.1 © Alan Denton, Figure 5.4 © Alan Denton

Data on pages 234-235 © NASA/CXC/SAO https://chandra.harvard.edu

Acknowledgements

Every effort has been made to trace all copyright holders, but if any have been inadvertently overlooked, the Publishers will be pleased to make the necessary arrangements at the first opportunity.

Although every effort has been made to ensure that website addresses are correct at time of going to press, Hodder Education cannot be held responsible for the content of any website mentioned in this book. It is sometimes possible to find a relocated web page by typing in the address of the home page for a website in the URL window of your browser.

Hachette UK's policy is to use papers that are natural, renewable and recyclable products and made from wood grown in well-managed forests and other controlled sources. The logging and manufacturing processes are expected to conform to the environmental regulations of the country of origin.

Orders: please contact Hachette UK Distribution, Hely Hutchinson Centre, Milton Road, Didcot, Oxfordshire, OX11 7HH. Telephone: +44 (0)1235 827827. Email education@hachette.co.uk Lines are open from 9 a.m. to 5 p.m., Monday to Friday. You can also order through our website: www.hoddereducation.co.uk

ISBN: 978 1 5104 6258 8

© Association for Science Education 2021

First published in 2000.
Second edition published in 2011.

This edition published in 2021 by
Hodder Education,
An Hachette UK Company
Carmelite House
50 Victoria Embankment
London EC4Y 0DZ

www.hoddereducation.co.uk

Impression number   10 9 8 7 6 5 4 3 2 1

Year   2025 2024 2023 2022 2021

Cover photo ©Leigh Prather – stock.adobe.com
Illustrations by Integra Software Services Pvt., Ltd.
Typeset in India by Integra Software Services Pvt., Ltd.
Printed and bound by CPI Group (UK) Ltd, Croydon, CR0 4YY

A catalogue record for this title is available from the British Library.

MIX
Paper from
responsible sources
FSC™ C104740
www.fsc.org

Schools have a *Licence to Copy* one chapter or 5% for teaching ✓

CLA Copyright Licensing Agency

Contents

Contributors

James de Winter decided he wanted to be a physics teacher when he was 14 and while no longer in the school classroom still sees himself in that role. Having gained his PGCE from Cambridge, he taught in Hertfordshire and Suffolk. He works at the Faculty of Education at the University of Cambridge, leading their secondary PGCE physics course. In addition, he teaches on the secondary biology, chemistry and primary PGCE courses, helping to support those who have yet to realise how much joy teaching physics can bring. In 2020 he was the winner of the best lecturer award in the University-wide student-led teaching awards.

James is a member of the Physics Education Research Group at the University of Uppsala, Sweden where he is researching the development of beginning and early career teachers, with a particular focus on the subject-specific aspects of being a physics teacher. He has a long-standing relationship with and commitment to the Ogden Trust and is their national lead for initial teacher education and early career teacher development. A member of ASE since the first day of his training, James supports their work including writing, editing, and running conference sessions. For many years he also worked with STEM Learning, designing and running CPD courses. He works with the IOP in various consultancy and advisory roles.

James has written many books and resources for teachers, teacher educators and students but thinks his book *How to Catapult a Castle* has the best title. His column for the local parish magazine is mainly focused on natural history but he does occasionally sneak physics in. The column he co-writes for the IOP *Classroom Physics* magazine is more cerebral, focusing on physics education research. James' favourite physics lesson ever involves the teaching of sound through birdsong and is available from www.physicsandbirdsong.com.

Mark Hardman is an Associate Professor at the UCL Institute of Education. He taught physics in London before becoming a teacher educator in 2007. Since then he has developed and worked on a range of teacher education programmes across London and nationally, developing undergraduate teacher education programmes and combining university outreach with teacher education to ensure that cutting edge science reaches the classroom. He recently joined the Centre for Teachers and Teaching Research and now focuses on educational research. His primary research interests centre on the processes of learning and draw on cognitive neuroscience, video studies and philosophical perspectives such as complexity theory to frame learning in new ways. He also works with collaborators internationally to better understand how the characteristics of physics as a subject influence teaching and learning. In line with the research centre, Mark also conducts research into the processes of developing as a teacher and the working conditions of teachers in relation to recruitment, retention and professionalism.

Richard Brock is a Lecturer in Science Education at King's College London. After working as a secondary physics teacher, he now lectures on the science PGCE, MA programmes and supervises doctoral students. His research focuses on learning in science education, in particular the nature of scientific understanding and fine-grained models of conceptual change. His work with trainee teachers has spurred an interest in teacher wellbeing and he researches how policy related to teacher wellbeing has been enacted in schools. With the support of the Institute of Physics, he has produced a collection of stories for use in physics teaching.

Carol Davenport is a senior lecturer at Northumbria University and the Director of the NUSTEM outreach group. She is passionate about education and STEM as a way of improving the life chances of young children. Carol has worked in education, as a teacher, teacher educator, and lecturer for 25 years. She started teaching as a physics lecturer in a large further education college, then became a science/physics teacher in the state sector, and later a professional development leader for STEM Learning. Carol is also a governor of a large secondary academy, and a governor at a learning partnership. In her 'spare time' Carol writes textbooks and has recently published a story book for toddlers based on robotic exploration of the solar system.

Alan Denton is a former Head of Science and Physics of a large school in Bury St Edmunds, and he now writes and leads teacher training courses across East Anglia, nationally and internationally. He enjoys working with teachers as a coach for the Institute of Physics and a Senior Facilitator for STEM Learning. As Head of Physics his department consistently increased the uptake of science as well as improved their results, but he is equally proud that he got an Apache helicopter to land in the school field for a physics lesson.

Peter Fairhurst taught physics and science for 28 years in a wide variety of secondary schools in Barnsley, Guyana, Harrogate, Tadcaster and York. He has had leadership roles for special educational needs, physics and KS3 science, and for 15 years led a large school science department. Peter has a passion for developing high quality, research informed, resource materials and schemes of learning, and is now a curriculum specialist in secondary science and a researcher with The University of York Science Education Group. He is the lead physicist for the Best Evidence Science Teaching (BEST) project.

Stuart Farmer is the Scottish Education Manager for the Institute of Physics. Prior to this he taught physics in four secondary schools in Scotland for 35 years, almost all of this time as Principal Teacher of Physics. Throughout his career he has been an active member of the Association for Science Education, including a term as Chair of Trustees, and of the Institute of Physics, including Chair of the Institute in Scotland and a Teacher Network Coordinator. He has extensive experience leading curriculum and assessment development, helping shape education policy, and organising and delivering professional learning for teachers of physics and science. He has a particular interest in researching and improving the career-long professional learning of teachers of physics. In 2016 he was awarded the Bragg Medal from the Institute of Physics for his work promoting and enhancing the teaching of physics.

Rachel Hartley leads the Institute of Physics' Professional Practice Group to develop diverse and inclusive physics education based on evidence from research across the IOP's education programmes and the wider education community. After graduating with a joint honours degree in Chemistry and Physics from King's College London, Rachel began teaching adults GCSE maths while working as a research student. She was hooked and taught in South London for 13 years in a range of schools, gaining extensive experience as a GCSE maths and A-level physics examiner. Rachel played a key role in the IOP's Stimulating Physics programme since its inception in 2007 and based her Masters by Research on impact data from the pilot phase; she continues to put evidence at the heart of her work. Rachel has led CPD programmes in over 50 science departments in Leeds and North Yorkshire along with IOP summer schools for teachers. Rachel is passionate about physics education, making it accessible to all and dispelling the myth that it's too hard!

Judith Hillier has been at the University of Oxford Department of Education since 2007, where she leads the science PGCE programme, teaches on the Masters in Learning and Teaching and the Masters in Teacher Education, and also runs the Teaching Physics in Schools option for 2nd year physics undergraduates. She is Fellow and Vice-President of Kellogg College, Oxford. Prior to that, after completing a degree in Physics at the University of St Andrews and her PhD in condensed matter physics from the University of Leeds and the Institut Laue Langevin, Grenoble, Judith studied on the Oxford PGCE programme and taught for several years in an Oxfordshire comprehensive school, becoming Key Stage 3 Co-ordinator. Judith's research interests lie in the education of science teachers, the recruitment and retention of physics teachers, the role of language in the development of scientific explanations in the classroom, and gender and diversity in STEM education.

Alex Manning spent several years teaching science/physics in inner London secondary schools. She is now a lecturer of Science Education at King's College London, where she completed her PhD, 'Urban science teachers, exploring how their views and experiences can influence decisions to remain in post or not' (2017). Alex contributes to a number of teacher education programmes. In addition to science education, her research areas of interest are teacher wellbeing, teacher experiences, department dynamics and teacher retention.

Tom Norris is a practising physics teacher. He has taught physics to 11–18 year olds in state schools in England since 2010, including 7 years as Head of

Physics at Huntington Research School. During this time Tom has also worked as a Physics Coach for the Institute of Physics, supporting numerous teachers and science departments to develop their practice and curricula. Tom can often be found talking about teaching physics on Twitter using the handle @physicsuk, and he occasionally blogs about aspects of physics and science education. He is currently based in Newcastle upon Tyne.

Charles Tracy is Head of Education at the Institute of Physics. His main interests are in the physics curriculum, teachers' professional learning and building professional communities of teachers. He also advises on education policy, particularly relating to teacher retention and recruitment. He started teaching in Hertfordshire in 1987, where he worked as a physics teacher, Head of Physics, Head of Science and as an adviser. He has also worked as a consultant for the BBC and Channel 4 and has developed educational websites.

Over the years, he has written textbooks, overseen major national CPD projects and been involved in curriculum development. He is particularly interested in how the physics curriculum can be structured to develop rich and lasting ideas about physics and its practices. Among other things, he has spent more than 30 years worrying about the teaching of energy.

Kevin Walsh teaches physics and astronomy at Westminster School, where he is Director of the Westminster China Schools Project. He is an Honorary and Adjunct Professor of Science Education at Shaanxi Normal University in Xi'an, China where he lectures and is currently involved in researching dialogic teaching methods in the Chinese science curriculum and the feasibility of using computer simulations to assess science practical skills.

He is a Fellow of the Institute of Physics and a former member of the editorial board for Physics Education. He is also a Fellow of the Royal Astronomical Society with whom he is involved in a number of outreach projects with various groups including Open Age, the Scouts and Guides Associations and HM Prison Service. He is the editor of the Bulletin of the Society for the History of Astronomy.

Acknowledgements

In writing this book, we have drawn on material from the previous editions from 2000 and 2011. Some chapters have been rewritten and others updated and revised but in all cases the work and thinking of the previous authors have contributed to what is here and we offer our thanks to them all: Bob Kibble, Robin Millar, Jonathan Osborn, David Sang, Robert Strawson and Carol Tear.

We would also like to thank the reviewers of the book: Richard Brock, Euan Douglas, Suzanne Gatt, Nicola Percy, David Rennie and Pete Robinson.

Thanks to Dan Cottle for ideas and input to the Energy chapter and Jackie Flaherty for her suggestions to help improve the Forces chapter.

In addition to their contributions to specific chapters, Charles Tracy and Judith Hiller acted as advisers across the whole book and we offer our thanks to them.

We are particularly grateful to Mary Whitehouse for the thorough, wise and detailed scrutiny that she offered on the individual chapters and to the book as a whole, correcting physics, improving content and helping with consistency. We would also like to thank Marianne Cutler for project management on behalf of ASE and Ralph Whitcher and the ASE's Health & Safety Group.

Finally, as co-editors, we'd like to note the significant contribution that Chris Harrison has made to shape this final book. In addition to being series editor and a science education giant, she was wise counsel, project manager, negotiator and friend. Thanks, Chris.

In memory of Ian de Winter and Dan Shearman

The principles behind secondary physics teaching

Mark Hardman and James de Winter

This book is one of a series of three Association for Science Education (ASE) handbooks, the others being parallel volumes in chemistry and biology. The 1st edition of this book was published in 1999, over 20 years ago, the 2nd edition in 2011, almost a decade ago. This 3rd edition has been substantially revised and brought up to date.

The author team has kept in mind a secondary teacher confronted with the task of teaching a specific topic, for example forces, and the plans and preparation they need to do. What does such a teacher need to produce a series of effective lessons that will also engage learners, and both enhance and sustain their curiosity? Some teachers will approach this task with an excellent understanding of the topic. However, we have kept in mind that not all teachers of secondary physics have a degree in the subject and that, even if they do, very few degrees cover all of secondary physics. We hope that all teachers of secondary physics, even if they have been teaching the subject for some time, will find much of value in here.

In this book, our aim is to encourage and support teachers to use approaches that convey the essential features of physics and the nature of science. This is important so that students learn not just the content of physics, but also what physics is and how it relates to their world. As such, this chapter reflects on the discipline of physics and approaches to teaching that enable students to engage in that discipline and build an identity that connects them to physics. Our hope is that considering the nature of physics, and teaching it, will also support teachers in reflecting on and developing their own identities as teachers of physics, whatever their background.

In the chapters that follow we will look at some of the main topics covered in the study of physics: forces, electricity and magnetism, energy, matter, atomic physics, waves and the Earth in space. In each of these chapters the author team will cover the content that we feel will be useful for a teacher to plan a series of effective lessons in that topic, highlighting specific examples of the ideas and thinking that will help develop and strengthen understanding of physics.

What is physics?

Physics develops and provides deep and satisfying explanations of phenomena; often those explanations will be based on what the world is made of and how those constituents behave. Furthermore, these explanations will be built on consistent and well tested relationships between identified and carefully defined quantities. As a discipline, physics is concerned with the smallest things we can conceive, and the largest, and everything in between; from the behaviour of individual electrons to galaxies containing millions of stars, not to mention the nature of time and even how social networks develop. This is one reason why it is helpful to frame physics around the development of explanations, to provide coherence to all these areas of physics.

The enormous scope of what physics tries to do presents challenges around how to 'see' complex and sometimes abstract ideas. To help, physicists often use models as ways to make particular aspects of what they are studying easier for them and others to conceptualise and communicate. As such, the use of models is a central part of the study and development of physics. Models in physics can have descriptive, explanatory and often predictive power; they are useful abstractions about an aspect of the world that can be elegant and that help us understand how and why phenomena happen. The kinds of models we consider in physics are incredibly diverse: they include simple linguistic analogies that could be spoken or written (such as 'a force is a push or a pull') to more sophisticated narrative explanations such as describing the formation of a star in terms of a balance of gravitational and nuclear forces. Other models include various representations such as schematics, diagrams, animations and graphs, as well as physical and computational models, often involving mathematics. In every case the model will have value for the physicist. For a magnet sitting on a table, we cannot 'see' field lines that come out of it but imagining these helps us describe what would happen if another magnet was brought near it. Equally, when considering the design of an aeroplane wing, a complex computational model of air flow can help optimise the design of the wing shape, so that it will generate the upwards force on the bottom of the wing needed to lift the plane.

Another strength of physics is how models of one phenomenon can be applied to other situations. For example, a model that provides an explanation of waves can be used in considering light, radio communications, earthquakes and waves in the ocean. At an advanced level, waves are also important in understanding electron orbitals and quantum phenomena. Models in physics can go beyond the description of a single phenomenon in one context to the same phenomena in other contexts and sometimes (but not always) different phenomena altogether. Models in physics can have a 'generalisable' nature but we must also recognise the limitations of all models in perfectly describing aspects of the world. Models in physics also have the power to link different scales of analysis, often microscopic and macroscopic. For example, a sub-atomic account of electrons helps us understand the current in a circuit and the phenomenon of electricity, and this can be developed further to include electromagnetism. An explanation of gravitation helps us to understand both why a ball falls to the Earth and how stars are formed.

However, the use of models is only part of the nature of physics as a discipline and it is true that biology and chemistry also use and develop models that link phenomena and scales: think of DNA and phenotypes, or atomic structure and elements. We suggest that it can be problematic to present students with hard distinctions between the traditional school sciences of biology, physics and chemistry, and that this doesn't reflect the work of professional scientists anyway, in which collaboration among specialists is common practice. Physics is frequently described as 'abstract' and this is often given as a reason why some find studying it hard. It is true that physicists attempt to reduce the details of a situation to describe fundamental processes and relationships. This is because physics has been successful in finding a way to describe natural phenomena with a small number of formulae that describe the relationship between physical quantities ('universal laws') and that can be applied in multiple situations.

The way in which mathematical formulae are used in physics is a key aspect of the discipline: relationships and equations are at the heart of many areas of physics. We hope you agree that this in itself is appealing: the elegance of being able to describe aspects of the Universe through simple mathematical relationships. Yet, appreciating the elegance of a mathematical relationship requires linking the mathematics to conceptual understanding; knowing the equation is a far cry from relating it to phenomena in the world and only once the mathematics is given meaning does it become elegant. This also links back to the need for recognising the limitation of models. A mathematical formula might describe a relationship that appears to hold anywhere in the Universe, but bringing this to bear on a particular situation requires an understanding of those particulars, knowing when the model is not sufficient and whether it needs to be refined or superseded by a different one.

It can be easy to see the formulae that students need as a list that just has to be memorised and recalled in an exam. It would be a shame to simply commit these equations to memory rather than use them to develop and strengthen understanding. In many cases they describe how nature works, giving order to the Universe and identifying what causes things to happen. Ohm's law can help us to calculate a current, but knowing that current will flow *because* there is a difference in potential across a conductor is part of conceptual understanding contained in that equation. We can convert mass to weight by multiplying it by 10, but realising that near the surface of the Earth an object will fall *because* its mass is attracted towards the centre of the Earth is more important as this is something that happens with all objects.

In physics, things happen for a reason and events occur as a result of the previous situation. Physicists attempt to break down events in order to understand causal chains, although these can be complex. In this way, physicists are concerned with exploring what has happened and why, often using derived ideas to make further predictions about the future.

In summary, physics provides descriptions and explanations of phenomena and helps scientists make predictions. It does so through models that can take many forms, but are often abstractions which try to get at the mechanisms that link different scales of phenomena, and different phenomena. As well as being beautiful and refined, the power in these models is that they are often generalisable and can be applied to multiple contexts and situations. Many of the fundamental equations of physics provide elegant ways to understand the world on whichever scale you choose to look at it, from the level of an atom to a galaxy.

1.2   Doing physics

Characterising physics as a domain is part of showing young people what role physics may play in their lives and how it can help them understand how the world around them works. Another aspect of this is painting a picture of what it means to do physics. This is not to assume that all students should aspire to become professional physicists, but many careers, hobbies and interests involve 'doing physics'. Watching the International Space Station pass overhead with a pair of binoculars and working out how fast it is travelling, considering how a higher temperature might cook the outside of a cake more, working out the most stable position when riding a horse or how best to scale a climbing wall and keep your balance all involve some understanding and use of the laws of physics. As teachers we should look to find and highlight these connections in students' everyday lives whenever we can, and build from these an appreciation of what professional physicists do, but also that many aspects of life involve 'doing physics'.

Because physics is about elegant and often abstract models that are generalisable, then it is perhaps understandable that it might be mistakenly considered to involve a set of fixed truths. The language of physics may not help here. For example, instead of using the term 'generalisable' we could have used 'universal', and rather than 'models' and 'fundamental equations', we might have focused on 'laws'. It is an often painted caricature that physicists are concerned with uncovering universal laws that describe the secrets of the Universe. Indeed, this is appealing to some young people and many physicists still talk in these terms. However, very few physicists still hold this view of the nature of physics.

A further confounding factor here is that school curricula still refer to the canon of classical physics for the most part, and might be seen to feature almost exclusively the academic triumphs of the dead, wealthy, white men who span history, from Galileo to Newton to Stephen Hawking. Doing physics was never really like this, and it certainly is not today. Helping your students to see the role that Jocelyn Bell Burnell played in discovering pulsars, or Lisa Meitner's research on atomic physics and radioactivity, or Shirley Ann Jackson's pioneering work in telecommunication or how Persian scientist Avicenna had developed ideas around motion hundreds of years before Newton demonstrates that physics is valued and done by all genders and ethnicities. Each of these physicists worked within a community and built on the ideas of others. We suggest that widening the appeal of physics involves giving students a sense of what it is really like to do physics.

If we are to contend that physics is about explanatory models therefore, it follows that teaching secondary physics should convey the nature of how models develop in physics and the processes involved in this. Physicists recognise that models change over time, and that models are often the answers to the specific questions asked in research. Part of physics is about the development, testing and modifying of ideas and models. Many of the ideas presented in school physics have been updated, and this involves more sophisticated models rather than the direct replacement of many theories. For example, we suggest that it is still incredibly important for students to learn about Newtonian physics and this forms a key part of Chapter 2 Forces. Nevertheless, we know that Einstein's theory of relativity and quantum mechanics can describe and explain aspects of the world that Newtonian physics cannot.

Physics changes over time because models are continually tested and revised. However, it is worth noting that many models are robust and have survived a great deal of testing over the years. At any one time, there are often competing theories to explain something, for example how the Moon was formed. What physicists (and other scientists) do is develop models that take into account the available evidence at that time and can then be used to make hypotheses that can be tested in the future. This often involves collaborations between scientists from multiple disciplines and backgrounds, with each of these categories containing a huge number of different specialisms (e.g. biophysicists, geophysicists, electrical engineers). The international collaborations around particle physics at CERN, the European Organization for Nuclear Research, or around space missions are examples of this, in which theoretical physicists who deal with abstractions work in collaboration with experimental physicists and engineers who have to build and operate the equipment to test the predictions and theories.

The scale of large projects can make it easy to forget that physics is used on smaller, more local scales. For example, a radiographer uses physics to provide images of the body, as does a dentist when taking X-rays. Engineering is very closely related to physics, although it also has its own characteristics as a range of disciplines with more emphasis on design, testing, creating objects and solving real-world problems. In many countries, including the UK, engineering is not a school subject in its own right at secondary level, so the role of physics in engineering is worthwhile highlighting to students and also looking for places where these connections could be made. For example, the study of force and extension of materials could be followed by an activity using glue guns and spaghetti to build the strongest structures or widest span bridges. When you can, try and include in your lessons information about the careers that might include physics, to strengthen the feeling that students see physics as 'for them' (organisations such as the Institute of Physics have resources and guidance to help here). Authors have included links to careers throughout the chapters in this book. Studying physics teaches critical and logical thinking, problem solving and understanding complex systems, skills that can make students highly successful in careers such as finance, software design, plumbing, being an electrician, product design, architecture, journalism and broadcasting, and in the armed forces, for example.

Many students you teach are unlikely to study physics after the age of 16 and so it's worthwhile highlighting the role that physics plays in their everyday lives to help them feel the subject is relevant and worth studying. Many of your students will be interested in the role that physics plays in new developments in technology, understanding sport or how rollercoasters work; using these everyday contexts allows students to understand and value physics. This is where there can be benefit in looking beyond the formal curriculum, even if you don't explore the detail. For example, analysis of vectors, momentum and friction will help describe the optimal path of a ten-pin bowling ball (the one that is likely to get a strike) and explain why a curved trajectory is likely to be more successful that a straight-line trajectory. GPS systems would not work without incorporating Einstein's theories of relativity and even the humble LED is a quantum physics device rather than just a direct replacement for the filament light bulb. Physics often leads to technological advances that permeate our lives: the internet and Wi-Fi, mobile phones, cameras, music production, ballpoint pens, seatbelts, solar panels and many other everyday technologies owe their existence to physics ideas.

There are also questions to which physics cannot yet provide an answer, such as what happened before the Big Bang, what happens inside a black hole or how gravity and quantum physics link together. The impact of physics on the world is not always positive though, and this needs to be explored too. Nuclear physics has provided an alternative to fossil fuels and helped us understand how the Universe was formed, but has also led to the development of atomic weapons and sometimes damage to our environment, such as the nuclear power plant disaster at Chernobyl. So looking at the impact of physics from a societal viewpoint is important and it might be useful to bring in aspects of debate and discussion around topical issues such as the pros and cons of cars, or the expansion of internet technologies or the choice and siting of alternative energy plants. There are questions that physics may never be able to answer though, and ethical and social questions can, at best, only be informed by physics. Not only does physics have a 'cutting edge', which shows students that the discipline is ever moving, but it also has 'permeable boundaries' requiring physicists to engage with broader social and ethical debates.

1.3 Learning physics

When learning physics, it is important that students don't just learn the conceptual ideas like a shopping list or song lyrics; we want them to see the physics all around them in their daily lives and see how studying physics can make the world seem more beautiful. As well as the laws, theories and experiments that help us and students to understand how the Universe works, one of the joys of teaching physics is that you can pick almost anything lying around and find a physics lesson in it or use it to show a physics principle. Air resistance can be taught with cupcake (muffin) cases, electrical resistance with a pencil line and the nature of transverse waves can be shown using cocktail sticks and jelly babies. One of the habits that physicists and physics teachers get into is that they start to see physics everywhere and relish asking questions, even if they don't know the answers. This inquisitive nature about how the world works and how we might be able to find answers is something that is worth trying to foster in class. The fact that asking the right questions can be as important as finding the answers means that we shouldn't worry too much if we don't know all the answers ourselves. We hope that your lessons can enable students to 'do' physics, as well as develop a sense that it is something that extends well beyond their classroom.

Like all worthwhile pursuits, the path to success isn't always easy and in this section we will highlight some of the common challenges that students (and their teachers) can face when learning physics. We will include some suggestions for how to deal with these in the classroom and the chapters that follow will provide more specific examples. The main areas we address here are:

→ students' prior conceptions and how these may differ from the accepted scientific view
→ the challenges of visualising and working with abstract ideas
→ the role of language and multiple representations in the teaching and learning of physics
→ the role of mathematics in the teaching and learning of physics.

In some areas of physics, for example in aspects of nuclear physics, pupils may not have strong preconceptions around how things work. However, often, students come to classrooms with their own ideas about how the world works, and sometimes these differ from the way that physics describes and explains the world. This can sometimes cause problems in the physics classroom as their experiences and interpretations may run counter to the scientifically accepted explanations. Most students will have seen heavier things fall faster than lighter ones, tell you that they cannot see anything moving inside wires and observe that it does not look like anything comes out of a remote control. As the ideas they hold have often emerged from their experiences of the world around them, just telling them that they are wrong and 'this is how the world works' is not necessarily the best teaching strategy.

Prior conceptions and how they may differ from the accepted scientific view

Part of being a good physics teacher is being aware of, and sympathetic to, the views and intuitions that students have about how the world works. Students need opportunities to make their ideas explicit, to encounter alternative ideas and to evaluate these ideas in relation to their own. Social interaction between teacher and students allows such processing of ideas, and rich dialogue also helps students engage with their own preconceptions by drawing on different funds of knowledge. When learners' prior ideas are very different to scientifically accepted knowledge, these ideas have classically been labelled as 'misconceptions', although many educators now prefer to refer to these as 'alternative conceptions', recognising that such ideas are simply learners' attempts to make sense of their world using common sense. It is difficult for students to give up their alternative conceptions, so lessons and learning activities need careful design.

Before teaching any topic, we strongly recommend that you explore the alternative conceptual ideas that students commonly hold in that topic. The book *Making Sense of Secondary Science* (see Resources at the end of this chapter) provides a comprehensive overview of many of the views that you may encounter, but other resources are available. In many physics topics, diagnostic assessment questions have been developed to help. These types of questions are tightly focused on a particular conceptual idea. They are often multiple choice with the incorrect responses representing common alternative conceptions that students have. The power of these questions is that they do more than just tell us who is right and who is wrong; we can get an idea of what an individual student is thinking. There are a number of online repositories of these types of questions (see Resources for links to the Institute of Physics, IOPSpark, and Best Evidence Science Teaching, BEST). The physics education research (PER) community has produced many of these, often referred to as concept inventories, many of which are hosted on the PhysPort site.

Having access to and using these types of questions can be a key part of planning and teaching and they can be powerful tools, not just at the start and end of a topic, but through using them in teaching to generate discussion activities. As well as knowing the 'right' answer, if we are forewarned of the most common conceptual problems, then we can adapt what we do in order to help to support students to move from their current thinking and towards accepted ideas in physics. Helping students realise that their ideas may be naive, by showing the differences between their own ideas and the evidence, is one approach to begin changing their ideas. For example, a teacher may ask students to make a prediction before a piece of practical work or simulation, based on their prior ideas. This makes those ideas explicit to the teacher, but also to the students themselves, and the data they collect may conflict with the students' initial ideas (White and Gunstone, 1993). Concept cartoons can help achieve the same aims, but through dialogue (Keogh and Naylor, 1999). A concept cartoon provides a picture of a scientific phenomenon, with different people giving inferences about or alternative explanations of that phenomenon. By inviting students to say what they think or decide how much they agree with various statements, and then justify their positions to each other, you can create dialogue that can help students to unpick their current understanding.

The challenges of visualising abstract ideas

The role that modelling plays in physics has been highlighted as a key one in the discipline. One of the reasons why it is also relevant at the school level is that much of what we ask students to study is based around abstract ideas. Concepts and ideas such as forces, magnetic fields, energy and atomic stability are not tangible in the way that an apple falling from a tree is and this can cause challenges for students. One of the reasons we use representations in these situations is to help us connect between the tangible world and the ideas and explanations that sit behind them, but it is important that we distinguish between reality and theory.

In the electricity chapter, the rope model is explored in detail and we hope a case is made for its value, but it's important to remember that there is not actually a rope inside the wires. This may seem like an obvious thing to say, but it can be easy to slip from the model: 'as I pull harder on the rope, it will move faster', into reality: 'the increased potential difference causes a greater flow of electrons' and back again, without highlighting this transition between model and reality. The difference is not always obvious to students. Physics teachers develop their own ways to present this difference, for example standing on one side of the room and saying '*I am in model world*' when discussing the model and then, when talking about the real world moving to the other side of the room, sharing '*I am now in the real world*'. This may seem a little over the top but, for the novice, the distinction is not always clear and so we need to signpost it as clearly as we can.

This provides one strategy to support students in helping them visualise some of the abstracted ideas they meet in physics. Others include the use of 'forces glasses' (see Chapter 2 Forces, Section 2.1 page 21) and marbles on ramps to appreciate potentials and nuclear scattering (see Chapter 6 Atomic physics, Section 6.1 page 173). The important thing for physics teachers to consider is that there is often a certain leap of imagination that we ask of students in lessons and we should consider what we ask of them and look for ways to help.

The role of language and multiple representations

Language presents a specific issue in physics education, because many of the terms used in physics in a very specific way are used in a different way in everyday life. Words like 'force' and 'energy' have everyday uses that are, in some way, connected to their correct use in physics, but sometimes not with the level of preciseness needed in physics. Sometimes physicists are criticised for being pedantic, but some words have very specific meanings and it is critical to use them appropriately to avoid confusion. For example, in Chapter 2 Forces we'll suggest ways to help students correctly use the terms 'speed', 'velocity', 'acceleration' and 'momentum', which are often conflated. Similarly, in Chapter 3 Electricity and magnetism, we'll explain how to help students be clear about the difference between 'current' and 'potential difference', and why it matters.

As well as the examples above, other technical words used in physics can cause problems and so it can help when introducing or using words in science to consider how and if students may have encountered them before. If one considers the words we use in physics, they may have a very specific technical meaning (for example, diffraction) or one that is more common (such as energy). Sometimes the common usage of the word can be close to the way it is used in physics (as in the case of repel), but sometimes the meaning is quite different (for example, field) and can cause problems. The ways in which mass/weight and speed/velocity are often used interchangeably in everyday life is also problematic. Providing clear definitions with examples and insisting on their correct use is an important part of teaching and learning physics well and in the individual chapters we will suggest ways to help students become fluent and confident in using the correct language.

As well as the precise use of technical terms, physics also has the tools to communicate details about the same situation in multiple ways, each having their own strengths and limitations. For example, a question about the acceleration of a bird in flight may be presented in multiple ways including:

→ in words; 'a peregrine falcon, flying at 20 m/s accelerates to 80 m/s in 10 s'
→ with a labelled photograph
→ a diagram of the bird, with labelled force arrows
→ a speed–time or velocity–time graph
→ in equation form with symbol algebra or with numerical values $a = (v - u)/t$.

The expert physicist will find it easy to navigate fluently between each of these representations. However, students often find this a greater challenge. When working with students we suggest that you pay particular attention when moving between representations and emphasise that they are only one way of communicating the situation being considered. In some cases, it may be that questions can be successfully answered by using more than one representation and so consideration should be given to promoting more than one 'right way' of answering questions.

The role of mathematics

The critical role that mathematics has in the doing and learning of physics can sometimes send a message to students that much of physics is about using equations and doing calculations. While this is an important part of the subject in school, the difficulties that some students have with their mathematical skills can create a barrier for success in physics that needs some careful navigation.

There are three aspects of mathematics that commonly cause difficulties for learning physics, which you may wish to consider in your teaching:

→ a balance between conceptual understanding and calculations
→ algebra and memorising formulae
→ drawing and interpreting graphs.

A balance between conceptual understanding and calculations

While formulae play a pivotal role in the teaching and learning of physics, they are used to describe the relationships between quantities in real-life situations rather than just representing numbers that need to be combined in some mathematical fashion. As such it's important not to lose sight of these concepts and slip into a 'plug-and-chug' mode in which students become skilled at getting the correct numerical answer while bypassing any consideration for what the numbers actually represent and the interrelationship between the variables. Fluency with the associated calculations is desirable, but we suggest that a stress on the conceptual understanding of the ideas needs to be highlighted in your teaching. Try and strike a balance between practice with the numerical questions and questions that will allow students to discuss their thinking and ideas. Physics *is* mathematical but if the focus is too much on the computational side of things, then the real meaning and heart of the discipline can be lost or obscured. Using questions that cannot be answered mathematically in small group discussions can provide an environment where students may be more confident in expressing their ideas and challenging each other's openly without the potential embarrassment of 'getting it wrong in front of the whole class'. There is a large collection available free online, called Next Time Questions and they can be a powerful resource for you to check your own understanding before any lesson.

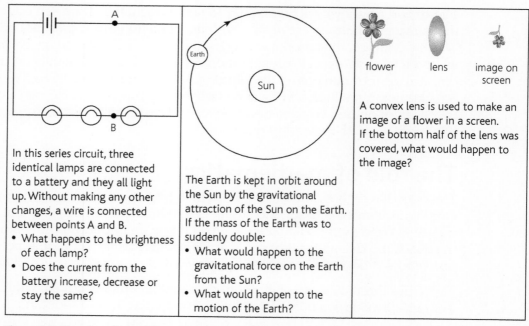

In this series circuit, three identical lamps are connected to a battery and they all light up. Without making any other changes, a wire is connected between points A and B.
- What happens to the brightness of each lamp?
- Does the current from the battery increase, decrease or stay the same?

The Earth is kept in orbit around the Sun by the gravitational attraction of the Sun on the Earth. If the mass of the Earth was to suddenly double:
- What would happen to the gravitational force on the Earth from the Sun?
- What would happen to the motion of the Earth?

A convex lens is used to make an image of a flower in a screen. If the bottom half of the lens was covered, what would happen to the image?

Figure 1.1 Questions designed to promote conceptual thinking

Algebra and memorising formulae

As we have discussed, equations are powerful and elegant simplifications of how quantities in the Universe are related. Students can see letters in an equation represent missing numbers, but in most cases the letters represent quantities that are related. This is one of the reasons why always including units with measurements in physics is so important. Adding the unit is what transforms the numbers into quantities. As a teacher, always insisting on units is not about convention or exam marks, it is about giving these numbers meaning. Students may use an equation to find one particular answer but part of the power of equations in physics is that they are often generalisable: they do not just apply to the situation in question, but *all* situations.

The formula $KE = \frac{1}{2}mv^2$ might be used by a student for a runner, but the same formula can work out the kinetic energy of a bicycle, an aeroplane or a meteorite.

It is a good habit when introducing new relationships to begin with a word equation so that you can talk about the relationship in conceptual terms. If you jump straight to the shortened, algebraic form, then the connection between the letters and symbols and the real world can be lost or weakened. Once the conceptual ideas and the relationships are established, you can then move on to mention the quantities, units, symbols and the equation that links them all together. We have included a table of all the quantities, units and symbols used in this book as an appendix.

Drawing and interpreting graphs

Students are likely to have had some experience of drawing and interpreting graphs from their primary education in mathematics and other science topics. Table 1.1 shows some of the common difficulties that students face relating to graph drawing in physics, with suggestions for how you might address them.

Table 1.1 Common difficulties related to graph drawing in physics

Difficulty	Suggestion
Students may be able to read data points on a graph, but it can be more challenging to interpret and explain relationships and trends in such points.	Developing narratives about the story that the graph might be telling can be a way to communicate that the graph is representing a relationship.
When asked to draw a graph, students can often find it quite challenging to select the scales needed on each axis.	Initially, you may wish to consider providing graphs with pre-drawn axes or providing different scales to choose from, to help them develop confidence in doing this.
Students can often omit the units on the labels of the axes. As with equations, these are as important as the quantity.	Always insist on these in graphs and, initially, you may want to provide pre-drawn scales, with units.
Their experience of drawing best-fit lines can be limited, and some may simply join the dots on a line graph. If students have to try and develop their procedural skills in graph drawing at the same time as learning new conceptual ideas in physics from the graph, that can be a large cognitive load.	Allocating time to support and develop a student's graph drawing skills using decontextualised or everyday data can be a good investment.
Some find language such as 'Draw a graph of a versus b' confusing, not being sure which variable goes on which axis.	Liaising with the maths department to find common language and being consistent in physics and, if possible, across the sciences can help here.
Many students struggle to correctly calculate the gradient of a line graph, even if they have done so successfully in maths.	Try to develop a consistent protocol for how you do this, making it easier for students to develop confidence and fluency.
Students do not always appreciate that the gradient of a graph and the area under it can be meaningful and allow them to work out extra information about the situation.	It is common for physics to deal with rates of change (e.g. velocity, power, current) and accumulations (e.g. displacement, gravitational potential energy) and so these may be ideas that you wish to introduce and regularly refer back to when using graphs.
Some students do not realise that calculated values for the gradient of a graph and the area under graph have units.	When calculating gradients or areas under graphs, include the units of each axis in the calculation to show that they are an important and relevant part of the calculation.

The Association for Science Education (ASE) publication *The Language of Mathematics in Science* provides much more detail about these and other issues with examples of best practice. It can also be really valuable in talking to your maths department and, when possible, developing common strategies or approaches.

Practical work

Physics is a practical subject, from the work of massive experimental facilities such as CERN and the Laser Interferometer Gravitational-Wave Observatory (LIGO) to students exploring the behaviour of a diode in a classroom. Practical work hugely enriches the understanding of students when done well and can be a powerful tool in helping students connect the ideas that physics is built on and the reality of what they can see, touch and measure in front of them.

For any practical activity, it is important to be clear about what you hope students will learn from it and, once this is established, you can then help steer the situation to support that learning. There will be a manipulative demand related to the use of the equipment, setting things up and taking precise measurements. There is also a procedural demand relating to the order in which things need to be done, the control of variables, and the processing and analysis of data. Finally, there will be a conceptual demand that is related to the physics ideas behind the experiment. Each demand can be important but it's worth being clear in your mind which is your primary focus in the practical work you choose to do.

If the focus is conceptual, then you may want to provide partly set-up equipment (for example, providing a set-up with a ruler and a spring attached to a weight holder on a clamp) so the student only has to add 'weights' and take measurements of the spring extension and can focus on the relationship between load and extension. In other cases, collecting accurate and reliable data may be your focus. As such, you will need to get the students to consider potential errors and how confident they are in their findings. Graph drawing and analysis is another core skill in physics and so, in some cases, you may provide exemplar data to allow enough time for the analysis. Like so many things in teaching there is rarely a clear 'right' or 'wrong' thing to do; what matters is that you are clear in your focus for the learning and steer the lesson that way, with consideration for the competing demands you place on students.

A useful way to consider the purpose of practical work in physics is to see it as a way to connect the domain of ideas with the domain of observables, helping students 'see' what might be abstract ideas in the ways in which objects behave and interact. When planning or evaluating the effectiveness of practical work, it can be easy to consider it as successful if the students do or see the things we want them to, rather than considering whether they actually connect the conceptual ideas to what they were observing. These ideas are explored in more depth by Robin Millar and Ian Abrahams in their paper 'Practical work: making it more effective' (see Resources at the end of this chapter). A simple but powerful phrase from that paper which can help us keep an eye on what matters is that effective practical work should be 'hands on and minds on'. Specific suggestions for how this approach can be applied to many of the common practicals carried out in secondary physics lessons can be found in the book *Enhancing Learning with Effective Practical Science 11–16* (See Resources at the end of this chapter).

You might also wish to develop an enquiry approach in your physics teaching so that students experience, to some extent, how research physicists work and how science knowledge is built and challenged through practical work. There is a range of enquiry activities developed through EU funding in recent years and these can be found on the Scientix website.

Using digital technologies

The development of new technologies has provided all kinds of tools to support teaching and learning in physics. Sensors and measurement devices that were once confined to research laboratories now sit in students' pockets. Most smartphones contain accelerometers, GPS, magnetic field sensors, compasses, light and sound meters from which you can take direct readings in the classroom. When studying earthquakes, the readings from accelerometers can help students to appreciate how a seismometer works and, at the same time, show them why vectors are important. Students can take their smartphones on theme park rides and measure the forces they experience; they can track their speed and acceleration on their journey to school and use high speed camera settings to capture things that happen in fractions of a second. Conversely, astronomy simulations can help them explore changes that happen over long periods of time in a few seconds and imagine 'what if' situations when exploring the orbital speeds and height of satellites. Spreadsheets can allow them to process large data sets into meaningful graphs almost instantly, such as the experiment in Chapter 6 Atomic physics in which a class of students use coins, sweets or dice to model half-life and draw a graph representing hundreds of random events.

Advances in technologies are often so rapid that any specific detail included here could easily be superseded, but there are some messages to draw out that will remain true. When possible, it is important to collect data to be analysed and explore relationships in physics lessons. Simulations and visualisation tools can help us to see the massive and the microscopic, play with relationships and vary things we could not do in a practical situation. However, they can build on, but not replace, real practical work.

 ## 1.4 Final thoughts

We hope that this chapter helps provide a foundational understanding of what physics is, what physicists do and some key issues to consider in your teaching. Hopefully we have made a strong case that physics is not just a collection of facts and equations, rather the study of how the Universe works and the connections within that. We have tried to lay out clear narratives around how physics describes, explains and predicts aspects of the world and how it uses a variety of different types of models to do this. We have also advocated that teachers develop a sense of what it means to 'do physics' within their students: showing how physics is relevant to everyday life, impacts society and provides skills which will help students in their careers and lives. Finally, we have given some guidance on the aspects of teaching physics which can be challenging, and what might be done to ease these challenges. In this introductory chapter therefore, we hope that we have stimulated thoughts about what it means to convey physics as a discipline. Readers may not agree with all the suggestions made here, and that is very much part of the developmental process in becoming a teacher of physics. Our aim is to support that development and give you confidence as physics teachers. In the chapters that follow, the authors further lay out their thinking on how to convey a particular area of physics to students, and what is important in doing so. We hope that readers will engage with these chapters critically also, as they develop their own ideas around teaching physics.

1.5 Resources
Online resources

Please go to **spark.iop.org/asebook** for a set of curated resources from the IOP Spark website to match this chapter.

The Best Evidence Science Teaching (BEST) from the University of York has many diagnostic questions, follow-up activities and detail on the progression of conceptual ideas in this and other topics: www.stem.org.uk

The Institute of Physics provides a comprehensive set of teacher support curated through their spark website: www.spark.iop.org

Next Time Questions are a set of conceptual thinking questions: www.arborsci.com

The PhysPort site features many resources and papers from the physics education research (PER) community: www.physPort.org

References

Abrahams, I. and Reiss, M. J. (eds.) (2017) *Enhancing Learning with Effective Practical Science 11–16*. London: Bloomsbury.

Boohan, R. (2016) *The Language of Mathematics in Science*. Hatfield: Association for Science Education.

Driver, R., Squires, A., Rushworth, P. and Wood-Robinson, V. (1994) *Making Sense of Secondary Science: Research into Children's Ideas*. London: Routledge.

Keogh, B. and Naylor, S. (1999) Concept cartoons, teaching and learning in science: an evaluation. *International Journal of Science Education*, 21 (4), 431–446.

Millar, R. and Abrahams, I. (2009) Practical work: making it more effective. *School Science Review*, 91 (334), 59–64.

White, R. T. and Gunstone, R. F. (1992) *Probing Understanding*. London: The Falmer Press.

Further reading

Knight, R. (2003) *Five Easy Lessons: Strategies for Successful Physics Teaching*. San Francisco: Addison Wesley.

Redish, E. F. (2003) *Teaching Physics with the Physics Suite*. Hoboken, New Jersey: Wiley.

2 Forces

James de Winter

Introduction

One of the wonderful things about physics is how efficiently it can describe the Universe. With a few measurements and some rules that will fit on a postcard we are able to describe and predict the motion of most things on the planet and even travel to the Moon. This chapter looks at those measurements and rules and, while many situations can get complex, the underlying principles are accessible to all students in their study at this level. It starts with primary education experiences and then moves on to developing a sense of what forces are and how we can 'see' them, as well as understanding how forces can change the motion and shape of objects. It then looks at how we describe and quantify the motion of objects, paying particular attention to the terms 'speed', 'velocity' and 'acceleration', together with their associated equations and graphs which represent motion. Once these ideas are established, the chapter will look at how Newton's laws connect everything together. Other sections deal with how forces are linked to changing the shape of objects, freefall, momentum and circular motion. Examples are taken from many different contexts and you can reinforce the idea that forces and physics are everywhere and not confined to a single situation.

Teams designing the latest sports clothing to reduce air resistance, aeronautical engineers working on supersonic flight, medical physicists developing replacement body parts and many others who use physics in their everyday jobs will find the ideas that underpin this topic relevant and important in their work. From the forces between planets to those between atoms and everything in between, an understanding of how forces change the motion of an object is one of the most powerful ideas in physics that permeates our daily lives and hopefully we can communicate this to students.

A teaching sequence

It is unlikely that all of the ideas relating to forces and motion will be dealt with in a single set of lessons at secondary level. It is more likely that these topics will be returned to a number of times as students pass through their physics education. Rather than trying to provide a route that will tightly map to any particular curriculum or exam specification, the flowchart below shows a route through the whole topic in a sequence that is designed to build up ideas and concepts in a logical order that broadly increases in conceptual challenge as the chapter progresses. Topics such as momentum, circular motion and more detailed analyses of motion, such as freefall and terminal velocity, are usually studied by older students (14–16 years old) building on work covered in earlier years. The hope is that you can use this when planning for your specific context and classes.

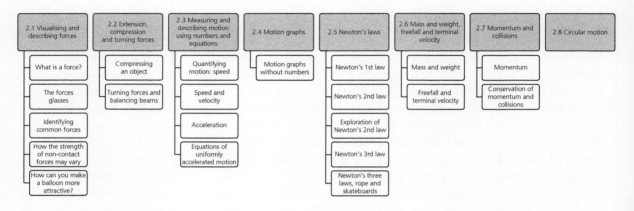

Prior experiences

Forces are commonly studied during primary education and students will have had the experience of thinking about them in everyday situations. This work is likely to have begun in an exploratory or structured play situation, such as pulling, pushing, stretching or squashing objects or experimenting with floating and sinking, and dealing with contact and non-contact forces (such as weight and magnets). Although there is likely to be a limited formalised use of language, they may have talked about the 'heaviness' of things, how 'stretchy' a material is or how 'rough' or 'slippery' a surface is and connected forces to what happens. This might include exploring questions like 'How much force does it take to push the table across the floor?' or statements such as 'there is an upwards force making the boat float'. Students are likely to have had some experience of measuring forces directly with a simple force meter. In many cases the analysis of numerical data will be more comparative (e.g. the force to lift X was more than needed to lift Y), although it is likely that some students will have seen or presented experimental data graphically.

As many of their experiences will link pulling and pushing to movement, a direct connection between forces and motion is almost inevitable. Although initially helpful, this causes problems later on, particularly when students have to consider the forces on an object in equilibrium. Helping students appreciate that there may be multiple, but balanced, forces acting on stationary objects and those moving at a constant velocity is a significant challenge and this is addressed later in this chapter.

There are a number of alternative conceptions that students hold about forces and motion. Some of the ideas taught in this topic seem to be counter to intuitive understanding, such as the naive ideas that without air resistance, objects fall with the same speed towards the ground or need a force to make them carry on moving in a straight line at constant speed. Collections of these alternative conceptions from research are widely available, the book *Making Sense of Secondary Science* (Driver, Squires, Rushworth, and Wood-Robinson, 2014) is highly recommended. As we can only see the effect of forces and not the force itself, forces are difficult to visualise and so students may need help to do so. Strategies covered later in this chapter, such as the use of force arrows and 'forces glasses', are designed to help. Many examples and questions that students are given are simplified (for example, 'assume that there is no air resistance') and, while this can help, it can be a struggle for some to imagine the 'ideal' situation, such as one without friction.

Good quality diagnostic questions can be valuable in identifying what students already know or believe. Rather than traditional, generic questions, these are targeted at a particular, single conceptual idea. The questions are often multiple choice with the distractor answers representing common alternative conceptions, which allow teachers to identify if a student understands that idea but also if not, what they do think. The Best Evidence Science Teaching (BEST) and AAAS project 2061 and the *Concept Cartoons* books are particularly helpful here (see the end of this chapter for more details). This evidence about students' current ideas can then be used to inform what you do next for the whole class or on an individual level.

 ## Science literacy

The correct use of language can create challenges for some teachers and students. In physics, we use words deliberately to express complex ideas efficiently and clearly. Examples are mass and weight; it is true that in everyday conversation these are interchangeable terms, but they have precise and different meanings that we need to use in the physics classroom, even if this may contradict what students hear elsewhere. A language teacher would not accept 'apple' to be an appropriate substitute for 'banana' on the grounds that they are both fruit. We should take our lead from them and, when it matters, insist on the correct language and take care to use it ourselves.

Teaching and learning challenges

In this topic, there are a number of common and persistent alternative conceptions that students can hold and which cause difficulties. In the rest of this chapter, we will try and provide sufficient background and activities to support you in addressing these alternative conceptions with your students. However, at this point it is perhaps worth identifying some of the most common conceptual challenges faced by students studying this topic.

→ Students often think that if an object is moving then there must be a force acting to keep it in motion. For example, they might think that when you push or throw an object there must still be a force in the direction of motion once you let go.
→ Students often think that moving objects will slow down and come to a stop by themselves without a force being needed.
→ Students often conflate words that have similar meanings, not always realising the important differences between them. The most common ones are speed/velocity, distance/displacement, mass/weight and force/pressure.
→ Students often think that acceleration means speeding up only, when in fact the term can also describe slowing down or changes in direction. This is particularly important when considering circular motion (covered later in the chapter).
→ Students often think that all forces require objects to be in contact, not appreciating that some can act at a distance (for example, magnetic or electrostatic attraction and repulsion, gravitational attraction) and that the strength of these forces can vary with distance.

2.1 Visualising and describing forces

In physics, some quantities that we are interested in have a magnitude (size) and a direction, and these are called vectors, whereas other quantities only have a magnitude and they are called scalars. Examples of vectors are velocity, force and acceleration. Examples of scalars are speed, mass, temperature and time. Vectors are common in this topic and sometimes vector and scalar quantities are easily confused, such as velocity and speed. Although you may not wish to use the terms 'vector' and 'scalar' or differentiate between 'speed' and 'velocity' in early lessons on forces, appreciating that many quantities in this topic have size *and* direction and that both are significant pieces of information should be a consideration in your teaching.

A note on notation: In this chapter we have chosen to keep notation as simple as possible but it's worth being aware that some books use particular protocols such as vectors written with arrows over them (for example, $\vec{F}, \vec{v}, \vec{a}$) and scalars written in italics (such as m, T, t). Subscripts are sometimes used on forces to clarify what force is acting on what object, an example being the upwards force on a book from a table written as $F_{T \text{ on } B}$. The balance between clarity and additional detail is not always easy to strike and you will need to be guided by your own views, confidence and knowledge of your class.

What is a force?

It is useful to begin by trying to define what a force actually is. It can be quite insightful to ask a class 'What is a force?' and then work through their responses. The response 'a push or a pull' is a common one that may come from their primary science experience and is a useful starting point that can form part of an initial working definition, before moving on to one that perhaps focuses on ideas around Newton's laws. Part of the challenge here is that forces are not tangible in the way that a table is. Much of our classroom talk about forces moves between a real experience of objects and models such as the use of force arrows, and so our examples and language should be geared to help students connect the objects and the models. The use of arrows and the forces glasses are strategies designed to help here.

The forces glasses

Looking at real objects and talking about the forces acting on them, such as weight or air resistance, and/or drawing diagrams or labelling photographs is a process of modelling. A downward arrow labelled 'weight' on a falling ball is a model that tries to represent the invisible effect of the unseen gravitational field of the Earth on the ball. We could draw many downward arrows from each part of the ball, but this is not practical or helpful and so we draw a single downward arrow. This is usually drawn starting from the middle of the object (centre of mass).

To try and acknowledge that the use of these arrows is a particular way of looking at the world, the idea of forces glasses can be used. When you look at the world normally, you see objects. When you put the forces glasses on, you can 'see' the forces as well. In class I would show an object such as an apple hanging from a thread and then I would put on the forces glasses. You might want to model putting the forces glasses on or show a slide on the board of what you see with and without the forces glasses, so that your students understand the ideas that you are helping them with. In my demonstration, once 'wearing the force glasses', I could then 'see' the forces and would add cardboard arrows with tape to the apple to show what the world looks like with the forces glasses on.

To help with the aspect of the modelling process that focuses on the key information, there are some rules that I suggest students follow when wearing the forces glasses:

→ You can only look at one object at a time.
→ It is easier to consider one direction at a time (so, up/down, then left/right, then combine).

By focusing on one object at a time, you help to move students into situations where they can talk about which of Newton's 1st and 2nd laws would be most appropriate in this type of situation (these laws are covered in more detail later in this chapter). It can help to initially pick examples that have forces only in one dimension to remove the complications than can come with adding forces at angles to find a resultant force. These ideas are dealt with at higher levels, but at this stage it is likely to complicate things without much benefit to understanding.

Once you have established a way for students to observe and talk about forces, a good follow-up exercise involves providing students with a set of pre-prepared force arrows (described below) and some diagrams or photographs showing situations that are as unambiguous as possible. A picture of a ball after it has been kicked, a helicopter hovering over water, skydivers as they fall out of a plane, a bungee jumper at the bottom of the fall and a bird in level flight are all good examples. Students then try and add what they feel are the most appropriate arrows to the diagram and use them to help describe and explain what is happening in potentially less threatening small group discussions.

I suggest using arrows of two or three different sizes which have the following design features:

→ *Smaller arrows are exactly half the length of the next biggest one.* This allows students to 'add' forces, and identify balanced and unbalanced situations without the need for calculations. At higher levels, students will have to draw forces arrows to scale and so this can prepare them without over-complicating work at this stage.

→ *They are all the same width.* The length of the arrow is the representation of the size of the force, so all other variables are kept the same.
→ *They all have FORCE written on one side only.* The direction of motion should be represented or indicated separately from the direction of the forces as they can be different. The non-labelled side can be used to show the direction of movement, but the side labelled FORCE can only be used to represent a force.

Just as we use specific words deliberately, sometimes the images we use are constructed in a very particular way to help communicate and highlight the things we care about. When drawing diagrams showing forces, it is common to draw what is called a 'free body diagram'. Figure 2.1 shows an apple suspended on a string, the same apple viewed through the forces glasses and in a free body diagram.

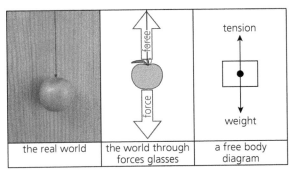

| the real world | the world through forces glasses | a free body diagram |

Figure 2.1 Three ways to represent the same situation (the one on the right is a free body diagram)

A free body diagram is a type of diagram that provides the simplest version of what is happening. It treats objects as a single point and shows all the forces acting on it and nothing else. As with all diagrams in physics, it highlights the relevant information and removes as much of everything else as possible. There are several approaches to drawing free body diagrams; here we suggest the following approach:

→ Identify the object that is being considered.
→ Treat it as if it were a single point.
→ Draw force arrows, all starting from that point and going in the direction of the force.
→ Label the arrow with what is causing that force and/or the size of the force in newtons.
→ If you have more than one force in the same direction, draw them tip to tail (→→), not side by side.

Science in context

Bicycles are a good context to help students study forces on an object. Unlike many powered vehicles, such as cars and aeroplanes, it is relatively easy to see where the forces that cause changes in motion (dynamics) are acting, as well as it being relatively easy to measure the motion of the bicycle (kinematics).

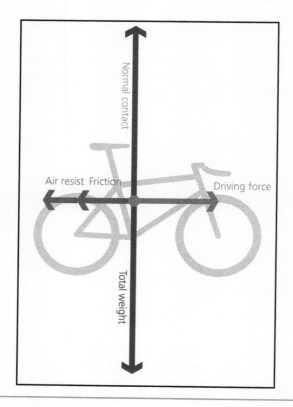

Identifying common forces

Table 2.1 lists some of the forces that students should be aware of. It is important to try to be consistent with terminology. Students will find it very confusing if you label a force as a normal contact force, but your colleague labels the same force as a reaction force, and your exam board labels it a support force!

Table 2.1 Common forces

What is the force?	Where does the force come from?	Examples
Weight	This is the gravitational force of attraction acting on one object by another object's mass. This is usually the downwards force on an object caused by the mass of the Earth. There is a gravitational attraction between any two masses but it is normally too small to measure. Can also be called the 'force due to gravity' but never just 'gravity'.	An object in freefall The downwards force on an object sitting on a surface
Normal contact or normal force	This is the force that acts on an object caused by any object that is supporting it. It is sometimes referred to as a support force.	Someone standing on the floor Sitting on a cushion
Friction	This is a force that opposes motion or attempted motion. There is still a force acting on something that is stationary but being pushed. This force always acts in the opposite direction to the movement or potential movement.	A wardrobe being pushed across a floor The horizontal force between bicycle tyres and a flat road
Air/water resistance	When there is movement between solid and a fluid (liquid or gas) then there is a particular type of friction between them, also known as drag. Unlike the friction on a sliding object which remains constant, this force increases with the speed of the object and is always in the opposite direction to the motion.	A fish swimming A dropped brick, falling down
Upthrust	The upwards force on an object in a fluid (liquid or gas). Most examples will involve objects floating in liquids, but it is important to note that there is an upthrust in all fluids and even if the object is sinking. Things sink because the upthrust is less than the weight.	A block of wax floating in water A helium balloon floating in air
Electrostatic forces	The non-contact forces between any charged objects. These often act on a submicroscopic scale, acting between molecules to keep structures together.	A charged balloon sticking to a wall
Magnetic forces	These non-contact forces act between: • magnets • magnets and magnetic materials • charged particles moving in a magnetic field.	Two magnets repelling or attracting A fridge magnet holding a note on the fridge door
Strong and weak nuclear forces	These forces act between and within subatomic particles and only act over very small distances.	The force within the nucleus of an atom that holds matter together (strong) and the force involved in beta decay (weak)

How the strength of non-contact forces may vary

In addition to showing different types of non-contact forces in context, consideration should be given to the ways in which they can vary. An example might consider the effect changing the mass of the Earth would have on its gravitational field strength and thus the weight of an object. The following simple demonstrations can be used to demonstrate other ways in which students can be shown how the strength of some of these forces can vary with distance.

How can you make a balloon more attractive?

While it is not possible to take readings, it is possible to also show qualitatively how the strengths of an electrostatic force changes with distance. If you move a charged balloon near to, but not touching, a thin stream of running water, you will see it deflecting. This shows that there is a force between the balloon and water. As you move the balloon closer to the water, the stream will deflect more indicating a greater force when they are closer.

 Technology use

The PhET simulation Balloons and Static Electricity can be really helpful in explaining in terms of charges why these and similar phenomena occur. More detail with respect to charges and electrostatic forces is provided in Chapter 3 Electricity and magnetism (see Section 3.1, page 59).

KEY ACTIVITIES

How strong is a magnet?

Students will be familiar with magnets and the forces between them, but it can be hard to try and measure how strong the force is. This simple demonstration can help them appreciate that there can be an attractive or a repulsive force between the poles of two magnets and that the strength of this force changes with the distance between the magnets. Place a magnet upright on a balance and then move another magnet towards and then away from it. It is a good idea to fix the lower magnet on a block or with modelling clay so it does not fall over or cause damage to the balance.

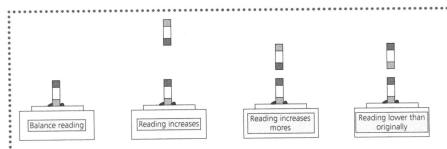

| Balance reading | Reading increases | Reading increases mores | Reading lower than originally |

The observed changes should be enough to show that there is a force between the magnets, that it has a direction, and its strength changes with the distance between them.

Safety note: Make sure that steel, not neodymium, magnets are used.

Extension, compression and turning forces

Students are likely to have had prior qualitative experience of stretching and compressing objects, but during teaching at this level they should move into data collection, looking to identify and quantify patterns. In this topic, a conceptual hurdle you may face is to explain how a motionless surface, such as a tabletop, can exert a force acting upwards. When teaching about normal contact or support forces (those forces which stop objects from falling through the floor, for example) you will require the use of models that draw on microscopic stories of forces between particles. Some macroscopic support systems, a mattress, for example, can help learners appreciate how the deformation of springs results in an upwards force. Ask students to imagine that the surface of the table, considered microscopically, is like the springs in a mattress. This is a good starting point.

When experiments are carried out to measure the extension of springs and elastic bands when loaded, it is important to reinforce the point that, within certain limits, the observed behaviour can apply to many things including strawberry lace sweets, human bones, glass and metal wires.

27

An initial activity to show how forces affect the shape of objects is to ask students to carefully stretch steel springs and measure their extension. The resulting proportionality, up to the elastic limit, allows their results to be presented in the form of a law – in this case Hooke's law (extension is proportional to the load added). Some schools get students to make their own springs from copper wire wound around a pencil in which case reaching the elastic limit does not ruin a good steel spring. If wires are to be stretched near or past their elastic limit, then eye protection will be needed. The important physics learning point in all cases is that here is a simple pattern, one that can be described by an equation (Hooke's law).

This is a good practical activity to develop student conversations by asking them to describe the data they collect. The students may refer to their table of results and begin with simple descriptions such as the 'extension goes up in steps' or 'the same each time'. Asking the students to qualify and compare their statements, and gradually moving them to using more scientific language helps their understanding, as does comparing what they have deduced from tables to what they have interpreted from graphs. There is useful guidance on teaching students to plot and interpret graphs in the ASE publication *The Language of Mathematics in Science*.

Before you introduce the formal equation for Hooke's law to students, they should be guided to develop the relationship themselves or use their data to predict an unknown force from a known extension. In any graph showing a relationship between variables, if the line is straight and passes through the origin, we can say that the quantities are directly proportional. If you double one, you will double the other, triple one then you'll triple the other and so on. Elastic bands are sometimes used in place of springs and these provide an interesting challenge for graph plotting and another opportunity to encourage students to talk about their data. The stretching behaviour of an elastic band is unlikely to be linear. It is more likely to yield a curve with the band's stretchiness changing throughout the process – easier at first and then stiffer later on.

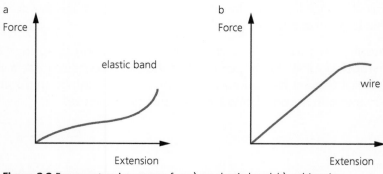

Figure 2.3 Force–extension curves for: a) an elastic band; b) a thin wire

For situations in which the object stretches according to Hooke's law, the following expression is used to describe the relationship:

$$\text{force (N)} = \text{spring constant (N/m)} \times \text{extension (m)}$$

$$F = kx$$

With younger students (11–14 years old) it is common that the relationship between force and extension is the main focus. For older students (14–16 years old) the level of analysis of this relationship is developed, usually with a focus on the energy stored in the stretched object. The area under a force–extension graph represents the work done in extending the object. To a good approximation, this is the same amount of energy as that stored in the stretched object. If the graph is a straight-line graph, this can be worked out using the formula for the area of a triangle:

$$\text{energy stored elastically (J)} = \frac{1}{2} \times \text{force (N)} \times \text{extension (m)}$$

$$E = \frac{1}{2}Fx$$

For lines that are not straight, an estimate can be made by counting squares under the line, but caution is needed to ensure that the correct units are used, as often extension is measured in centimetres.

The spring constant can also be calculated from the graph if it is straight, as it is equal to the gradient. You might want to use these ideas to turn pinging an elastic band upwards into a physics experiment, ensuring suitable eye protection is worn. Ask students how they think the vertical height reached changes with the extension of the stretched band? This is an inefficient energy transfer. The energy stored elastically when the band is stretched is far greater than the energy stored gravitationally as the band reaches its greatest height but, usually, the more you stretch, the higher it goes and so this activity should be able to generate some good conversations about energy and efficiency.

Compressing an object

The concept of compression is often neglected in favour of tension when deforming materials in the school lab, but it is worth explaining to students that the same principles apply and similar graphs and calculations could be done. It is possible to get compression springs that you can load with masses and measure the compression. A simple and more engaging approach is to use large marshmallows. Place a marshmallow in a plastic cup and then put another plastic cup inside the first one, on top of the marshmallow. You will them be able to add masses to the inside of the second cup and measure the compression by seeing how much closer the top of the inner cup moves towards the top of the outer cup. Load it with small masses and you should be able to get a good set of force versus compression data that show an approximately linear relationship between force and compression.

29

Turning forces and balancing beams

There are some nice demonstrations and activities that can be done in class to help students get a feel for the idea of moments. The door challenge simply asks a student to close a door by pushing the door right next to the hinge; it's almost impossible. Move along, away from the hinge, to the handle and it can be moved with one finger. Similarly, the force required to pull down a student's arm held horizontally near the shoulder is much greater than near their hand. In this and other examples, it is important to stress the key terms (force, pivot, distance, moment) and make the point that a moment depends on force and the distance from the pivot where that force is applied.

Although simple machines like a lever may have been used in primary schools, at this level we will be quantifying their effects and can use rules to find unknown values. Turning forces are quantified as moments and this is worked out by multiplying the force by the distance from the line of action of the force to a pivot. It is best to try and use the term 'moment' rather than 'turning force' as a moment is not a force, a distinction that students often fail to make.

$$\text{moment (Nm)} = \text{force (N)} \times \text{perpendicular distance from the line of action}$$
$$\text{of the force to a pivot (m)}$$

$$M = Fd$$

Careers

Engineers and builders work with forces and moments all the time. These range from the large counterweights on the back of a construction crane to the supports for an overhanging balcony. Here and elsewhere, calculations involving force and moments are critical to designing safe and secure buildings. It is more common for engineers to use the term 'torque' (also measured in Nm and calculated in the same way) to describe the turning force, usually in a rotating system.

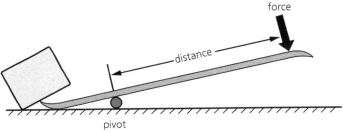

Figure 2.4 The moment of a force = force × perpendicular distance from the line of action of the force to the pivot.

KEY ACTIVITIES

Class practicals can be carried out to explore the law of moments, which says that if the clockwise and anticlockwise moments are equal then an object will not start rotating. This can be done by balancing a metre ruler on a wooden triangular pivot with different masses at different distances from the pivot. An alternative version involves suspending a metre rule from a clamped nail or in a bulldog/foldback clip. Weights are hung on string loops on each side of the metre rule, making them easy to slide. Students can see if the law holds true or find unknown weights with known ones. Confusion between mass and weight can be an issue here, as the calculation of a moment uses the force. An easy solution is to place a sticker over the 100 g label on the mass and write 1 N on it (or 0.5 N for 50 g).

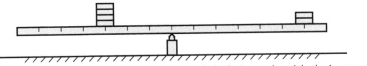

Figure 2.5 A balanced beam showing equal clockwise and anticlockwise moments.

Measuring and describing motion using numbers and equations

Students will be familiar with the concept of speed, although it is likely that they will use the term interchangeably with velocity. Many will have measured the speed of objects, but here they will start to take a more formalised approach to measurement and equations in physics, as well as graphical representation of data. When we look at the motion of objects, even if it is not obvious, this is a process of modelling. We consider a simplified version of reality and interrogate what is happening. Complex objects with many moving parts, such as bicycles or aeroplanes, are reduced to a free body diagram (see Section 2.1, page 23) and we then ask some questions about that object.

→ Where is it?
→ How fast is it moving?
→ What direction is it moving in?
→ How rapidly is it speeding up or slowing down?

The key terms in this section, 'speed', 'velocity' and 'acceleration', are sometimes merged by students into a single term, 'motion', rather than being clearly distinguished. While all are connected, each term describes a different aspect of motion and so it is good for us to be precise in our language and encourage our students to do the same.

 Science literacy

This is a good opportunity to encourage students to talk and share their ideas about a number of different examples, so that they can become more confident in both using and responding to situations using clear physics language. Measurements and discussion of speed are normally covered in the earlier stages (11–14 years old) of this topic, sometimes with simple speed–time graphs. At higher levels (14–16 years old), the difference between speed and velocity is addressed together with acceleration, more complex motion graphs and calculations from them.

Quantifying motion: speed

If an object is moving, it will travel a certain distance in a particular time, and this relationship is represented by the equation for speed. It helps to introduce the word equation first to ensure that the conceptual ideas are considered before numbers are used. You then need to make sure that you highlight that use of the correct units is important and finally show that this can all be written in a shortened symbol form. The equation for speed is shown below:

$$\text{speed (m/s)} = \frac{\text{distance travelled (m)}}{\text{time taken (s)}}$$

$$v = \frac{d}{t}$$

The abstract nature of algebra means that students can sometimes see the symbol form as just letters, perhaps not appreciating that they represent things that can be measured in a real-world example and could have many possible values in many different situations. The letters used in the symbol form of an equation can cause further problems as they are not always logical and based on the first letter of the quantity. Here, v has been used for speed but some books use s. Other teachers use s for displacement and x for distance, adding to potential confusion that can only really be resolved by knowing what your awarding body requires and always being consistent and clear with the language, units and symbols you use.

Very few moving things travel at a constant speed and so, when considering motion, it is usually better to consider an 'average speed' for a whole journey. If you are considering the speed of an object at a particular point in time, then the term 'instantaneous speed' is used. There are multiple opportunities to measure the speed of real things in or around the classroom. Slow-moving things or those that travel comparatively long distances work well, such as wind-up toy cars or even real cars, providing you take appropriate care. When dropped, a cupcake case usually reaches a constant speed almost immediately and falls slowly enough to make measurement easy. Once students are confident in taking these measurements and calculating speeds, you could progress to more complex situations in which speed varies during the motion. Experimentally, this will require interim time and distance measurements, rather than single distance and time readings for a whole journey. Getting students on the athletics track is a way to do this, but only use willing volunteers. Place student timers every 10 m along the track and collect a data set for a 50 m sprint. Usually, for the first part of the race the runner is accelerating and then they reach a steady speed, although you may need to ask students to deliberately vary their motion to show the ideas you wish to.

Science in context

- The fastest sprinters travel at about 10 m/s, with downhill skiers travelling at around 60 m/s.
- The fastest bird is the peregrine falcon, which can travel at up to 90 m/s (around 300 km/h).
- The fastest speed a human being has ever travelled is 11 km/s (around 40 000 km/h). This was reached by the crew of Apollo 10 as they re-entered the Earth's atmosphere.

In these examples we have used multiple units as in some cases m/s is not the most practical unit, which may also be the case in some questions students are given.

Speed and velocity

For younger students these words are often interchangeable, but making a clear distinction as early as possible at secondary level is recommended. Speed is a scalar quantity; it tells us how fast something is moving but not the direction it is travelling in. Velocity can be seen as the vector version of speed; it tells us how fast something is moving *and* the direction it is travelling in. Direction is important for velocity, so we use displacement to work it out. Displacement is very similar to distance but, like velocity, it has direction as well. The equation for velocity is shown below:

$$\text{velocity (m/s)} = \frac{\text{change in displacement (m)}}{\text{time (s)}}$$

$$v = \frac{s}{t}$$

Table 2.2 shows how speed and velocity are connected and the similarities and differences between them.

Table 2.2 Equations for moving objects

If the direction is not important, use scalar quantities. For example...		If the direction is important, use vector quantities. For example...	
speed = distance/time		velocity = displacement/time	
$v = d/t$		$v = s/t$	
Quantity (symbol)	**Unit**	**Quantity (symbol)**	**Unit**
distance (d)	metres (m)	displacement (s)	metres (m)
time (t)	seconds (s)	time (t)	seconds (s)
speed (v)	metres per second (m/s)	velocity (v)	metres per second (m/s)

It is easy to sympathise with students who ask, 'Does it really matter; they are more or less the same?' and for many situations students face early on, they may well be right. However, the following question helps to make the point about why it can matter. '*A cyclist travelling at 12 m/s moves towards a cyclist travelling at 11 m/s, what is the difference in velocities when they crash?*' Without knowing the direction of the slower cyclist, you don't know. The answer could be 1 m/s or 23 m/s and the collision could end up causing very different injuries. It also matters when studying circular motion for which ideas around changing direction and velocity are important (see Section 2.8, page 53).

Thankfully, when we consider vector quantities at this level, it is only in one dimension and so life is relatively simple. We normally use the symbols + and − to indicate direction and we can just pick whether + is up, down, left or right and, as long as we are consistent, there shouldn't be any problems. I recommend that when dealing with vectors such as displacement and velocity you should use a positive or negative sign before all values to be consistent and show that all vectors must have a direction.

Acceleration

The simplest way to describe acceleration is to say that when the velocity of an object is changing, it is accelerating. Students can think acceleration means speeding up or slowing down and while this is not untrue, it is not the whole story. Velocity has a magnitude and direction and so, as well as speeding up or slowing down, acceleration also describes changing direction. As with velocity at this level, directional considerations are simple and so + and − are all that we need to show whether the velocity is increasing or decreasing. Acceleration is calculated using the following equation, commonly using the symbol v for final velocity and u for initial velocity.

$$\text{acceleration (m/s}^2) = \frac{\text{final velocity (m/s)} - \text{initial velocity (m/s)}}{\text{time taken (s)}}$$

$$a = \frac{v - u}{t}$$

The unit m/s^2 for acceleration can cause confusion for students and so when introducing it you might want to say something like 'acceleration measures how much the velocity changes in metres per second *every second*'. You can tell them that this is a little clumsy to say or write and so (meters/second)/second is shortened to m/s^2. As $v - u$ is a *change in* velocity, it is sometimes shown as Δv. Δ is the capital Greek letter delta, and it is used as a shortened way of writing 'change in'.

For all accelerations, students will need to say whether the velocity is increasing or decreasing and so, while not wrong, deceleration is not needed as a term. Here, and elsewhere, you should feel able to use the language you wish to communicate ideas, but it is worth checking the requirements of your examination specification in case they have particular expectations.

When helping students develop fluency with calculations, don't forget that initially they are having to deal with a procedural demand (the mathematical skills) and a conceptual one (the physics ideas). This can provide a significant cognitive demand and so it's best to start with fully worked examples to show the 'right' way, so that you can then follow with partly completed ones, before you hand them over a list of practice questions to do on their own.

Equations of uniformly accelerated motion

For older students (14–16 years old), the analysis of motion can become more complex, using the equations of uniformly accelerated motion. These equations contain more variables and can be intimidating to students, but they are simply mathematical rearrangements and combinations of the equations for velocity and acceleration that they have already encountered. For example, the equation for acceleration, $a = \dfrac{v-u}{t}$, can be rearranged to calculate the final velocity, $v = u + at$.

Another equation that students may see is $v^2 = u^2 + 2as$. To derive this requires a little more mathematical work, but again this is not a new idea, just a different rearrangement of the equations for velocity and acceleration, done to make calculations easier. Rearranging equations is known to be challenging for some students. In addition to the considerations noted in the introductory chapter, the ASE publication *The Language of Mathematics in Science* provides much more detail about strategies and approaches you could take.

2.4 Motion graphs

Students may have some experience of drawing graphs in other physics topics or science lessons, but it is best to be alert to the support students may need with graph drawing and you may have to provide extra support here. In addition to the challenges mentioned in the introductory chapter, there are some additional issues specific to motion graphs:

→ Students can struggle to connect the static image of a graph to the dynamic situation that it represents, meaning they cannot always see the 'story' the graph is telling.
→ This topic can include distance, displacement, speed and velocity against time graphs, where similar looking lines mean different things and students can get confused. For example, a horizontal line on a distance–time graph represents a stationary object but on a velocity–time graph this means constant velocity.

Motion graphs without numbers

 Maths

In order to develop students' fluency with the ways in which motion can be represented graphically you can get them to interpret and draw graphs of different motions without adding numerical detail on the axes. Use journeys to school and shopping trips, for example. Focusing on the meaning of the shapes without numerical data is a deliberate effort to reduce the cognitive load.

You can move an object, such as your hand, and get students to graph its motion on mini-whiteboards. Or you can show students a graph and then get them to move their hands to show they understand what the graph represents. Table 2.3 shows one possible sequence of the graphs you might ask them to draw. You may wish to adapt it if you are not covering all graphs (for example, omitting displacement–time graphs). By graphing an observed motion rather than working from a prose description and by describing the motions from a graph, the hope is that the connections between real, dynamic situations and the graph can be reinforced.

Table 2.3 A way to introduce motion graphs

Graph	Motion	Notes
Distance–time	Moving in one direction at a constant speed. Then the same motion at a faster and slower speed.	These to develop the following ideas: • constant speed is represented on a distance–time graph as a straight line. • the steepness of that line represents the speed.
Distance–time	Motion in stages, for example moving in one direction slowly, then stopping for a few seconds and then moving off in the same direction at a faster or slower speed.	This allows discussion about what a horizontal line on a distance–time graph represents (stationary object).
Displacement–time	Repeat of distance–time examples above, and then again but with changes in direction.	These motions can be used to show how distance is different from displacement and how direction can be represented on a graph.
Speed–time	Moving in one direction at a constant speed. Then the same motion at a faster and a slower speed.	These to develop the following ideas: • constant speed is represented on a speed–time graph as a horizontal line. • the height of that horizontal line can be used to compare different speeds (higher = faster).
Speed–time	Motion in stages, for example moving in one direction slowly, then stopping for a few seconds and then moving off in the same direction at a faster or slower speed.	The fact that the motions here are exactly the same as those in the second examples but the graphs are different is a way to show how distance–time and speed–time graphs are connected but look different.
Velocity–time	Repeat of speed–time examples above, and then again but with changes in direction.	These motions can be used to show how velocity is different from speed and how direction can be represented on a graph.

An alternative is to ask students to sketch a motion graph for a particular sport and then in small groups look at each other's graph and try and work out what the sport is. It's best to start with distance–time graphs, but using other motion graphs helps to reinforce how similar looking graphs describe different motions. Examples that have been found to prompt good discussion include:

→ 200 m sprint (where runners accelerate for the initial part of the race and then reach a roughly constant speed for the rest of the race. This provides an opportunity to talk about the average and maximum speeds)

→ 4 × 100 m relay (showing overlapping lines and acceleration and deceleration at changeover)

→ vertical displacement–time for high jump or diving (where the athlete lands above or below the ground level).

 Technology use

In addition to the activities described above, there are a number of online simulations, such as PhET's The Moving Man, which can help connect dynamic situations and their associated motion graphs in real time. Many smartphones have accelerometers which allow motion data to be captured and these can be used in interesting situations such as on playground equipment, theme park rides or aeroplanes, although caution is needed as the data can be quite complicated and calibration is not always reliable.

The hope is that the qualitative activities mentioned above will help students to become fluent with the different types of graphs, as well as with what different shapes represent, making it easier to move to the quantitative stage. There are two common procedures that they will need to carry out when analysing motion graphs. The first is to calculate the speed of an object from a distance–time graph (or the velocity from a displacement–time graph); in both cases this is equal to the gradient of the line. Care is needed as some questions ask for speeds or velocities for part of the journey and so it is important to find the gradient of the appropriate part of the graph. The second common procedure is to work out the distance travelled from a speed–time graph (or displacement from a velocity–time graph); in each case, this is equal to the area under the graph. Sometimes students will need to calculate the distance for a motion that has changing speeds and, in almost all cases, this can be done by splitting the motion into sections, calculating individual areas and adding them together. Calculating the gradient of a graph and the area under it are techniques also covered in mathematics courses, so it is worth talking to your maths department. By knowing when they cover this content, how it is taught and the language used, you can reinforce the message that this is not a new skill, merely something that is needed and used in both subjects.

 Maths

Whenever drawing or analysing motion graphs, students should be encouraged to always include or check the labels of the axis and their corresponding units. It is very common for students to mix up distance–time and speed–time graphs and carry out the wrong calculations. Also, some graphical and numerical questions will require unit conversions between the data given and the required answer, and students should be alert to this.

2.5 Newton's laws

Newton's laws underpin most of the study of forces and motion at school level. It is often said that Newton 'discovered' gravity when an apple fell on his head but, while it is a nice story, it is not really true. Objects had always fallen to the ground; Newton's leap was to suggest that whatever caused the apple to fall was the same thing that caused the planets to orbit the Sun. Newton suggested a 'universal' law that always worked, regardless of the objects and distances. This was the majesty of his thinking and a lovely example of why a simple idea in physics can be so powerful; it doesn't just describe one situation, it can describe *all* situations involving motion. Newton's laws of motion describe how the forces on an object are related to changes in its motion. Ideas around Newton's laws are relevant to study at all ages, although the numerical analysis of Newton's 2nd law is usually covered by older students (14–16 years old).

 Science literacy

If a law in physics is said to be 'universal', it applies to all situations, everywhere, every time. We can measure the way that masses interact gravitationally on Earth and then apply this to the Solar System and beyond. Similar principles apply to the forces between charged objects and the way that all electromagnetic waves behave and interact with matter. The idea of a universal law is a powerful one that allows physicists to explore situations which may not allow easy direct measurement or be based on work that can be verified experimentally.

Science in context

Newton's contribution to physics was profound, but should not eclipse the work of many brilliant scientists who came after him and developed his work further. Émilie du Châtelet was a French natural philosopher and mathematician who translated Newton's book *Principia* into French, but also advanced understanding in the fields of conservation of energy, kinetic energy and motion of objects. The book *Passionate Minds* by David Bodanis provides more detail of du Châtelet and her work and an insight into society and gender in 18th century France.

Newton's model was good but it turned out that it didn't work for very large, very small or very fast-moving objects. At higher levels of study, students will discover that Einstein developed his theories of special and general relativity that give us better predictions. It would be unfair to say that Newton was wrong, it is just that his model turned out to be a simplification of what we now know. Einstein developed a better and more powerful model, and with the development of quantum physics we have produced other models that predict what happens with even more accuracy. As yet, we haven't been able to connect all the recent best models into a single framework, but this is one area of current research in physics.

The Perimeter Institute for Theoretical Physics in Canada is an internationally renowned centre where researchers from many branches of physics work together to explore the current unanswered questions in physics. Their website highlights current research, hosts webcasts and lectures and provides free teaching resources aimed at bringing modern physics to secondary school classrooms.

Newton's 1st law

Translated from Newton's original Latin, his 1st law reads something like this:

Every object continues in a state of being at rest or moving uniformly straight forward, unless it is compelled to change its state by force impressed.

This law says that if all the forces on an object are balanced, the object will experience no change in its motion: stationary objects will stay stationary and things moving at constant velocity (constant speed in a straight line) will carry on doing that. However, if there is an overall force on that object then it will change what it's doing. The word 'inertia' is sometimes used to describe the fact that objects tend to carry on doing whatever they are doing, obeying Newton's 1st law. You don't necessarily need to use this term in class but as it often appears in textbooks it is worth knowing. Many students, and adults, struggle with the idea that if something is moving at a constant velocity then the forces on it are balanced and that there is no overall force. In most situations there will be lots of forces on a moving object, it is just that when considered all together an overall unbalanced force is needed to cause a 'change in motion' and so if there is no change, all the forces must be balanced.

Similar confusion can occur when students observe moving things slowing down. It's hard to see the frictional force that is causing this change in motion, so it is more than reasonable to think that moving things slow down all by themselves without any force causing this. But slowing down *is* a 'change in motion' and so the law tells us that there must be an unbalanced force. You can use ice skaters, battery-powered hover pucks or an air track to show that, once pushed, objects tend to carry on moving but, however good your examples are, things do always come to a stop as you cannot totally eliminate friction, at least on Earth.

Figure 2.6 presents Newton's 1st law in an alternative, simplified way to help students deal with the two situations they will encounter.

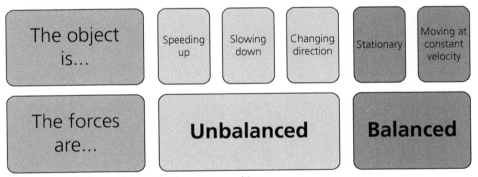

Figure 2.6 Relating motion to the forces on an object

The word 'equilibrium' can also cause problems, as students can think it only applies to stationary objects. When forces are in equilibrium it means that all the forces are balanced and so this can describe an object which is either stationary or moving at a constant velocity. The terms 'resultant force' or 'net force' are often used to describe all the forces on an object together and can be more helpful than phrases such as 'the forces cancel out' which can wrongly imply that they are no longer there.

Once you feel students are secure in Newton's 1st law ask them to observe or imagine someone throwing a ball upwards in the air. Get them to draw the ball and the forces on it just after it has left the hand, at the top of the path and on its way back down. Some students think that there is an upwards force on an object after it has left the hand, but this is not the case. Throughout the whole motion, going up, changing direction at the top or going down, there is only one downwards force, the weight of the ball. As a follow-on question, you could ask them to sketch the corresponding motion graphs for this throw.

Newton's 2nd law

We know from the 1st law that an unbalanced force will accelerate an object. The 2nd law provides a quantitative relationship between the force on a particular object, its mass and its acceleration. The equation is:

$$\text{force (N)} = \text{mass (kg)} \times \text{acceleration (m/s}^2)$$

$$F = ma$$

The fact that it is a force acting on a mass that causes an acceleration means that some teachers prefer to write the equation as $\dfrac{F}{m} = a$ as it can be easier to see that, for a fixed mass, a bigger force will result in a bigger acceleration. Although the equation might seem new, the ideas behind this law are intuitive for most people. Ask students to imagine a situation in which they pushed a bicycle as hard as they could and then pushed a car with the same force. Would there be any difference in what happens? Figure 2.7 shows this situation represented in a way that can be used to support students in becoming confident with the conceptual ideas before moving on to formal calculations.

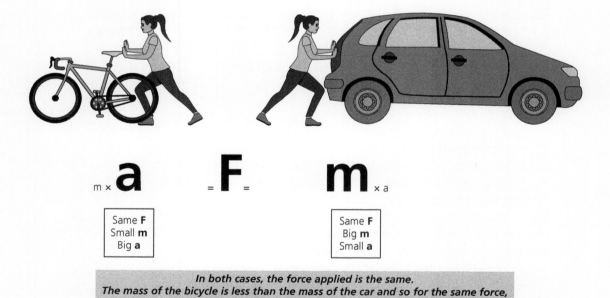

$$m \times \mathbf{a} \quad = \mathbf{F} = \quad \mathbf{m} \times a$$

| Same **F** Small **m** Big **a** |
| Same **F** Big **m** Small **a** |

In both cases, the force applied is the same.
The mass of the bicycle is less than the mass of the car and so for the same force,
the bicycle will experience a greater acceleration.

Figure 2.7 The relationship between force, mass and acceleration without using numbers

Exploration of Newton's 2nd law

A simple activity to help students appreciate the ideas in Newton's 2nd law in a qualitative way can be done with an elastic band, golf ball and ping-pong ball. This can show the effect of mass on the acceleration of objects with a constant force. Pull back an elastic band with a golf ball and a ping-pong ball next to each other and held against the stretched part of the band. Let go and watch what happens to the balls as they fly off. It should be clear that the ping-pong ball moves away with a greater acceleration than the golf ball. There is no need to measure the acceleration, but it is important to focus on acceleration rather than velocity or distance travelled in questioning and class discussion.

In both cases the force from the elastic band is approximately the same, but the greater mass of the golf ball means that this force will result in a comparatively smaller acceleration. It is possible to do this experiment with one ball at a time but it becomes harder to easily compare as you will end up measuring a proxy for acceleration such as distance travelled. You could use any two objects that have roughly the same size but quite different masses such as blocks from the density kit. Whatever you use, consider safety issues, for example using safety eyewear and avoiding objects falling on feet. Don't pull the elastic band too far, to reduce the chance of injury from flying objects.

KEY ACTIVITIES

An experiment that is commonly used to demonstrate and quantify the relationship $F = ma$ is shown below:

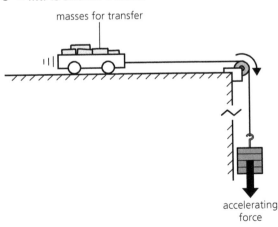

masses for transfer

accelerating force

In this experiment, the trolley is placed on a smooth, low friction surface and accelerated by varying the mass hanging down below the pulley. One end can be lifted *very* slightly to compensate for friction; check that the trolley rolls freely without slowing down or speeding up when given a small starting push. The weight of the masses hanging down provides the accelerating force; as this is varied, the acceleration of the trolley is measured. Light gates are often used to measure the acceleration although smartphone accelerometers can also be used. Caution is needed if you do this, as it involves putting the phone on the accelerating truck. It will need some protection, and make sure to also use a cushion or foam to stop the masses crashing into the floor. Make sure that all measurements are taken before the masses hit the floor so the trolley is still being accelerated.

A graph of force against acceleration should show a straight line, illustrating the directly proportional relationship between force and acceleration. The mass of the *whole system* can be calculated from the gradient. A common difficulty is that some students don't correctly connect the equations to the equipment. In the equation $F = ma$, the value of the accelerating force, F, is calculated from the weight of the masses hanging down below the pulley by using $W = mg$. What students sometimes fail to consider is that the m in the equation is the mass of the *whole system*, which is the hanging masses, the trolley and the connecting string. A clear relationship will only emerge if this total m is kept constant throughout the whole experiment. This requires students to keep the total number of masses constant and just move them from the trolley to the hanger or back to allow them to vary F.

Newton's 3rd law

Newton's 1st and 2nd laws focus on a single object, so we use simple examples. The 3rd law is different in that it looks at 'interactions' between two objects. A shortened form of the law suggests 'every action has an equal and opposite reaction', but this can be misleading as it does not make clear that the action and reaction forces mentioned are acting on *different* objects. The word reaction can also be problematic as it implies these forces occur sequentially whereas they happen instantaneously, another aspect of this law that is often not highlighted. This is more important than it may sound. If the law described a single object, nothing could ever accelerate as all forces would be balanced. Physics can be beautiful in the way it can reduce things to a simple law or equation but here is an example where over-simplification causes problems. Being more precise in your language can take a bit of getting used to, but if you are clear from the outset you can hope to avoid problems later on. A more precise but longer version of the law, closer to its original Latin version, is;

If object A exerts a force on object B then object B exerts an equal and opposite force of the same type on object A.

This version of the law makes it clear that the forces are on different objects, as well as showing that you can never have a single force on its own, forces can *only* happen if there is an 'interaction' between two objects. If you push an object, the force you feel on your hand will be the same magnitude as the force you apply to the object; these forces occur as your hand and the object interact, and not one after another. You can only push things as hard as they are able to push back. You cannot push a floating balloon as hard as you could push a brick wall, because the balloon is not able to push back as much as the wall.

Science in context

Water and gas jetpacks that can keep a pilot hovering in the air can be explained with Newton's 3rd law. The jets provide a downwards force pushing on the water or gas. At the same time the water or gas produces an equal and opposite upwards force on the pilot. If this force is the same size as the pilot's weight, they stay in the air.

Newton's three laws, rope and skateboards

A good way to explore all three of Newton's laws together with a class is by using some skateboards, or wheelie chairs, and some rope. Caution is needed here as students can fall off, so we recommend sitting rather than standing on the skateboards and individuals should start at least 2 m apart to avoid collisions. You may need large skateboards to carry out the third situation suggested, but all of these can really help illustrate Newton's laws in an accessible, classroom situation. Figure 2.8 below shows multiple situations, in a recommended order to work through. In each case, before anyone pulls the rope as directed, ask all students what they think will happen and why. In each case we have identified possible responses and explained what should happen and why, with reference to which of Newton's laws is applied.

Situation	Possible responses	Correct response
pulls rope / holds rope does not pull	Some students may think that the person holding the rope will be pulled towards the person pulling the rope and the person pulling the rope will remain stationary as no one is pulling them.	*Both people will move, towards each other.* The person holding the rope is being pulled by the rope to the left and so will accelerate that way (Newton 1), towards the middle. The person pulling the rope applies a force to the rope to the left. The rope applies an equal and opposite force on them to the right (Newton 3). This force accelerates them in that direction (Newton 1), towards the middle.
pulls rope / pulls rope	Students will usually appreciate that they will both move together.	*Both people will move, towards each other.* As with the previous situation, there is the same force on each person. This acts towards the middle and so they will each accelerate in that direction and move towards each other (Newton 1).

| 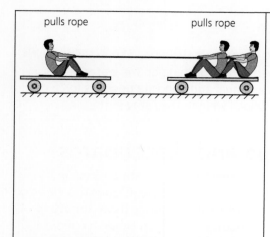
pulls rope   pulls rope | Students may think that this will be the same as the previous situation. | *They will both move towards each other. The single person will move faster than the pair.*

In this situation, although the force is the same on each side, because the masses on each side are different the acceleration will be different.

The mass of the pair is greater than the mass of the single person. The same force is acting on the single person as the pair. The mass of the pair is greater and so this force will result in a smaller acceleration (Newton 2). |

Figure 2.8 Demonstrations of Newton's three laws of motion

2.6 Mass and weight, freefall and terminal velocity

It is quite likely that your lessons on mass and weight will be the first point at which the difference between these terms will have been addressed. A solution may be saying something like 'I know people say other things outside, but in this room and in the exam, this is what the terms 'mass' and 'weight' mean'.

The term 'freefall' is used to describe unsupported, falling objects that are being accelerated by the downwards force due to gravity (weight). In some situations, air resistance is considered and sometimes not, so when using examples make this clear. The activity suggested in this chapter that explores the motion of a skydiver may be the first time students are asked to consider air resistance that does not remain constant, increasing as something gets faster. Even though they may be comfortable with the underlying ideas from previous lessons, combining them in one context can be a challenge.

Mass and weight

The mass of an object, measured in kilograms, is an inherent property of that object, just like its colour or volume. It will be the same wherever the object is. If an object has a large mass, it will be much harder to accelerate it with a force compared with a small object. A common definition of mass that can be helpful is 'the amount of matter in an object' as this gives us a sense that the mass of an object depends on what the object is made of and so it is fixed.

Weight is a measure of the gravitational force exerted on an object and, in almost all cases, this will be the downwards pull on an object by the gravitational field of the Earth. As this is a force, it is measured in newtons. If the strength of gravitational field changes then so does the weight and this change is one of the ways in which it is different from mass. If you take an object to the Moon, it remains the same object and so the mass stays the same. The gravitational field strength of the Moon is less than that of the Earth and so the weight of the object will be less on the Moon. The gravitational field strength at the surface of the Earth is approximately constant and has been measured to be 9.81 N/kg, meaning that every single kilogram will be pulled down with a force of 9.81 N. Some books use the value 10 N/kg, which is less precise but makes the calculations easier. On the Moon, the gravitational field strength is 1.63 N/kg, about six times less than on Earth.

We can use this idea, a little bit of logic and some imagination to explain the apparently counter-intuitive idea that, in the *absence of air resistance*, all objects will accelerate towards the ground at the same rate. Imagine dropping a brick with a mass of 1 kg. It has a weight of 9.81 N and so we can use Newton's 2nd law to work out the acceleration. Then imagine two and then three bricks tied together and do the calculations again. A pattern soon appears; the acceleration is always the same. These calculations are shown in the table below.

Table 2.4 Force and acceleration for different falling masses

1 brick	2 bricks	3 bricks
Mass = 1 kg	Mass = 2 kg	Mass = 3 kg

Weight = $m \times g$
    = 1 kg × 9.81 N/kg
    = 9.81 N
 	
Acceleration = F/m
    = 9.81 N / 1 kg
    = 9.81 m/s²
	Weight = $m \times g$
	    = 2 kg × 9.81 N/kg
	    = 19.62 N
	
	Acceleration = F/m
	    = 19.62 N / 2 kg
	    = 9.81 m/s²
		Weight = $m \times g$
		    = 3 kg × 9.81 N/kg
		    = 29.43 N
		
		Acceleration = F/m
		    = 29.43 N / 3 kg
		    = 9.81 m/s²

Adding bricks increases the mass and weight proportionally, and so the acceleration will always stay the same however many bricks you have. In each situation, the masses and forces are different and so it is important to be precise with your language. It is only the acceleration that is the same in each case. An alternative way to get students to consider this is to have two tennis balls, one of which has been completely filled with water carefully using a syringe. When falling over a few metres, both balls are indistinguishable, falling at the same rate. Once you have shown the balls to be 'exactly the same' you can pass both to students who might offer a surprised look. What they see and think (the balls fall the same and so they must be the same) does not seem to align with what they expect (one is heavier than the other and so it should have fallen faster) and so they are forced to challenge their preconceptions.

Freefall and terminal velocity

The motion of a skydiver from when they leave the aeroplane to when they land involves many of the ideas of forces and regularly appears in questions. Working through this motion step by step, looking at the forces and the velocity–time graph and connecting them, is a good way to model how to answer these types of questions, as well as how physics works more generally:

Figure 2.9 suggests the stages you should break the motion into and the points to highlight. You can act this out (lying on a table if you wish) or use a video that you pause at each point. At each point, take the following approach in small groups or class discussion.

→ Be clear about the point in the motion you are focused on (e.g. just after they have opened their parachute).
→ Identify the forces on the parachutist, their direction, relative size and if they have changed.
→ From the resultant force, identify if the parachutist is accelerating and, if so, in which direction.
→ From this acceleration, describe any changes in velocity.
→ Sketch a velocity–time graph for that part of the motion.

Graph (positive velocity is downwards)	Forces diagram	Description/Explanation	Teaching notes/Learning challenges
	 air resistance weight	The weight acting downwards is greater than the air resistance acting upwards. There is an unbalanced downwards force and so the skydiver accelerates downwards. The upwards slope of the velocity/time graph shows a downwards acceleration.	It is a good idea to use the velocity–time graph and the force diagrams together. You can show the graph and ask students about the forces or the other way round. In both cases you will get the correct answer, the key is to connect forces and motion using Newton's laws.
	 air resistance weight	As they accelerate, their downwards velocity increases. Throughout the fall, the weight remains constant but air resistance increases with velocity, so the upwards force increases but is still less than the weight. This means that there is still an unbalanced force downwards, but it is decreasing. The decreasing gradient of the graph indicates that the acceleration is getting less, even though the velocity continues to increase.	Students may think that the increase in air resistance means that the skydiver is slowing down here. This is not the case. They continue to speed up; it is the acceleration *not* velocity that is decreasing. Being precise about language and whether you are talking about forces, velocity or acceleration is very important and can help unravel these confusions.

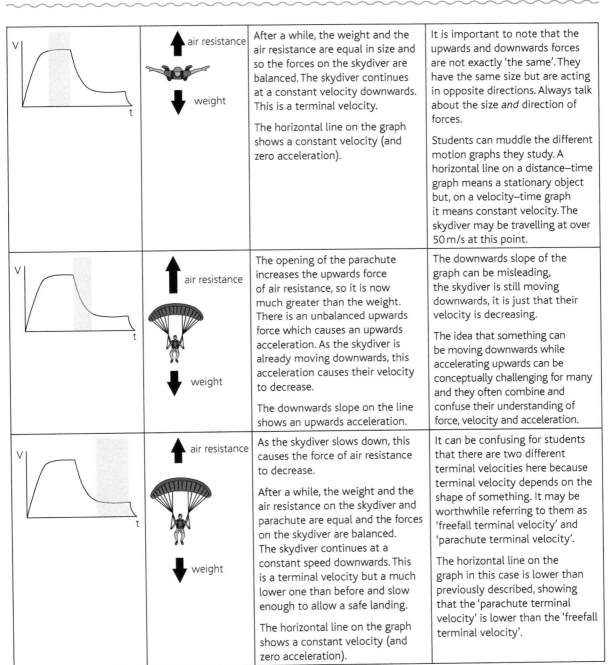

		After a while, the weight and the air resistance are equal in size and so the forces on the skydiver are balanced. The skydiver continues at a constant velocity downwards. This is a terminal velocity. The horizontal line on the graph shows a constant velocity (and zero acceleration).	It is important to note that the upwards and downwards forces are not exactly 'the same'. They have the same size but are acting in opposite directions. Always talk about the size *and* direction of forces. Students can muddle the different motion graphs they study. A horizontal line on a distance–time graph means a stationary object but, on a velocity–time graph it means constant velocity. The skydiver may be travelling at over 50 m/s at this point.
		The opening of the parachute increases the upwards force of air resistance, so it is now much greater than the weight. There is an unbalanced upwards force which causes an upwards acceleration. As the skydiver is already moving downwards, this acceleration causes their velocity to decrease. The downwards slope on the line shows an upwards acceleration.	The downwards slope of the graph can be misleading, the skydiver is still moving downwards, it is just that their velocity is decreasing. The idea that something can be moving downwards while accelerating upwards can be conceptually challenging for many and they often combine and confuse their understanding of force, velocity and acceleration.
		As the skydiver slows down, this causes the force of air resistance to decrease. After a while, the weight and the air resistance on the skydiver and parachute are equal and the forces on the skydiver are balanced. The skydiver continues at a constant speed downwards. This is a terminal velocity but a much lower one than before and slow enough to allow a safe landing. The horizontal line on the graph shows a constant velocity (and zero acceleration).	It can be confusing for students that there are two different terminal velocities here because terminal velocity depends on the shape of something. It may be worthwhile referring to them as 'freefall terminal velocity' and 'parachute terminal velocity'. The horizontal line on the graph in this case is lower than previously described, showing that the 'parachute terminal velocity' is lower than the 'freefall terminal velocity'.

Figure 2.9 Forces on and motion of a skydiver

In addition to exploring terminal velocity using the skydiver example, it is possible for students to investigate terminal velocity in the classroom. One possibility involves using falling cupcake (muffin) cases, which fall quite slowly making reasonably accurate measurements possible and they often reach terminal velocity very quickly. Students can design an experiment to test if the cupcake case does reach terminal velocity and if so, what that velocity is. A simplified version involves dropping a cupcake case from a height of 2 m, measuring the velocity of the first 1 m of the fall, second 1 m of the fall and the whole distance, and comparing them.

Technology use

More accurate measurements with data loggers or video analysis software provides a way for students to explore the motion of other falling objects in more detail and consider other variables. Tracker is a free software package that can analyse most video files (see resources section at end of chapter for more details). If you are using video analysis software such as Tracker, make sure that there is a metre rule or an object of a known length in the video shot so you can calibrate the data.

2.7 Momentum and collisions

Students are likely to be familiar with and have carried out calculations of velocity and acceleration, and so it will be important to introduce 'momentum' as a different, but related, term that is connected to motion. The conceptual challenges here mean that momentum is often covered towards the end of the study of forces.

Some students can erroneously see momentum and (kinetic) energy as the same thing, possibly compounded as they both have mass and velocity in their associated formulae. There are connections between the two, but they are different. At this level, one key distinction is the vector nature of momentum in which direction is important and needs to be known for calculations. This then provides a way to explore a universal law relating to the conservation of momentum in all interactions. Although the total amount of energy is always conserved, kinetic energy is not conserved in all interactions as it can move into a different energy store.

Momentum

If you ask a student if it's easier to stop a fast or slow cricket ball, they would have no trouble in giving you an answer. Extending the question to a more unlikely situation, ask them if it would be easier to stop a slow-moving car or a fast cricket ball and they will usually find it easy to provide another correct answer. Momentum is a way of measuring the 'motion of an object' and, as the examples illustrate, depends on two things: velocity and mass. In the first case the masses of both balls were the same, but the faster ball had a greater momentum. In the second case, even though the ball is travelling faster, the mass of the car is so much bigger than the ball, it has more momentum and so is harder to stop.

Momentum is defined as follows:

$$\text{momentum (kg m/s)} = \text{mass (kg)} \times \text{velocity (m/s)}$$
$$p = mv$$

Note that lower-case p is used as the symbol for momentum, upper-case P is used for pressure.

As with all vectors, direction matters but, like velocity and acceleration the questions and examples students will usually encounter will be restricted to one dimension and so + and − can be added to terms to indicate direction.

Conservation of momentum and collisions

Imagine you were sitting on a stationary skateboard; a heavy rucksack was thrown at you. You caught it perfectly and didn't lose your balance. What would happen? Most students would have an intuitive sense that you'd start moving in the same direction as the rucksack was moving and that, if the rucksack was heavier, you'd move faster. If you were to talk about the situation in terms of momentum, you would call this a 'collision', a term used when two or more objects collide, stick together, move or break apart. One of the universal laws of physics is that, if there are no external forces (the term 'closed system' is sometimes used) the total momentum before and after every collision will always be the same.

 Technology use

Using video analysis or data loggers and light gates you can ask students to test this law. Trolleys with springs or coupling mechanism (often magnets) can be used to explore collisions in which moving objects join and move off together as one, or bounce off each other. In addition to this classroom activity, there are some videos taken on the International Space Station available from the *Astro Academy: Principia* project that can be used to show various collisions in a friction-free environment (see resources section at end of chapter for more details).

The rucksack example describes two objects combining but the law also applies when a stationary object splits with the parts moving in opposite directions. This why when a gun or cannon fires, it recoils in the opposite direction to the projectile. Figure 2.10 shows this happening; the cannon moves backwards as the cannonball flies forwards. The mass of the cannon is so much larger than the cannonball that it only recoils at a fraction of the cannonball's speed and in the opposite direction. The size of the forward and backward velocities are not the same, but the momentums are.

Although all the examples used here have involved large objects, as the law of conservation of momentum is a universal law it is used to help interpret the collisions of sub-atomic particles that happen at the Large Hadron Collider at CERN. The calculations are a lot more complex and involve three dimensions, but the principles are the same, and have helped us discover new particles and learn about their behaviours.

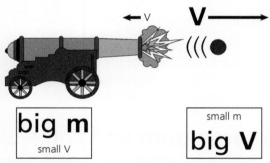

Figure 2.10 The total momentum after firing the cannon remains zero.

2.8 Circular motion

Most of the examples of moving objects that students examine at this level will be travelling in a straight line, so considerations relating to direction will be simple (up or down, forwards or backwards). Motion in a circular path is different as the direction of an object is constantly changing and so it must be accelerating even if its speed does not change. Circular motion is particularly important when studying the orbit of planets and satellites, and is also detailed in Chapter 8 Earth in space. This topic builds on multiple ideas about forces and motion, and so is usually covered at the end of the study of forces.

An engaging way to begin a look at circular motion is to swing a rubber bung attached to a string around your head in a circular path. This activity is often better done outside. You will need to group the class carefully, wear eye protection, ensure that the bungs are secure on the string and make sure nothing breakable is nearby. You can use a soft toy to replace the bung to reduce the risks.

Good questions to ask students are:

1 Is there a force on the bung and, if so, what is the direction of this force and where is it coming from?
2 What will happen if I let go?

These questions will allow you to draw out ideas around circular motion. These are:

→ When an object is moving in a circular path its direction is constantly changing. This means its velocity is changing and so it must be accelerating.
→ The force causing that acceleration always acts towards the centre of the circle and is described as a centripetal force.
→ If the force is removed, the object will carry on in a straight line at a tangent to the circular path.

The term 'centripetal force' is not a new type of force. It is a descriptive word for *any* force that causes circular motion (centripetal means centre-seeking). It can help to use multiple examples of circular motion that have different causes of the centripetal force, such as a car going around a track (friction), planets orbiting the Sun (gravitational) and an electron orbiting a nucleus (electrostatic). In each case, identify what is the cause of the force and then use the term 'centripetal' as an overarching description. Some students may have heard or used the term 'centrifugal' force, describing a force that 'pushes things outwards' when moving in a circular path, but this is not a correct description of what is happening. If you are on a roundabout, it *feels* like you are being pushed outwards by an imaginary (centrifugal) force, but in reality, your body is simply obeying Newton's 1st law by trying to carry on moving in a straight line. It is the inwards (centripetal) force towards the centre that keeps you in place, assuming you are holding on.

To reinforce these ideas, ask students to stand in a line and swing a (very) soft toy attached to a string around as shown in Figure 2.11. Ask them what will happen if you let go of the string at point A.

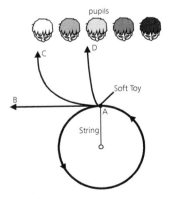

Figure 2.11 Investigating circular motion (top view)

It is common for students to think that D or C represents the path that the toy will take when you let go, but it will follow path B, carrying on in a straight line at constant speed, in accordance with Newton's 1st law.

A second demonstration illustrating the same behaviour involves an extra-long sparkler. This should only be carried out as a teacher demonstration. Bend the sparkler at a right angle to the handle end and, when lit, spin it carefully in a hand drill. When it rotates, sparks fly off in straight lines, showing that when they are no longer attached to the sparkler they no longer move in a circular path.

The sparkler should rotate in the vertical plane, preferably with a clamped hand-cranked drill. If it is done with a cordless drill, it must be set to a slowish speed (at higher speeds, the unbalanced mass will cause considerable vibration and instability). All students must be wearing safety eyewear, and the students should stand well back. The demonstrator should wear a lab coat and, if necessary, have their hair tied back. Make sure the area around the sparkler is free from combustible material. Students can capture pictures using, for example, phone cameras. In addition to these safety considerations, you should carry out your own risk assessment and ensure you consider any nearby smoke alarms.

2.9 Resources
Online resources

Please go to **spark.iop.org/asebook** for a set of curated resources from the IOP Spark website to match this chapter.

The American Association for the Advancement of Science (AAAS) *Project 2061* has a whole collection of indexed diagnostic questions on forces and many other topics: www.aaas.org

Astro Academy: Principia is a collection of classroom resources and teachers' guides on teaching the forces topic and in particular Newton's laws, momentum and circular motion. These include videos of experiments carried out by Tim Peake aboard the International Space Station that can be analysed with Tracker: www.astroacademy.org.uk

The Best Evidence Science Teaching (BEST) from the University of York hasmany diagnostic questions, follow-up activities and detail on the progression of conceptual ideas in this and other topics: www.stem.org.uk

The Physics Factbook contains lots of different velocities, accelerations and other motion data measurements for many real-life situations that can provide alternative contexts and examples to use in class: www.hypertextbook.com

The free Tracker software allows detailed motion analysis of video files: https://physlets.org/tracker/

The Universe and More website has a number of interactive physics games: www.theuniverseandmore.com

Simulations

PhET simulations 'Balloons and Static Electricity' and 'The Moving Man': https://phet.colorado.edu

References

ASE. *Concept Cartoons* series. Millgate: Association for Science Education. Provides questions for discussion based around common alternative conceptions.

Boohan, R. (2016) *The Language of Mathematics in Science*. Hatfield: Association for Science Education. Offers a summary of many of the mathematical challenges that students face in physics, many of which occur in the forces topic.

Driver, R., Squires, A., Rushworth, P. and Wood-Robinson, V. (2014) *Making Sense of Secondary Science: Research into Children's Ideas* (2nd ed.). New York: Routledge. A comprehensive summary of the research on common conceptual difficulties that students have.

Further reading

Bodanis, D. (2006) *Passionate Minds: The Great Enlightenment Love Affair*. New York: Crown. Detail of the life and work of Émilie du Châtelet including translating Newton's work and her own contributions to maths and Physics.

Brock, R. *Stories from Physics Booklet 2: Forces and Motion*. Institute of Physics. This booklet has many interesting and engaging stories around this topic that you can use in your teaching.

The *Force Concept Inventory* is a widely used and very well researched assessment tool covering many basic ideas in Newtonian physics with questions. Hestenes D, Wells M, Swackhamer G 1992 Force concept inventory. The Physics Teacher 30: 141-166.

Rankin, W. (2010) *Introducing Newton: A Graphic Guide*. London: Icon Books. This provides an accessible overview of Newton's life, the society in which he lived, his work and the ideas that came before him. Suitable for teachers as well as something to recommend to students.

3

Electricity and magnetism

Rachel Hartley, Peter Fairhurst and Tom Norris

Introduction

Students may think of electricity and magnetism as somewhat magical, with instant control at the flick of a switch. From light bulbs to electric cars, electronic devices have changed work, study, entertainment and communications. Many devices respond to our touch; some display information in an instant. They can communicate and link with other devices nearby. Understanding that these devices are, in fact, not magical is a crucial part of any young person's education. The devices work in fixed and predictable ways according to fundamental physical laws. In exploring these, students are learning the foundations on which all complex electronic technologies are based.

Furthermore, electrical impulses are central to many biological systems: keeping your heart beating; controlling muscle responses; the firing of neurons and reinforcing connections in the brain as you think and dream. These are complex processes beyond the scope of this chapter, but all are based on the fundamental laws of electricity.

Electricity
Prior experiences

In primary school, students are likely to have investigated current electricity. They should have learnt about the difference between conductors and insulators. They will have progressed from making a bulb light up in a simple circuit to investigating bulb brightness or the loudness of a buzzer. Students will have used a variety of devices and some will have used circuit symbols and diagrams. They may have designed and made a set of traffic lights or an alarm. At home, students will have seen a single cable from home appliances to the socket, so students may have unknowingly developed separate models and schema for 'school electricity' and 'home electricity'. Your challenge may be to reconcile the two.

The electricity topic presents conceptual and practical challenges for the teacher. Given that our understanding of 'electricity' stems from centuries of debate, it is unsurprising that some highly-skilled, experienced science teachers admit that they've never really understood electricity. Teachers may find themselves fire-fighting their way through the logistics of building circuits and wonder if it might be simpler just to use a simulation instead. In this chapter we hope to provide knowledge, ideas and encouragement to address these issues.

A teaching sequence

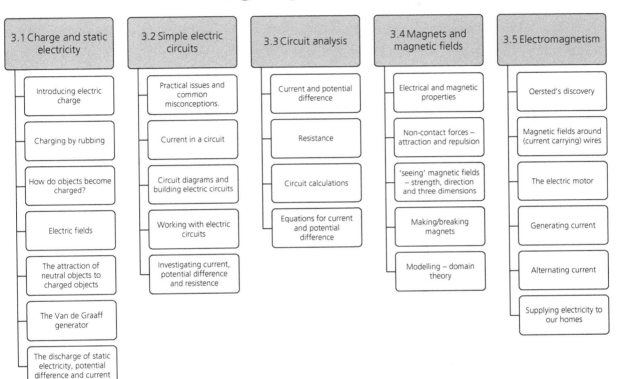

3.1 Charge and static electricity
- Introducing electric charge
- Charging by rubbing
- How do objects become charged?
- Electric fields
- The attraction of neutral objects to charged objects
- The Van de Graaff generator
- The discharge of static electricity, potential difference and current

3.2 Simple electric circuits
- Practical issues and common misconceptions.
- Current in a circuit
- Circuit diagrams and building electric circuits
- Working with electric circuits
- Investigating current, potential difference and resistence

3.3 Circuit analysis
- Current and potential difference
- Resistance
- Circuit calculations
- Equations for current and potential difference

3.4 Magnets and magnetic fields
- Electrical and magnetic properties
- Non-contact forces – attraction and repulsion
- 'seeing' magnetic fields – strength, direction and three dimensions
- Making/breaking magnets
- Modelling – domain theory

3.5 Electromagnetism
- Oersted's discovery
- Magnetic fields around (current carrying) wires
- The electric motor
- Generating current
- Alternating current
- Supplying electricity to our homes

 Science literacy

The word 'electricity' was first used in the 1600s, from the Greek *elektron* meaning amber (solidified tree sap, which becomes charged when rubbed). However, the word itself does not have a specific meaning. In everyday language, 'electricity' can always be replaced by a more accurate term:

- '*Electricity* is a flow of charged particles.' (current)
- 'Car batteries provide more *electricity* than an AA battery.' (potential difference)
- 'Turn the lights off to save *electricity*.' (reduce energy transfer)
- 'For lightning to strike, *electricity* has to build up in the clouds.' (charge)

Vocabulary instruction is crucial in helping students to unravel the complexity of this topic. Make sure they know that the word 'electricity' in isolation is just the title of the topic, and nothing else.

Progression

Electricity topics should *explain* what static electricity and electric current are. This clearly requires the concept of electrons. Electricity topics will, therefore, be much more meaningful for students if they *already* have an understanding of what electrons are. We would recommend teaching about atoms, atomic structure and electrons prior to covering electricity. At the very least, at the start of electricity topics you should establish that *all* materials contain an incredibly large number of tiny negatively charged particles called electrons, and that in *some* materials (called electrical conductors) *some* of these electrons are free and so able to move and indeed *flow* in the right conditions (such as when a potential difference is applied). You can then begin to discuss the causes and effects of such flows of charge through materials.

The topic of 'static electricity' is primarily about the effects of *stationary* charge, which stays in one place once transferred there. Do be careful with the term 'static electricity'; it may sound as if there are two kinds of 'electricity', one in which the 'electricity' is stationary and one where the 'electricity' is flowing. It is the word 'electricity' that causes the problem here; it is always better to talk in terms of charge, charged particles or electrons. So an 'electric current' always refers to a *flow of charge*; charge that is moving. This is much clearer and again illustrates why the concept of charge is fundamental.

3.1 Charge and static electricity
Introducing electric charge

Charge is a fundamental property of protons and electrons. So if students are already familiar with atomic structure this could be a logical starting point. Macroscopic objects become 'charged' if an imbalance arises between the electrons and protons on the object's surface. An excess of electrons causes a negative charge; a deficiency of electrons causes a positive charge.

The quantity of charge on an object is given the symbol Q (Q for 'quantity') and is measured in units called coulombs. However, the word 'charge' can also sometimes mean 'charged particle', so an electron *is* a charge as well as *having* charge. Charge is also a verb, objects become *charged*.

π Maths

When introducing the concept of charge to your students, it can be useful and interesting for them to learn about the magnitude of the numbers involved. Show students how small the charge on one electron is ($-0.000\,000\,000\,000\,000\,000\,16\,C$, or $-1.6 \times 10^{-19}\,C$) and then explain why this is often simplified to a relative value of -1 (and $+1$ for protons) elsewhere in science.

Science literacy

Unfortunately, the word 'charge' also has numerous different everyday meanings (associated with payments, moving forwards, and criminal accusations) that need to be separated from the scientific meanings. Even 'charging' a battery is misleading. 'Recharging' a battery has nothing to do with charge; it really means to reverse an electro-chemical reaction and replenish a store of *energy*.

Science in context

The concept of electric charge can be engagingly demonstrated and linked to students' own experiences. Ask if anyone has experienced a small electric shock, for example from a trampoline, door handle, woolly jumper, rug or carpet, car door or escalator. Give students some structure here: When was it? What happened exactly? What did it feel like? Value students' experiences and then link these experiences together by explaining that shocks are often received if you touch an object that is *charged* rather than *neutral*.

KEY ACTIVITIES

Make a show of touching nearby neutral objects and *not* getting a shock, and then demonstrate a spark using a Van de Graaff generator. It is essential that you are familiar with health and safety advice for this, the domes should be no more than 26 cm diameter. People with electrical medical implants should keep 4 m away. Please consult CLEAPSS for further guidance. Charge a rod or balloon by rubbing and show how it can attract small pieces of paper, whereas neutral rods and balloons have no effect. The contrast between the charged and neutral examples is important. A simple charge detector can be constructed from a plastic cup, cocktail stick and folded paper (see Figure 3.1). Charged objects, such as the rubbed balloon, will attract the paper and cause it to rotate, whereas a neutral object will not.

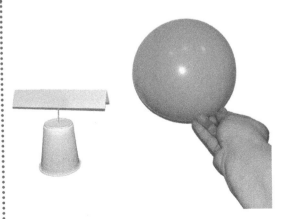

Figure 3.1 A simple charge detector

Students need to be taught that there are two types of charge that we call 'positive' and 'negative', and that there is an attractive *force* between oppositely charged objects, and a repulsive *force* between similarly charged objects. It is important to use the language of forces, rather than just saying 'opposites attract', to help students see the links between different areas of physics. Make it clear to students that the 'electrostatic force' between charges is different from the 'magnetic force' between magnets, despite a similar rule (opposites attract) applying to both.

Science in context

The history of the development of ideas about electrical effects is fascinating, and involves experiments with Victorian parlour tricks, dangling charged schoolboys and twitching frogs' legs. Rogers (2018) and Brock (2019) provide excellent overviews.

Charging by rubbing

Students need to know that some objects can become charged when rubbed. Students can easily do this using plastic rods and cloths or dusters, or simply balloons rubbed on jumpers. When polythene is rubbed it will become positive; other plastics and glass will become negative. You should warn students that touching the charged portion of a rod will cause a transfer of charge and return to neutral. For this reason, testing the rules for attraction and repulsion can be fiddly. A simple method is to balance a charged rod horizontally on an inverted evaporating basin. Another similar charged rod can then make the first rod spin by repulsion, but a differently charged rod will do the same by attraction. It is also very simple to charge a rod or balloon to attract small pieces of paper (however, note that the attracted paper was neutral – see Section 3.1, page 61). Be careful not to say the paper 'sticks'; there is an 'electrostatic force of attraction' responsible for this, not glue.

How do objects become charged?

This is much easier to explain if students are already familiar with what electrons are. This is much preferable to explanations or diagrams that refer to mysterious 'charges' (+ and – signs) within materials.

The idea is simply that friction (rubbing or contact) transfers electrons from one object to the other, resulting in a charge imbalance. One material gains extra electrons so becomes negative and the other loses electrons to become positive. Providing students with a diagram of an atom, with the electrons in shells around the outside of every atom, may help explain why it is only electrons that get transferred.

Science literacy

Static electricity is sometimes called 'triboelectricity'. Look up 'the triboelectric series' for a list of materials ordered by their tendency to gain or lose electrons on contact.

Electric field: just a name for the space around charged objects

The concept of an electric field sounds complicated but it is really just a *label* for the space around a charged object, where another charged object will experience a force (attractive or repulsive). In other words, if you put a charged object 'in the electric field' of a second charged object, that first charged object experiences a force and vice versa. It really is that simple. The concept of a gravitational field is very similar – a gravitational field is similarly just a *label* for the space around a mass (for example, a planet) where another mass experiences a (gravitational) force. Gravitational forces act on objects with mass in a gravitational field and electric forces act on objects with charge in an electric field. Gravitational forces are always attractive, but electric forces are either attractive or repulsive depending on the charges involved.

Electric fields are 3D however they are usually represented using 2D diagrams. Field lines represent the direction and intensity of the force that would act on charges placed the field. The force caused by electric fields is called the 'electrostatic force', although you will also see 'electric force' and sometimes 'coulomb force'.

The attraction of neutral objects to charged objects

The attraction of apparently neutral objects (such as small pieces of paper or dust) to charged objects is a common static electricity phenomena. The idea is that a charged object, when brought close to a neutral object, causes charged particles *within* the neutral object to move or rotate slightly, to be attracted or repelled as far as possible. The neutral object therefore remains neutral as no charge has been gained or lost, but the positive and negative charges within it now all *align* in a certain way. This creates areas of positive and negative charge within the object while it remains neutral overall. These areas of charge are then attracted towards the original charged object.

Technology use

A visual explanation of the alignment of charges in a neutral object, such as the PhET *Balloons and Static Electricity* simulation, works well to help students to connect their observations to the microscopic causes (see Resources at the end of the chapter).

The Van de Graaff generator

A Van de Graaff generator can help to demonstrate many different physics ideas and it is a memorable part of physics teaching. It is not just an add-on or a 'fun lesson'; it should be used in lessons strategically to help students to learn specific ideas. Gain confidence by practising with your colleagues or attending training such as from the Institute of Physics in the UK. Always discharging the dome (using the small sphere connected to the Earth connection) before touching the equipment will avoid any shocks. Detailed safety guidance is available from CLEAPSS and Scottish Schools Education Research Centre (SSERC) (see Resources at the end of this chapter). It is important to be aware that people with heart conditions or medical implants (such as pacemakers or cochlea implants) should be at least 4 m from an operating Van de Graaff generator. The strong electric field can disrupt or damage nearby electronic equipment. Students may be involved in demonstrations, but only one at a time and they should be volunteers.

The dome of the generator becomes charged due to the triboelectric effect of the belt on the pulley. The comb provides a conduction path to transfer the charge. There is no safety reason to prevent lifting off the dome while the Van de Graaff generator is off and discharged. Electrons are transferred *from* the dome, and *from* anything touching the dome, *to* the belt. The dome and anything touching it therefore become positively charged.

Many Van de Graaff demonstrations are just different ways of showing that like charges repel. To perform the classic 'hair standing on end' demonstration, a volunteer should stand on an insulating platform and place their hands on the (switched off) dome. When the generator is turned on, they do not receive a shock but instead gradually become charged. Their hair stands on end as charge spreads through their body; every hair becomes positively charged and so repels from every other hair. When finished, turn off the motor and pass the student the end of a wooden metre ruler, which safely discharges them when they take it; they can then step off the insulating platform. Alternatively, balance a stack of small metal pie cases on top of the Van de Graaff dome. When the machine is switched on they will float upwards, one by one, as they all gain the same charge so repel each other.

 ## Technology use

The Resources section at the end of the chapter lists links for further ideas, guidance and explanations about using the Van de Graaff generator, including a useful YouTube video from CLEAPSS.

A lesser known use of the Van de Graaff generator is to allow students to *experience* an electric field. Supervised students can bring the back of their hand to within 15 cm of the charged dome (so within the dome's electric field), and will feel a tingling sensation. This is because tiny hairs on the skin are affected by the electric field and so stand upright, repelling each other.

A demonstration of earthing is also effective. Ensure the smaller sphere is connected to the Van de Graaff generator's Earth connection, and hold it in place touching the dome. The dome is now 'earthed'; this means that there is a conducting path from it to the ground. The dome should now be perfectly safe for anyone to touch: any charge that builds up on the dome immediately flows away to Earth through the smaller sphere connection. Note that the charge is sometimes said to 'flow away to Earth', despite the fact that electrons really flow 'up' from Earth when neutralising a positive charge.

Discharge of static electricity, potential difference and current

When you touch a charged rod, it discharges as the charge is transferred to your skin and spreads out. Like charges will always repel away from each other if they can. This is why charge flows away to Earth if there is a conducting path available for it to do so.

Another way of describing this is to say that a build-up of charge (lots of charges in the same place or a high charge concentration) creates a region with a high *electric potential*, whereas the Earth has a very low *electric potential*, as it is effectively neutral. Whenever there is a *difference* in electric potential, this can be thought of as what causes charges to flow, if they can. This makes for a lovely lead in to learning about circuits, which is all about *flows* of charge (current), caused by the potential difference of a battery, measured in volts.

Potential difference is commonly called 'voltage', however the term 'potential difference' seems much more meaningful; it is the size of the *difference* in potential between two regions that determines how quickly the charge moves (the rate of flow of charge, that is, the current) between the two regions for a single conduction path. Note that with an alternating potential difference, the net movement of charge (over time) is zero (since charges are oscillating back and forth within wires and components, not flowing). There would be no flow of charge at all between a 9 V region and another 9 V region because there is no *difference* in potential between the two regions. The number of volts is unimportant, it is the *difference* in the number of volts (the potential difference) between two locations that is important. In England the most recent national curriculum and exam specifications now prefer the term 'potential difference' instead of voltage, and we would encourage you and your students to adopt this terminology too.

3.2 Simple electric circuits
Practical issues and common misconceptions

The key to teaching electric circuits is to have a structured approach and to challenge misconceptions as they arise. Often students are taught a set of definitions and formulae that they need to memorise, with a focus on identifying the specific equation to solve a particular problem from the variables given. If, instead, the primary focus is developing students' descriptions and explanations of what happens in circuits, then they are more likely to be able to understand and solve more challenging circuit problems later in their learning.

While, from their earlier learning, students may appreciate that batteries have two terminals and that a closed loop of wire is needed for the bulb to light, their models of what is happening in a series circuit may be quite different from the accepted scientific model. Research suggests that many students hold one of the alternative models 1–3 below, rather than the accepted scientific model 4:

1. **Consumption model:** 'Electricity' emerges from one end of the battery and is all consumed by the bulb which lights up.

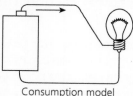

Consumption model

2. **Clashing current model:** Two types of 'electricity' emerge from the battery – one from each end – and react in the bulb to make it glow.

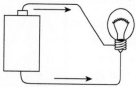

Clashing current model

3. **Attenuation model:** Some of the 'electricity' which emerges from one end of the battery is consumed in the bulb which lights up, while the rest returns to the other end of the battery.

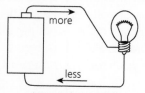

more

less

Attenuation model

4. Circulation model: All of the 'electricity' is initially contained in the wires and is pushed round the circuit by the battery. Current squeezing through the thin wire in the bulb's filament causes it to glow.

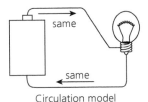

Circulation model

We suggest that to develop a good understanding of current, potential difference and resistance, only series circuits should be used. Parallel circuits should be introduced later, only when these initial ideas are embedded. An understanding of parallel circuits *begins* with a good understanding of potential difference that needs to be developed over time.

 Science literacy

In this chapter the word 'battery' has been used throughout for clarity. Strictly speaking, an 'electric cell' is a single device and a battery is a combination of one or more electric cells connected together to provide the potential difference required to operate some device or other.

Current in a circuit

Start teaching electric current with activities that prompt students to talk through their existing ideas about electric circuits. An 'energy stick', which is cheap and easy to find online, contains a battery and LEDs with a connection at each end. When it forms part of a complete circuit, made by students holding hands in a loop, it lights up and buzzes.

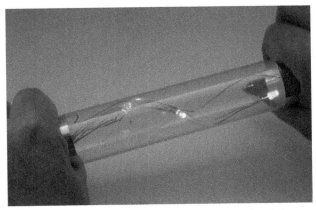

Figure 3.2 An 'energy stick' lights up and buzzes when it forms part of a complete circuit made by students holding hands in a loop.

KEY ACTIVITIES

Ideas for demonstrations:

- Complete circuit – students hold hands in a loop with an energy stick. Breaking the circuit *anywhere* stops the current *instantly*.
- Conductors and insulators – two students in a complete circuit hold either end of a conductor (piece of metal) or an insulator (wooden or plastic rod) between them and observe that the circuit is broken by an insulator.

During these demonstrations, ask students what they think is happening in the circuit. A common idea is that the 'electricity' leaves the battery and travels round the circuit very quickly. Instead encourage explanations in which 'electric charges' move round the circuit and form a 'current'.

In the demonstration, the energy stick turns on and off the instant a circuit is made or broken. Some students might imagine charges moving from the battery around the circuit at a high speed (models 1–3 on page 64). Instead, the charges move round the circuit quite slowly, at speeds in the order of a millimetre per second. The real reason the energy stick turns on instantly is because there are electric charges all around the circuit that all start moving at the same time as soon as there is a complete circuit. These charges are the electrons found in the energy stick and the humans which form the complete circuit.

The misconception that electric charges originate in the battery can be challenged with the second demonstration. In a circuit with an insulator, if the charges move from the battery they should flow through the circuit until they reach the insulator and then stop. If they did this, they would make the energy stick light for an instant, but no flash is seen. The explanation that the circuit is already full of charges, however, does work. If there is charge all around the circuit that all moves at the same time, if it is blocked in one place it cannot move through. This can also be shown to be the case in a conventional circuit, with a battery and a bulb.

Understanding exactly what is going on inside the wires of this circuit is conceptually demanding. This is where models can be very useful. The appropriate model helps to focus students' thinking and supports the development of a scientific understanding. If the model is not appropriate, it can introduce many more misconceptions than it tackles, so it is necessary to think through the model you intend to use carefully in advance.

The rope model is a particularly useful model for teaching current, potential difference and resistance in an introductory course. A rope loop is held loosely by a small number of students standing in a circle. Be careful to avoid rope burns when pupils pull the rope through one another's hands. One student acts as the battery moving charges around the circuit. Another acts as a bulb and gently squeezes the rope. More batteries or bulbs can be added and the effect on the whole circuit observed. The rope model demonstrates charge conservation and that all points in a circuit influence all others. It is useful for showing the effect of changing potential difference and/or resistance on current *everywhere* in a series circuit.

Table 3.1 Current, potential difference and resistance models

In a circuit	In the rope model	Potential difference, current and resistance in the rope model
Battery	A student moving the rope round.	The 'potential difference' is equivalent to the 'force' with which the rope is moved (and not how fast).
Bulb	Students holding the rope to make it harder to move round.	The friction between the rope and their hands transfers energy to each bulb. Greater friction represents a greater 'resistance'.
Wire	Students holding the rope loosely.	Conduction means electrons can move freely through a metal, which has a very small 'resistance'.
Electric charge (electrons)	The rope moves all around the circuit everywhere at the same time. Dots on the rope represent individual electrons.	'Current' is represented by the quantity of rope passing through each point in a second, which is the speed of the rope.

Care should be taken for each 'battery' to always move the rope with the same sized force. A common misconception is that current through a particular battery is always the same size, in any type of circuit. At this stage it is sufficient to describe the 'potential difference' of a battery as the size of its force on the current. If a battery is in a circuit with a bigger resistance, the current that it forces round is smaller.

The rope model illustrates that the electric charges (electrons), which the rope represents, are spread out through all of the wires *before* the circuit is turned on, and all move instantaneously as soon as the circuit is switched on. Use a climbing rope with a dot pattern so that students can see the 'charges' moving around the circuit.

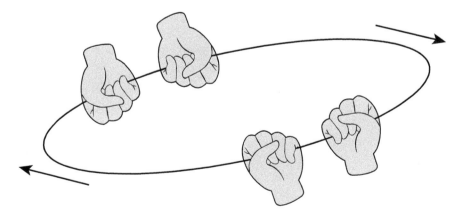

In this model the 'bulb' gently squeezes the rope and friction warms their hands. This illustrates the fact that electric charges are not used up by the bulb. If electric charges were used up, then a single wire connected to a bulb should be able to transfer energy to make the bulb light. A single length of rope between the 'battery' and the 'bulb' helps demonstrate that this is not the case.

One alternative 'donation' model uses sweets or potential difference money that is collected from the battery and taken around the circuit and given to the components. This model can incorrectly suggest that current takes time to get around the circuit and that the energy is transferred sequentially, one component at a time and so we do not recommend using it.

Science in context

The choice of which type of charge is called positive and which is called negative was made around 1750 by Benjamin Franklin. Alessandro Volta invented the first electric battery in 1800 and the direction of current was decided to be from the positive end of the battery to the negative end. It was almost one hundred years later that J. J. Thomson discovered the electron. In metal wires it is the electrons that move, but because of their negative charge they flow in the opposite direction to conventional current.

Circuit diagrams and building electric circuits

Once students are familiar with the concept of current, they can move on to setting up circuits from circuit diagrams. A circuit diagram is a schematic representation that shows the *order* of components and the *connections* between them. Where more than two wires or components join, connections are identified on a circuit diagram by a solid black dot.

A useful exercise for introducing circuit diagrams starts with students drawing pictures of electric circuits set up with different electrical components. Review the name and symbol of each component and scaffold students through the redrawing of each circuit as a circuit diagram, in order to prepare them for practice at building their own circuits from circuit diagrams.

When supporting students building circuits, teachers often suggest that students start at the battery and work round the circuit back to the battery. Although this helps students build working circuits, it can also reinforce the misunderstanding that the battery stores 'something' that flows around the circuit when it is turned on. It is better to start at a different component each time. For the same reason, it is a good practice to always use *two* hands to demonstrate the flow of current around a circuit or a circuit diagram. This has the added benefit of reinforcing the fact that *current moves in all parts of a circuit at the same time*.

When students are introduced to circuit diagrams, the battery is usually positioned at the top with one or more bulbs along the bottom. Using a selection of orientations, rather than sticking with the standard 'battery at the top', helps students to adapt their understanding when faced with a novel arrangement. It also helps them to realise that the orientation of a circuit diagram has no meaning, it is only the connections that matter.

Working with electric circuits

Practical work is a key element to developing a good understanding of electric circuits and in challenging misconceptions. However, without careful preparation, there are lots of things that can go wrong. A connecting wire might have a loose connector so it doesn't complete a circuit; a filament bulb may have 'blown' or a battery may be flat. Learning to identify damaged components and fault-check circuits at this stage can save a lot of frustration for everyone later. This section describes some of the things that you can do to make practical work with electrical circuits more successful.

Red and black wires are traditionally used to indicate the positive and negative ends of a circuit, but it is useful for students to know that the colours have no effect on how the wire works, and are just there to make a circuit easier to navigate. It may be challenging for some students to distinguish between coloured wires, so try to have a few sets of wires that are obviously different available, e.g. black and a much paler colour. It is not always clear to some students how these leads are constructed and so is helpful to show all students what a stripped wire looks like using these leads and a household electrical cable, identifying the insulating outer casing and conducting core(s).

Choosing appropriate circuit equipment can make a big difference to the success of practical work. Battery types need to be chosen carefully. Avoid batteries that have high discharge currents on a short circuit, therefore do not use rechargeable nickel–metal hydride (NiMH), nickel–cadmium NiCad, or lithium types. Zinc–carbon and smaller sized alkaline batteries are recommended. There is no 'right set' of equipment to use, but individual components connected by short plug-in wires tend to work well. There are several commercial sets that use standard 4 mm electrical plugs and sockets. Keeping wires short (about 15 cm) promotes well laid out neat circuits. Wires of this length do not tangle when stored together in a box, but a few longer wires will be needed for some experiments. It is more likely that students will disconnect longer wires by pulling on the wire rather than the plug, which can cause loose connections.

A simple circuit comprised of a battery and bulb with a gap can be used as a tester to check for faulty wires and bulbs. Batteries can be tested with a working bulb. Another quick check for a circuit that is not working is to make sure that all the batteries are the same way round. Encouraging students to fault-test their own components, and using a 'Circuit components for repair' box helps maintain a full set of working kit, which will save a lot of time and frustration in all practical work with electric circuits.

Bulbs

Due to variations in production and changes with use, not all filament bulbs will be exactly the same brightness as other *bulbs with identical ratings*. It is worth exploring this variation with students before using bulb brightness as a way to compare currents in a circuit.

Ammeters and voltmeters

Voltmeters and ammeters are now available that are relatively cheap and having a whole-class set is useful. If you use multimeters, you need to be aware that the protective fuses they contain blow very easily if the wrong setting is selected, and these need to be checked regularly. You may also need to explain the meaning of the prefixes k and M on the dial to the students so they understand the readings they are taking. Make sure that the multimeter is disconnected from the circuit before moving the dial, as this should avoid blowing the fuses.

3.3 Circuit analysis

Investigating current, potential difference and resistance in series circuits

Students should be able to identify materials as conductors or insulators and this can be extended to include the measurement of current through different materials with an ammeter, in order to distinguish between materials with different resistances. The quantity current (symbol I, from the French for 'intensity of current') is measured in amperes (amps), A.

Current and potential difference

Students can now explore currents (moving electric charges) at different points in series circuits to observe that the current is the same everywhere in a series circuit and that current is not used up. To do this, a series circuit containing two or more bulbs lit by two or more batteries should be used. This gives at least four points at which current can be compared. Students can use an ammeter to systematically measure current between each pair of components. It is unlikely that each ammeter reading will be *exactly* the same around a circuit, but each group should find that the current is at least very close to being the same all around. If you have a set of analogue ammeters, you might consider using them for this investigation, as tiny differences in current will be less obvious. A demonstration copy of the circuit can then be used to consolidate learning.

This contains several ammeters, with an ammeter connected between every pair of components. Changing the number of bulbs or batteries in this circuit shows the rule for current in a series circuit applies to all series circuits.

Voltmeters can now be introduced to measure the potential difference across a battery, or across other components. A voltmeter measures potential difference (symbol V) and is measured in volts (also V). The potential difference across a component in a circuit with a battery indicates how hard the current is being pushed through that particular component. Measuring the potential difference across the battery and each component in a series circuit leads to the rule that the potential difference across each component adds up to the potential difference across the battery:

$$V_{Battery} = V_1 + V_2 + V_3...$$

To help your students understand potential difference, talk through with them what will happen if another component is added to a series circuit. The first thing is that the extra component will increase the resistance of the circuit, but the potential difference across the battery will stay the same. The battery cannot push as much current around the circuit due to this increased resistance. There will be a reduced potential difference across each of the original components, and, if these are bulbs, then they will be dimmer than before. However, the total potential difference across all components will still be approximately equal to the potential difference across the battery.

Resistance

To understand the effect on the current of changing a resistor in a circuit, students need to be guided into thinking about an electric circuit in terms of a system, and to understand that when a resistor is added to the circuit, the current is affected throughout the circuit. Instead, it is very common for students to consider what happens to current one component at a time, moving in sequence around a circuit rather than a closed loop.

The rope model (see Section 3.2, page 67) is useful for thinking about an electric circuit as a system. Gripping the rope harder at any point in the loop slows the movement of the rope around the whole loop. Reducing the grip allows it to move faster showing that changing the resistance at any point in a circuit affects the flow of current through the circuit. This shows that changing the resistance at any point in a circuit affects the flow of current throughout the circuit.

Alternatively, changing the potential difference also changes the current everywhere, such as when you double the number of batteries in a circuit. This is analogous to moving the rope with different amounts of force, which changes the speed of the rope everywhere. Students can predict and observe the quantitative effects of doubling or halving resistance or potential difference. Students can be guided through these ideas using the rope model and then consolidate their learning through discussion and by taking measurements in real circuits.

These observations show how current, resistance and potential difference are related. For example:

→ Doubling the resistance halves the current flowing (for a given potential difference).
→ Doubling the potential difference approximately doubles the current flowing (for a given resistance).
→ Doubling the potential difference *and* doubling the resistance means that the same current flows.

All these observations are satisfied by the equation:

$$\text{current (A)} = \frac{\text{potential difference (V)}}{\text{resistance } (\Omega)}$$

$$I = \frac{V}{R}$$

This equation reflects the fact that current is affected by changes in either the potential difference or resistance of a circuit. This is one way of expressing Ohm's law, which states that for a given resistance, the current flowing between two points in a circuit is proportional to potential difference across the points. If the potential difference doubles, so does the current. Rearranging Ohm's law provides the definition of resistance.

Once students understand the qualitative relationship, they are ready to use a circuit with a voltmeter and an ammeter to measure the resistance of circuit components. Students can take a set of measurements to investigate how resistance changes as the potential difference across each component is changed. A resistor (or wire) at constant temperature can be shown to be an ohmic conductor (i.e. one that obeys Ohm's law), and a filament bulb and a diode shown to be non-ohmic. Guides for doing this can be found, for example, on the CLEAPSS website (see Resources at the end of the chapter).

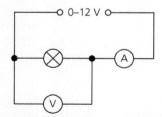

Figure 3.3 The simplest circuit to measure current and potential difference of a filament bulb is with a power pack of variable output connected to a 12 V, 24 W bulb.

Usually graphs of current against potential difference (*I–V*) are plotted from the results of these investigations to identify patterns in the resistance of each component as potential difference is changed. The resistance of a component is the potential difference divided by the current at a particular point; an increasing gradient indicates a falling resistance and vice versa. Some students will need help with reasoning; this is not an introductory topic and requires them to be secure with rearranging equations.

A common misunderstanding is to say the gradient of a current–potential difference graph equals $1/R$, (because $1/R$ equals current divided by potential difference). This is not true because resistance is calculated using the current at a particular potential difference. These are the values of a point on the graph.

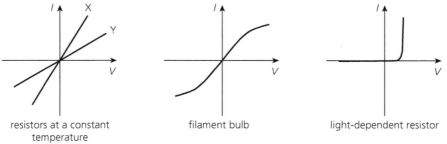

resistors at a constant temperature   filament bulb   light-dependent resistor

Figure 3.4 Current–potential difference graphs. Resistor Y has a higher resistance than X because a higher potential difference is needed to push the same sized current through it. As more current flows through the filament bulb its temperature rises and resistance increases. After a threshold voltage is reached, the diode conducts very easily and has a very low resistance. It does not conduct backwards because it has a very high resistance in this direction.

The hotter a metal filament is, the more quickly the atoms in it vibrate. If its atoms are vibrating more quickly, the electrons moving though the filament are more likely to collide with them. This means the hotter a filament is the greater its resistance. A filament heats up when a potential difference pushes current through, because moving electrons collide with atoms to make them vibrate more. A bigger potential difference pushes electrons harder and increases the number of collisions, which increases the temperature and resistance of the filament. The PhET *Battery-resistor circuit* can be useful for modelling this effect (see Resources at the end of this chapter).

> When metal atoms bond, outer electrons are no longer attached to specific atoms, resulting in 'metal ions' within a 'sea of electrons'.

Other components that students may encounter are the thermistor and the light-dependent resistor.

Table 3.2 Thermistors and light-dependent resistors

Name	Symbol	Behaviour	Uses
Thermistor		A resistor with a resistance that decreases as the temperature increases.	Controlling a thermostat, to turn heaters off if it is too hot, or on if it is too cold.
Light-dependent resistor (LDR)		A resistor with a resistance that decreases as the amount of light increases.	Controlling lighting, to turn lights on if it is too dark, or off if it is too bright.

The easiest way to measure the resistance of either component is to connect it directly to a multimeter set to measure resistance. The temperature of a thermistor can be changed by submerging it in hot or cold water. The amount of light reaching an LDR can be altered by placing layers of greaseproof paper over it.

Technology use

To demonstrate to the students, if you have a modular electronics kit, such as Unilab's Alpha, it is relatively straightforward to build circuits that show how thermistors and LDRs can be used to turn on a light when it is too dark, or turn on a heater if it is too cold. Alternatively, this can be shown using a short video clip from the internet.

Circuit calculations

Series circuits

Students need to practise applying $R = \dfrac{V}{I}$ to series circuits, and be able to explain the rules for current and potential difference in a series circuit. Initially, students should calculate missing values for circuits with a battery and a single component.

Maths

- Start by using $R = \dfrac{V}{I}$ to calculate a resistance when V and I are given.
- Next give the equations: $V = I \times R$ and $I = \dfrac{V}{R}$ to calculate missing values.
- Finally challenge students to calculate V, I or R by rearranging $R = \dfrac{V}{I}$

A calculation for a circuit with more than one component often requires two steps. The first step is typically to work out a potential difference or current from the rules for a series circuit and the second step is to apply $R = \dfrac{V}{I}$.

Parallel circuits

Once students can explain how potential difference and resistance affect the current in a series circuit, they will be ready to extend their understanding to parallel circuits. At its simplest, a parallel circuit can be thought of as a set of nested series circuits, each working off the same battery. Each series circuit behaves exactly as it would if it were the only one present.

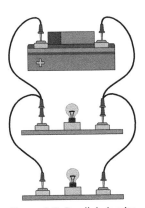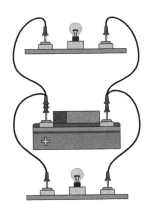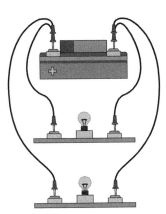

Figure 3.5 Parallel circuits

These circuits are equivalent to each other because in each one both bulbs connect directly to the ends of the battery. Students often need support in recognising equivalent parallel circuits. The first thing to establish when teaching parallel circuits is the idea that potential difference across each branch is the same as the potential difference across the battery. This can be observed by students using a voltmeter across the battery and across each branch of a parallel circuit. Repeating potential difference measurements on a wide variety of parallel circuits demonstrates that this is a general rule.

When students learnt about series circuits, it was useful for them to think of potential difference as a 'push'. In parallel circuits it is less clear how this idea can be applied. It is not clear what happens at points where a circuit branches. The gravitational model is useful for explaining how the potential difference of the battery can 'push' equally through each branch. In the gravitational model, the battery in a parallel circuit lifts electric charges to a 'higher level' and they fall back down to 'lower levels' as they pass through each branch of the circuit.

Note the orientation of the circuit diagram in Figure 3.6 which represents this approach.

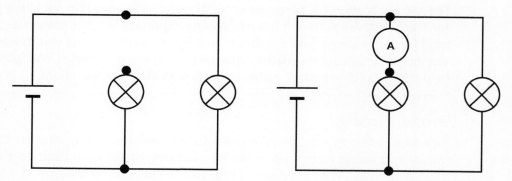

1 Disconnect the connecting wires from the middle branch.
2 Connect the ammeter from the connecting wires to the middle branch.

Figure 3.6 Connecting an ammeter to measure current through the middle branch of a parallel circuit is challenging.

The current in each branch of a parallel circuit can now be measured and compared with the current passing through the battery. It often helps students to use black wires for one loop and red ones for another. A common misconception is that current always splits equally at a dividing junction, but in most circuits this is not the case. To counter this misconception, place different components in each branch when students are measuring current, so that the current measured in each branch is different. Remember that the potential difference pushing the current through each branch in a parallel circuit is the same so, if a branch has a smaller resistance, more current is pushed through it. (If the branch is just a wire with little or no resistance, there will be a very high current. This is called a short circuit.)

The rule for current in a parallel circuit is that the current through each branch adds up to the current *through* the battery. Care should be taken not to say the current 'from' the battery, because this reinforces the misconception that current is something stored in the battery that is used up by components.

Students often think that adding an extra component in parallel to a circuit will increase the resistance of the circuit, whereas the opposite is true. Adding an extra branch to a parallel circuit does not affect the current through the existing branches because the potential difference across each of these remains the same. Additional current *does* flow through the new branch and this extra current also flows through the battery. Even if a new branch contains a very large resistor, it still provides an *extra* pathway for current to move through, which reduces the overall resistance of the circuit. It is rather like adding an extra door to a classroom – even if the new door is hard to push open, it still allows the classroom to empty more quickly at the end of a lesson by providing an alternative route.

Students need to practise answering questions about parallel circuits. Start off with questions to identify a missing potential difference to reinforce the potential difference rule; and then introduce questions with missing currents that can be worked out by adding or subtracting currents shown on a diagram. Harder questions often require students to use the equation $R = \dfrac{V}{I}$, in order to be able to apply the current or potential difference rule.

Power and energy

The purpose of an electric circuit is to do work of some kind. In an electric circuit, energy is transferred from the battery to the surroundings. Initially the energy is stored chemically by the battery. Once the circuit has been switched on for a while, some of this energy is now stored by the surroundings, usually thermally. To be able to calculate the amount of energy transferred in an electric circuit, students first need to calculate power. (Chapter 4 Energy discusses why it is better to discourage the term 'electrical energy', for continuous processes such as electrical circuits and why 'power' is a more appropriate descriptive term.)

Power is the rate at which energy is transferred each second. The unit of power is the watt (W), and one watt is equal to one joule per second:

$$\text{power (W)} = \frac{\text{energy transferred (J)}}{\text{time taken (s)}}$$

$$P = \frac{E}{t}$$

In an electric circuit, power can be calculated by simply multiplying current by potential difference.

$$\text{power (W)} = \text{current (A)} \times \text{potential difference (V)}$$

$$P = I \times V$$

Students can now calculate the energy transferred. All they need to do is multiply by the time taken:

$$\text{energy (J)} = \text{power (W)} \times \text{time (s)}$$

$$E = P \times t$$

Paying for domestic electricity

The 'energy = power × time' equation is the same equation that is used to measure the amount of energy used, and paid for, in the home. The only difference is that energy is shown on electricity bills as measured in kilowatt-hours rather than in joules.

π   Maths

Students need to be confident in using and converting between multiple units when performing calculations in this topic. Common conversions that they encounter are: 1 kilowatt = 1000 watt, 1 minute = 60 seconds, 1 hour = 60 × 60 seconds and 1 kWh = 3 600 000 J = 3.6 MJ.

After students can use the equation to solve simple problems, they can be given examples that involve domestic appliances. Students can be shown that converting power into kilowatts and time into hours gives an answer that is usually between zero and ten. All they need to do to work out how much this costs is to multiply their answer by the cost of a 'unit of electricity', which is the cost of one kilowatt-hour of energy.

Science in context

We pay for the number of 'unit of electricity' (sometimes called 'units') that we use. 1 kilowatt-hour = 1 'unit of electricity', this is actually a measurement of energy. One 'unit' costs about 15 pence in the UK.

Equations for current and potential difference

Once students have a good understanding of electric current as a flow of charge, they already know the story of the equation for current. The equation can now be introduced as a shorthand way of writing this down. Current is a measure of the amount of charge flowing past a point in a circuit in one second. The equation that describes this is:

$$\text{current (A)} = \frac{\text{charge (C)}}{\text{time (s)}}$$

$$I = \frac{Q}{t}$$

Potential difference can be usefully thought of as an electrical 'push', but in the section on power and energy it was linked to energy. This can make sense to students if they think about what a 'bigger push' by a battery does to the charges around a circuit. If a bigger potential difference 'pushes' charges harder, then the loop of electrons can do work at a higher rate.

Potential difference and energy (electrical working) are linked by the equation:

$$\text{potential difference (V)} = \frac{\text{energy transferred (J)}}{\text{charge (C)}}$$

$$V = \frac{E}{Q}$$

When the potential difference between two points in a circuit is 1 volt, then the loop of electrons does 1 joule of work between these points as 1 coulomb passes any point in that part of the circuit. An electric current is a continuous process. Although the volt is often defined by thinking of an isolated charge, it can help to define potential difference (in volts) using power. It would then be as follows: the power developed between two points in a circuit with a potential difference of 1 volt will be 1 watt for a current of 1 amp.

Magnets

3.4 Magnets and magnetic fields

Most of the learning about magnets and magnetic fields in school is based on observation. It is not appropriate or easy to give a full scientific explanation of how magnets work at this stage. However, students can find out about how magnets behave and there is an excellent opportunity to investigate non-contact forces. This part of the chapter explores magnetism from the macroscopic to the microscopic and provides a foundation for electromagnetism that follows.

Science in context

The magnetism topic is rich with applications, awe and wonder. From the early application of lodestone for navigation, to how the Earth's magnetic field gives rise to the most inspiring show on the planet (the aurora) and keeps us alive by protecting us against the solar winds. Magnetic stripes in the Mid-Atlantic Ridge provide evidence of sea-floor spreading, which led to the theory of plate tectonics, helping us to understand the Earth's geological history.

Prior experiences

Many popular toys use magnets, and students are often fascinated by their properties from an early age. In school, they will have described attraction and repulsion, and perhaps have already formed some idea of magnetic poles. There will have been investigations into magnetic materials and an attempt to classify them. A common misconception is that all metals are magnetic, which follows from dividing metals and non-metals into electrical conductors and insulators. It is very easy for students to get fundamental ideas about electricity and magnetism confused.

Electrical and magnetic properties

Start with a quick refresher on magnetic and non-magnetic materials, testing if they are attracted to a bar magnet. Include a range of metals that are not magnetic in order to draw a clear distinction between electrical and magnetic properties. Stress that a metal can be a good electrical conductor but not magnetic, for example copper.

> Prior to 1991, UK 1 penny and 2 pence coins were non-magnetic as they were made from a bronze alloy of copper, tin and zinc. Coins made after 1992 are copper-plated steel and so are attracted by a magnet. In 1998, coins of both types were made.

The needle of a magnetic compass is a small bar magnet that is free to spin. It will line up with any nearby magnetic field line. If there are no nearby magnets, the needle will point north, this is evidence that the core of the Earth itself is magnetic: compasses point in the direction of the Earth's magnetic field.

Science in context

The direction of the Earth's magnetic field has undergone a sporadic series of reversals, with the last flip occurring around 780 000 years ago. At the Mid-Atlantic Ridge the sea floor has spread out with stripes of magnetised rock, each corresponding to a change in the Earth's magnetic field direction. This provided evidence to support Wegener's theory of continental drift and led to the development of the theory of plate tectonics.

Non-contact forces – attraction and repulsion

Students often say that a north and south pole 'stick' together. It is important to clear up the difference between sticking and attracting. Students should be able to feel the force between the magnets when they hold them a little way apart. Get them to explain what 'attraction' means using the word 'force': *'The attractive force between the north pole of magnet A and the south pole of magnet B.'*

KEY ACTIVITIES

Students can use a bar magnet to pick up paper clips. Test *both* ends of the magnet to show that both a north pole and a south pole attract the paper clips. You may like to experiment with different shapes and strengths of magnets if you have access to them, checking how many paper clips can be attracted by each pole.

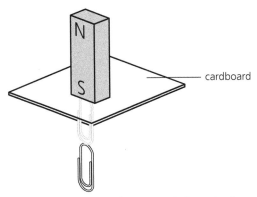

cardboard

Figure 3.7 A chain of paper clips shows how strong the magnet is; here, the force passes through a piece of cardboard.

When the magnet is brought close to the paper clip, the paper clip becomes a temporary magnet. The paper clip pole nearest the permanent magnet becomes an opposite pole; if the permanent magnet is a north pole, the paper clip end nearest becomes a south pole (and vice versa). There is always an attractive force and this is an example of magnetic induction: an opposite pole is induced as the magnet is brought near.

Students should experience the repulsion of magnets in a few guises. Chapter 2 Forces describes how to observe the magnetic force which results from resting a magnet on a balance and bringing another towards it (see Chapter 2, Section 2.1, page 26). If your school has a pair of large ring magnets, an excellent demonstration can be made by threading them over a suitable cardboard tube. The top magnet can then be pushed down and will spring back (see Figure 3.8).

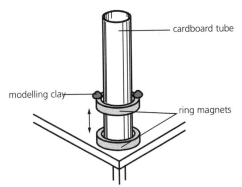

cardboard tube

modelling clay

ring magnets

Figure 3.8 Two ring magnets repelling. Add modelling clay to increase the downward force. The force of repulsion between the magnets is equal to the weight of the upper magnet.

'Seeing' magnetic fields – strength, direction and three dimensions

A magnetic field is the region of space around a magnet where another magnet experiences an attractive or repulsive force. Magnetic field lines are a way to visualise the direction and strength of the magnetic field.

There are three rules for magnetic field lines that need reinforcing:

1 They show the direction of the force that would act on a north pole placed in the field and so point North to South.
2 They never cross or touch.
3 The closer they are together (that is the 'denser' the lines of magnetic flux), the stronger the magnetic field. The magnetic flux density (B) is measured in tesla (T).

Science in context

Nikola Tesla was the inventor of the induction motor on which modern electric cars are based. His 'Tesla coils' could send and receive radio signals, but Marconi managed the first transmission across the Atlantic using many of Tesla's patents. Tesla was not a businessman and sadly failed with his lifetime's ambition of a transmission tower that would enable a 'wireless globe'.

The three-dimensional nature of magnetic fields can be investigated using a Magnaprobe, a small, gimbaled magnet that can rotate in three directions. This will be revisited when you move onto electromagnetism.

Figure 3.9 Use a Magnaprobe to see how the field changes direction around a bar magnet.

Try this on the magnetic cover of a mobile phone or tablet. You'll see that it keeps changing direction as you move along the edge, indicating that there are magnetic stripes similar to a fridge magnet.

The magnetic field of a magnet is strongest at the poles and gets weaker further away from the magnet: the strength of the magnetic field depends on the magnet you use and the distance from the magnet.

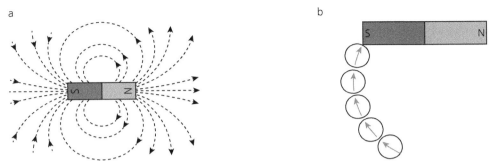

Figure 3.10 a) Field lines around a bar magnet; b) using a compass to plot lines of force

Using a compass to plot field lines and record direction

It is helpful for students to see a diagram of the field lines first (see Figure 3.10a) so that they know what to look for. Figure 3.10b shows the arrangement for plotting field lines around a bar magnet. In the lab, plotting compasses often become magnetised the wrong way round. This is due to the presence of strong magnets. It is relatively easy to re-magnetise them by passing a magnet over them and then retesting.

Science in context

Migratory birds and other animals use the Earth's magnetic field to navigate. A study from 2010 found that iron oxides in sense organs in a pigeon's beak intensify the Earth's magnetic field and stimulate nerve impulses that travel to the brain and assist in pigeons' navigation. The same structures have been found in many other species (see Resources at the end of this chapter). More recent research points to other magnetoreceptors in some birds including a light-dependent magnetoreceptor protein that is more strongly expressed during the migratory season.

Making and breaking magnets

Magnetising a piece of steel using a strong magnet is useful in developing a model of magnetisation. Use a modern high-strength magnet (see safety precautions on page 87). A length of iron wire or a small nail can be magnetised by repeatedly stroking it in one direction with a magnet.

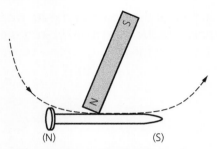

Figure 3.11 Magnetising an iron nail

Allow students to discuss and demonstrate that the magnetised nail displays magnetic properties by giving them access to other magnets, compasses and iron filings. If you then heat the nail in a Bunsen flame, this should demagnetise the nail. The demagnetisation can again be tested.

> Wear safety glasses when heating the nail, using long metal tongs. For the time it takes to heat a nail, the tongs handle will not warm appreciably. Submerge the nail in cold water directly after heating to avoid someone picking up a very hot nail.

Students can now bring together these experiments and use a simple model to explain their observations. The core of the argument is that iron atoms in the nail behave like small magnets. In a non-magnetised sample of iron, these 'atomic magnets' are randomly orientated.

unmagnetised   magnetised

Figure 3.12 Using a microscopic model to explain magnetisation

Modelling – domain theory

When a magnet is moved over an iron sample, the atomic magnets rotate so that they all lie in the same orientation. A permanent magnet can be produced using iron, nickel, cobalt or rare-earth metal alloy samples. In these cases the atomic magnets stay orientated in the same direction.

A 'soft' iron sample, like a nail, loses its magnetisation and the atomic magnets rotate back to random directions. Soft iron has been treated to reduce its hardness, making it more workable (hence, the term 'soft') and also reducing its ability to retain magnetisation when the external field is removed. This property is useful for electromagnets that need to be demagnetised at the flick of a switch.

In this simplified view, atomic magnets are locally lined up giving rise to 'magnetic domains'. These magnetic domains are themselves randomly orientated. The external magnet causes those domains that are favourably orientated to grow at the expense of those that are not. Thermal motion tends to randomise the domain direction (see Resources at the end of this chapter).

Careers

Radiographers use magnetic resonance imaging (MRI), which is a non-invasive technique that uses a magnetic field and radiofrequency waves to create detailed pictures of organs and structures inside the body and provides soft tissue detail that cannot be investigated by X-rays. Each spinning proton produces its own tiny magnetic field which interacts with the strong applied field, allowing images to be formed.

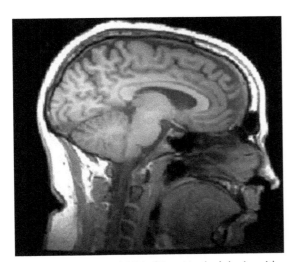

Figure 3.13 Structural MRI of Tom Hartley's brain, with permission

3.5 Electromagnetism

In 1820, Hans Christian Oersted was investigating electric current and the chance flicker of a nearby compass needle led to the discovery of electromagnetism. This was a major breakthrough on which much of today's technology is based. Since electromagnetism is a combination of ideas about magnetism and electric currents, teachers need to ensure that the foundations are laid for this next level. Some of the basic effects can be taught in the first few years of secondary school and then revisited. The rest of this chapter will build gradually on Oersted's linking of electric currents and magnetic fields, how to investigate this effect, applications and the generation of our electricity supply.

> Safety: Powerful neodymium magnets are widely available and make for some awe-inspiring demonstrations. They will magnetise steel, reverse the direction of magnetisation of compasses and can be very difficult to separate. There is also a danger that a student will get nipped by the magnet and suffer injury. People with electrical medical implants should not get too close to high intensity magnets such as neodymium types. Use with careful supervision and ensure they land on a soft surface when dropping them. Please consult CLEAPPS for further guidance on the use of rare-earth magnets.

Oersted's discovery

A natural place to start is with Oersted's original experiment with a simple series circuit including a battery, a switch and a bulb. Position one of the leads north–south above the compass, parallel to the compass needle. Close the switch and the needle rotates to lie east–west. The magnetic field produced by the current is at right angles to the wire. More details can be found at the Institute of Physics (see Resources at the end of this chapter).

KEY ACTIVITIES

Using similar equipment to Oersted, students can now look at the shape of the field near a single straight wire.

Use a long lead that is suspended vertically and a plotting compass. The right-hand grip rule is useful here. Students imagine gripping the wire with their right hand with their thumb pointing in the same direction as the conventional current (downwards from +ve to −ve). The fingers curl around the wire in the same clockwise direction as the circular magnetic field.

Ask students to predict, observe and explain what happens when:

1 the current through the wire is reversed (direction of the compass needle reverses.)
2 the compass is moved away from the wire (it aligns more with magnetic north as the field strength decreases with distance from the wire).

Safety note: Use a suitable high-current power supply designed for electromagnetism experiments as students will need currents up to 10A. Do not exceed 4V and switch the supply off between observations as the wire will get hot.

Quite a few people have issues knowing right from left, so be sensitive to this when teaching this topic.

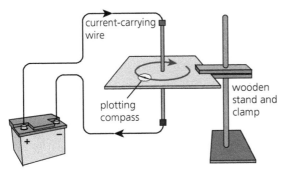

Figure 3.14 The magnetic field around a single straight wire (Oersted's experiment)

Making the magnetic field stronger

By making the single, straight wire into a coil you can increase the strength of the magnetic field and form a simple electromagnet.

Using an iron nail, the strength of the magnetic field can be shown to depend on:

→ the number of turns of wire (increasing them increases the strength of the magnetic field)
→ the presence or absence of the nail (the soft iron core becomes magnetised in the same direction as the magnetic field in the coil, leading to a stronger field)
→ the magnitude of the current (the strength of the field increases as the current increases).

This investigation works well as a demonstration or part of a circus of activities, if you don't have a class set of variable resistors.

> Safety note: The wire will get very hot and could cause burns, so stress that students only leave the circuit connected for a few seconds. Reinforce the idea that a high current has a heating effect and discuss what would happen to the wire if they allowed the current to flow for a long time. This links with future work on electricity supply and transformers.

Use an analogue meter, as digital meters are very vulnerable to the high-voltage spikes that can be produced when an electromagnet is turned off. You will need a meter with a range of about 10 A for this experiment.

It is difficult to measure the strength of the magnetic field, but the direction can be shown experimentally. When students investigate the field direction in and around a coil, use a wider diameter to create the coil (e.g. 2–3 cm diameter section of pipe or dowelling). A small compass or Magnaprobe (p.82) can then be placed inside the coil and used to investigate the direction of the field at each end. This is the foundation for understanding electric motors. Guides are provided at the Institute of Physics (see Resources at the end of this chapter).

The electric motor

So far, it has been discussed that magnets can attract and repel, and that a current-carrying wire can be a magnet. The next step for the students would be to investigate the forces involved and how this arrangement can be engineered to make an electric motor.

The force on an electric current in a magnetic field

You can start with a large-scale demonstration of the force on an electric current passing through a magnetic field. A series resistor (for example, a rheostat) is needed to limit the current or use a low-voltage, high-current power supply unit designed for electromagnetism practicals. The demonstration can be done using a slack length of aluminium foil as the conductor. The strip is suspended from a clamp between a pair of magnets (see Figure 3.15). When the current is switched on, the strip experiences a force at right angles to the current. Modern rare-earth magnets are best for this. If alternating current (AC) is used from the power supply, the strip will vibrate.

With this arrangement, you can show that reversing the direction of the current or of the magnetic field will reverse the direction of the force on the foil. You may also be able to show that increasing the current or field will increase the force. Ask your students to predict the outcome of each of these changes before making them.

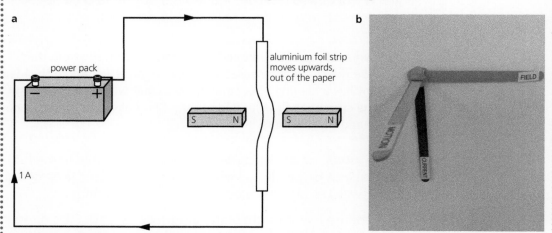

Figure 3.15 a) Showing the force on a current-carrying conductor in a magnetic field; b) Labelled lolly sticks in putty can be positioned alongside the experiment and are easy to rotate.

More detailed study in this area uses Fleming's left-hand rule to predict how the direction of the motion relates to the current and external magnetic field. In the above example, students can predict the direction that the aluminium foil 'kicks'. The thumb, first finger and second finger of the left hand are all at 90° to each other:

1 Thumb – direction of *motion* of the wire.
2 *First* finger – magnetic field direction from the N to S pole of the magnet.
3 *Second* finger – conventional current (+ to –) through the foil strip.

It can be difficult for students to maintain this hand orientation while investigating the motor effect. The lolly stick model is easy to place alongside the equipment and rotate in 3-D (see Figure 3.15b).

Making a motor

With a little engineering you can make a motor for your demonstration. A simple homopolar motor can be put together quickly and prompts some initial questions to ask the students:

→ What makes the magnet move?
→ How can you make it spin in the opposite direction?
→ Could you make it spin faster?

You may not have a class set of motor kits and building from scratch does take quite a lot of class time if the students are to end up with a working motor. It is probably best to have a few motors that have undergone strict quality control and that can be used as part of a circus, or to use a large demonstration motor. With help, your students should be able to identify the direction of the magnetic field and the two sides of the coil in which the current is at right angles to the field. It is the forces on these two sides that cause the coil to rotate. Many video clips are available showing homopolar motors and the use of motor kits to help you with your particular equipment.

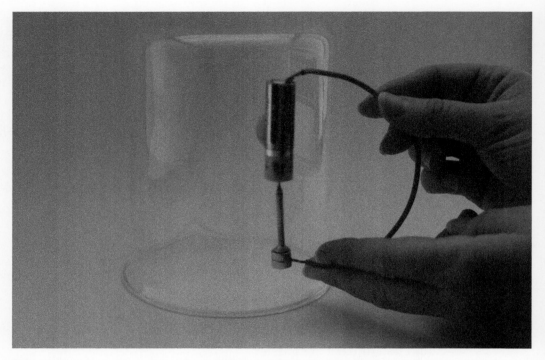

Figure 3.16 A simple homopolar motor: battery attached to a beaker with putty, with two small neodymium magnets attached to the head of a screw. A short length of wire connects one terminal of the battery to the outside edge of the magnets, completing the circuit. The current produces a magnetic field that interacts with the dangling magnets, making them spin. All electric motors use this effect. Take care not to let it run for too long and overheat.

It can be difficult to explain this effect using a 2-D diagram, so you might like to include an appropriate animation sourced from the internet, stopping at appropriate points to use the left-hand rule to identify the forces on the rotating coil.

Science in context

Loudspeakers are another application of the motor effect. In this case, the coil is attached to the speaker cone. The coil is attracted to or repelled by a permanent magnet as the current flows in and out of the coil. The cone vibrates at the same frequency as the AC flowing in the coil, which produces a sound wave.

Generating current

The previous section demonstrated that a current in a closed loop of wire creates its own magnetic field. The field can be made bigger by increasing the number of loops, adding an iron core or increasing the current. If this loop of wire interacts with another magnetic field, a force is produced and the wire loop moves. The inverse of this effect is that if you move a closed loop of wire through a magnetic field you will *induce a potential difference which will cause an induced current to flow*.

It is worth spending time investigating this effect systematically. Start by demonstrating a bar magnet moving in and out of a coil connected to a large analogue ammeter with high sensitivity or galvanometer, if available (see Figure 3.18).

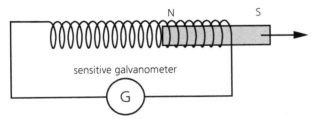

Figure 3.18 A simple demonstration of electromagnetic induction

This experiment produces very small currents and so a galvanometer should be used. A galvanometer measures very small currents and shows the direction, which is important when measuring induced currents. The best type of galvanometer to use is a sensitive, centre-zero, demonstration moving-coil meter (2.5–0–2.5 mA is a good range). Digital instruments are not suitable here. Use the strongest bar magnet that you can find and a coil of about 20 turns is suitable. First connect up the circuit with the magnet some way away. There should be no deflection on the meter. Deflection should only be observed when the magnet moves towards or away from the coil.

After an initial demonstration, this is a good class experiment for students to work on. Ask them to find out what produces the current. Leave time for a class discussion during the lesson to make sure that all students have grasped the essential points:

→ There is only a current when the magnet moves into the stationary coil. Holding the magnet still does nothing.
→ Moving the magnet the other way reverses the current.
→ Reversing the poles also reverses the current.

It is the relative motion of the magnet with respect to the coil that is important here. In most classroom situations it is easier to move the magnet but this idea should be mentioned even if it is difficult to show.

> Note: A current flows because the relative movement between the coil and magnet induces a potential difference in the coil. It does not matter whether it is the coil or the magnet that is moving. If there is relative movement a current will flow. With some equipment sets it may be possible to move the coil over a stationary magnet to show that this is the case. You can use a smartphone, visualiser or webcam to demonstrate this to the whole class so they can all see the motion and its effect on the current. The PhET simulation on Faraday's law is a great way of displaying all the essential points listed above (see Resources at the end of this chapter).

An alternative classroom generator

Drop a stack of neodymium magnets through a spool of wire or pre-wound transformer coil that has two light-emitting diodes (LEDs) connected in parallel across the ends, making sure that they are connected in opposite directions. As the magnet enters the coil one LED will light up and as it leaves the other LED will light up, showing current flowing in one direction when the magnets move into the coil and in the opposite direction as the magnets move out of the coil (LEDs will only conduct in one direction).

Filming the magnet drop in slow motion can make this easier to see. Take care that the magnets fall onto a soft object as they can break easily. Button neodymium magnets can be used by responsible students with suitable supervision. Always check that none have gone missing at the end of the practical. This demonstration can be used with younger students to get them thinking about why the LED lights up. It works very well along with the homopolar motor as a gentle introduction to electromagnetism.

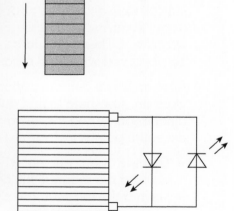

Figure 3.19 An alternative **generator**.

Some students will be able to reason this out for themselves and find it very rewarding but when giving an explanation or checking theirs, it is important to focus on the order in which things happen:

1 Relevant movement between magnet and coil
2 Induced potential difference in coil
3 Induced current in coil

The students should also note that the direction of the relative motion will affect the direction of the induced current, which can be shown by turning the stack of magnets over and seeing the LEDs lighting in a different order.

Alternating current (AC)

Students are now ready to see how AC is produced. Figure 3.19 shows how the coil can be rotated in a magnetic field; on an analogue meter the needle will move back and forth.

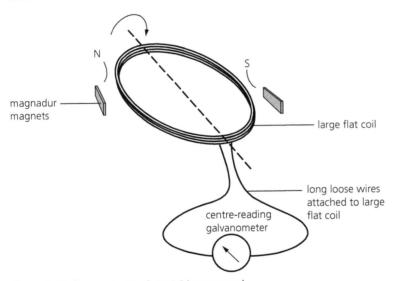

Figure 3.19 Demonstrating how AC is generated

It is generally better to show this demonstration to a small group of students, so that they can all see. Make a point of the fact that the long loose wires are getting twisted and that practical generators overcome this by using a 'slip ring commutator'.

This needs to be explained slowly, step by step, and for every student to see what happens as the coil spins rather than just referring to a 2-D diagram on the page.

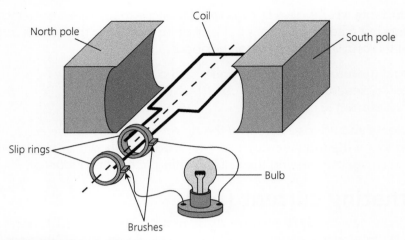

Figure 3.21 A basic AC generator

Science in context

Regenerative braking in electric cars uses the car's motor as a generator. When you take your foot off the accelerator pedal, the process that drives the wheels is reversed. The rotating wheels rotate the motor and this induces a current that is used to recharge the battery. Energy is stored in the battery and the charged battery can be used later to accelerate the car.

Supplying electricity to our homes

Generating the essential electric supply and ensuring that it reaches our homes safely is the last piece of the electricity and magnetism puzzle.

The heating effect in an electric wire has been highlighted a few times in this topic. Passing a high current through power supply cables would not be energy efficient or practical as the wires could melt. The current has a bigger heating effect on the wire than the potential difference and so the current must be kept as low as possible. Along the power supply lines the current is reduced to a minimum by *stepping up* the potential difference to very high values, to as much as 750 000 V, using a transformer.

At the substation, close to the point of use, the potential difference is *decreased to 230 V*. This is also done using another transformer: a *step-down* version. Transformers are also used in our homes, for example when we want to decrease the potential difference from the 230 V supplied to our homes to a lower voltage for a device such as a laptop.

Transformers

A transformer is made from two separate coils that are wound around the same, soft iron core. An AC in the first coil causes a changing magnetic field in the core that induces an alternating potential difference in the neighbouring coil. Remind your students that a soft iron core made their simple electromagnet stronger. By linking the two coils with a soft iron core the strength of the magnetic field is increased. In practice, the coils are overlapping, but this makes for a complicated diagram, so it is easier to draw each coil of wire on a separate branch of the core.

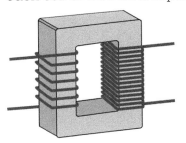

Step-up transformer
Fewer coils to more coils
Increases potential difference (V)
Decreases current (I)

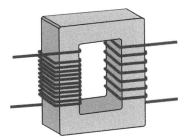

Step-down transformer
More coils to fewer coils
Decreases potential difference (V)
Increases current (I)

Figure 3.20 The basic structure of a transformer is a primary coil and a secondary coil wound on an iron core.

Both types of transformer alter the potential difference in the primary coil to meet the needs of the device by the following processes:

1 AC is supplied to the primary coil.
2 This produces a changing magnetic field in the iron core.
3 This produces an alternating potential difference across the secondary coil by electromagnetic induction.
4 The alternating potential difference causes AC in the secondary coil, if it is connected to an external circuit.

Students may think that there is a current in the magnetic core, but the coils are NOT connected. It is important to stress that there is *no current* in the magnetic core in an ideal transformer.

The ratio of the potential differences is equal to the ratio of the number of turns. In a step-down transformer the potential difference is *less* in the secondary coil (V_s) than in the primary coil (V_p) as there are *less turns* on the secondary coil. In a step-up transformer the potential difference is *greater* in the secondary coil as there are a *greater* number of turns on this coil.

$$\frac{\text{potential difference across primary coil } (V)}{\text{potential difference across secondary coil } (V)} = \frac{\text{number of turns on primary coil}}{\text{number of turns on secondary coil}}$$

$$\frac{V_p}{V_s} = \frac{N_p}{N_s}$$

95

Build your students' confidence by using proportional reasoning before introducing the equation. Discussions around doubling or increasing by a factor of ten are useful for any students who are less confident with algebra:

1 Are there more turns on the secondary coil? What type of transformer is it?
2 Show them the number of turns on the primary and secondary sides. What happens to the potential difference? Stepped up/down/stays the same?
3 Show them the number of turns on the primary and secondary sides. What happens to the current? Stepped up/down/stays the same?
4 Show them the current flowing in each branch. Is this a step-up or step-down transformer?
5 Introduce the equation and use some simple numbers, e.g. $N_p = 1000$, $N_s = 2000$, $V_p = 10$, $V_s = ?$
6 Practise using the equation to calculate each term using simple numbers first, before moving to more realistic values for V_p and V_s.

Transformers only work with an alternating current. If a constant current was used, the magnetic field in the iron core would also be constant, which would not induce a potential difference in the secondary coil. The flow of AC in the primary coil creates a continuously changing magnetic field in the coil and iron core. This has exactly the same effect on the secondary coil as if you were moving a magnet in and out of it, as explained in the earlier section on generating current (page 91). The transformer tab in the PhET Faraday simulation allows you to move the coils around and observe what happens when they are overlapping and what happens if you use DC instead of AC for the primary coil.

Science in context

An urgent refinement to our 'national grid' in the UK is the need to build the infrastructure that will support growth in the use of electric vehicles. At the time of writing a ban on petrol and diesel cars will be enforced in 2035. We need our students to be equipped to solve the technological challenges that will be faced to achieve such targets and develop creative ideas to support our demands on the planet.

(3.6) Resources
Online Resources

Please go to **spark.iop.org/asebook** for a set of curated resources from the IOP Spark website to match this chapter.

CLEAPPS provides support for practical science and technology and in particular safety advice: www.cleapss.org.uk

The Exploratorium has some accessible, hands-on activities that include a hand battery and simple generator: www.exploratorium.edu

The Institute of Physics has a number of curated collections to support teaching and practical work in this topic: www.spark.iop.org

The National Grid website has information on electric vehicles: www.nationalgrid.com

Phys Org has information about birds and magnetism: https://phys.org

Physics World has information about 3D images of magnetic domains: https://physicsworld.com

The Royal Mint explains why some coins are magnetic: www.royalmint.com

Scientific American has instructions for how to build your own loudspeaker (uses neodymium magnets, so supervision is required): www.scientificamerican.com

Scottish Schools Education Research Centre (SSERC): www.sserc.org.uk

The Smithsonian magazine provides further information on Nikola Tesla: www.smithsonianmag.com

Squishy circuits shows how to make electrical conducting dough for simple circuit work: www.squishycircuits.com

STEM Learning host many free resources including the BEST resources and their collection focusing on Electricity and Magnetism: www.stem.org.uk

Simulations

PhET simulations 'Balloons and Static Electricity', 'Generator', 'Faraday's Law', 'Faraday's Electromagnetic Lab' and 'John Travoltage': https://phet.colorado.edu

References

Boohan, R. (2016) *The Language of Mathematics in Science*. Hatfield: Association for Science Education. A comprehensive overview of the mathematical challenges students face in science with suggestion for classroom practice.

Brock, R. (2018) *Stories from Physics: Electricity & Magnetism*. IOP. Contains many interesting and engaging stories around this topic that you can use to enhance your lessons.

Rogers, B. (2018) *The Big Ideas in Physics and How to Teach Them*. London: Routledge. This book explores a narrative and historically contextualised approach to teaching physics with suggestions for classroom practice.

4 Energy

Charles Tracy

Introduction

If you ask a group of 12 year-olds what they think the word *energy* means, you will get a variety of responses: 'energy makes things happen', 'you get it in drinks', and 'if you run out of energy, you have to sit down'.

Trying to make sense of these ideas reveals two of the challenges of teaching about energy: energy is famously difficult to define (although we will have a go below) and it means many different things in everyday language.

This chapter is slightly different from other chapters in that it describes a complete approach to representing energy ideas – as a topic and across all of the sciences. We recommend spending some time on it and reflecting on how you and your colleagues will teach about energy.

Purposes: why should students learn about energy?

Although we cannot ignore or correct its everyday use, the term 'energy' has a specific meaning in the sciences. Furthermore, it is an important and revealing tool for making predictions. However, developing a good scientific conception of energy is also valuable for informing public discourse. A good grasp of energy ideas will allow all students (as adults) to make informed choices relating to food, transport and domestic use; and it can help them address some big questions – on both a national scale and in their homes:

1 What are our energy needs?
2 What sources are available to meet them?
3 What are the implications of limited resources?
4 How can we make the best use of what we have?

To answer these questions effectively, we need *numbers* and *values*. We need to know *how much* energy we require, and *how much* energy is stored in useful deposits.

That is to say: energy is fundamentally a tool for performing calculations that provide values. Those values allow for precise predictions and inform decisions.

What is energy?

The technical answer to this question is: energy is a *quantity* whose value can be calculated in various situations. The total energy of a system is conserved; and that conservation allows us to set up revealing calculations.

A less technical, but more intuitive and descriptive answer might be that the energy associated with a task tells us the total effort that is needed to achieve that task, for example, the effort needed to lift up a weight, to accelerate a bicycle or to boil a kettle.

Science in context

The conservation of energy began as an empirical law: experiments always showed that the total energy was unchanged. In 1918, the German mathematician Emmy Noether produced a theorem that allowed the law to be derived from the assumption that the laws of physics do not vary with time.

Science in context

Energy is measured in 'joules' after Salford-born brewer James Joule, who contributed to the unification of ideas about working and heating. He was motivated by trying to improve the efficiency of his brewery.

Big ideas about energy

The discussion above gives some sense of the lasting, big ideas that we would like students to take away from their secondary education:

→ Energy is a conserved quantity.
→ It provides a means of performing informative calculations.

To which we can add:

→ Energy is dissipated (becoming stored in less useable ways).
→ It is not energy that is 'used up' but energy resources, and there is a limited supply of them.

The more detailed outcomes at age 16 are shown below. In this chapter, we will aim to make you comfortable with the meaning of these outcomes.

A teaching sequence

The learning outcomes for this topic are as follows:

1 Systems store energy:
   a) Energy is stored by a system, which we can think of as comprising a group of connected or related parts, such as a person on Earth, a moving tennis ball or a cup of tea.
   b) There are different ways a system can store energy (see Table 4.1).
   c) It is possible to use formulae to calculate changes in the amount of energy that is stored in those different ways.
2 Conservation of energy:
   a) The total amount of energy always remains the same.
   b) Energy can be transferred between systems by two processes: working or heating.
   c) Working and heating can also result in changes in the *way* in which energy is stored within a system (for example, gravitationally or elastically).
3 Dissipation and reversibility:
   a) Energy is dissipated over time; it is stored in less useful ways.
   b) Power is the rate at which energy is transferred.

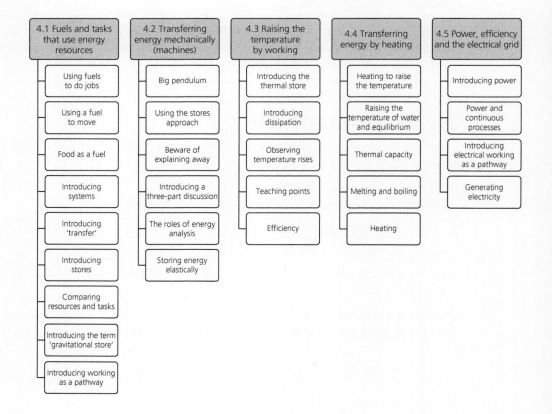

4.1 Fuels and tasks that use energy resources	4.2 Transferring energy mechanically (machines)	4.3 Raising the temperature by working	4.4 Transferring energy by heating	4.5 Power, efficiency and the electrical grid
Using fuels to do jobs	Big pendulum	Introducing the thermal store	Heating to raise the temperature	Introducing power
Using a fuel to move	Using the stores approach	Introducing dissipation	Raising the temperature of water and equilibrium	Power and continuous processes
Food as a fuel	Beware of explaining away	Observing temperature rises	Thermal capacity	Introducing electrical working as a pathway
Introducing systems	Introducing a three-part discussion	Teaching points	Melting and boiling	Generating electricity
Introducing 'transfer'	The roles of energy analysis	Efficiency	Heating	
Introducing stores	Storing energy elastically			
Comparing resources and tasks				
Introducing the term 'gravitational store'				
Introducing working as a pathway				

Energy and power

Power appears in only the last learning outcome. However, the quantity of power has equal standing to that of energy. Indeed, in many situations it is more informative. Furthermore, it is easier to give an intuitive sense of power: we can readily recognise machines and devices that are powerful and we have a sense of the brightness and loudness of 100 W devices.

While energy is helpful for analysing changes that occur over time, power is more helpful for processes that are *continuous over time*, such as listening to music, lighting a room or heating a house. You will know that you select loudspeakers, light bulbs and radiators based on their power rather than an energy value. We can summarise the differences as follows:

→ Energy *can inform us about* resources and tasks.
→ We use energy values (in joules) to analyse:
  • (resources): food, combustible fuels, nuclear fuels and a high tide
  • (tasks): stretching a spring, making tea and launching a ball in the air.
→ Power *can inform us about* devices and continuous processes.
→ We use power values (in watts) to analyse:
  • (devices): light bulbs, loudspeakers, kettles, circuits and power stations
  • (processes): lighting a room, generating electricity, moving at constant speed.

Preparing to teach about energy

Over the years, there have been a variety of approaches to discussing energy at school (such as 'types and transformation' or 'stores and pathways'). Given that energy ideas will be discussed in many topics across the sciences, it will be helpful if you and your colleagues choose a single approach and use the same representations across all science topics.

Stores and pathways: a helpful approach

In this chapter, we will not rely solely on any single approach. However, we will recommend one approach: 'stores and pathways'. Stores and pathways provide a useful shorthand way of discussing energy ideas in early secondary school without developing misconceptions. The approach works well with students and is derived from evidence of misconceptions. They are discussed in detail on the IOPSpark website (see Resources at the end of the chapter).

Stores

It is worth emphasising up front that stores are *not real*. They are an imaginary tool for illustrating and describing the way in which a system stores energy. They also enable us to represent how much energy is stored before students start doing calculations. You will notice that each one has a corresponding method for evaluating the amount of energy associated with a system (usually a formula). The eight stores below will allow you to discuss all the energy stories that you will need in early secondary school.

Table 4.1 Energy stores

Store	Method to evaluate how much energy is stored, E
gravitational	mgh
kinetic	$\frac{1}{2}mv^2$
elastic	$\frac{1}{2}kx^2$
thermal	$mc\Delta\theta$
vibrational	$\frac{1}{2}kA^2$
electric-magnetic	various including $\dfrac{q_1 q_2}{4\pi\varepsilon r}$
chemical	look up reaction in a data table
nuclear	

There is a discussion on IOPSpark on why these eight stores cover our needs in early secondary school (See Resources at the end of the chapter). Each of the stores above relates to a way of evaluating energy at a later point in the curriculum. Although students are unlikely to calculate all quantities unless they study post-16 physics, the language of stores is a placeholder for calculations that will come later. You should check your examination specification for those that are required.

So, for example, an elastic store is a shorthand way of referring to the amount of energy stored by a stretched spring up to age 13. Once students begin to use a formula ($E = \frac{1}{2}kx^2$), you can introduce the terminology 'the amount of energy stored elastically' to replace the placeholder of 'the elastic store of energy'.

Pathways

Pathways are placeholders for power calculations that will come later on. They are summarised in the table below.

Table 4.2 Pathways

Pathway	Method to evaluate power, P
Working mechanically	Fv
Working electrically	VI
Heating by contact	$kA\dfrac{\Delta\theta}{\Delta x}$
Heating by radiation	σAT^4

Note that the last two equations are included for completeness but are not a part of pre-16 physics courses.

Unless specifically stated, all the discussions in this chapter are quite general. So, for example, the helpful construction 'energy stored gravitationally' is general and is not a part of the stores and pathways approach.

Note that some examination specifications may use alternative symbols for some quantities.

Science in context

Energy analysis has revealed fundamental new knowledge. It led to the discovery of the neutrino as part of beta decay. In the 1930s, the calculated amount of energy stored by the unstable nucleus before the beta particle was emitted was larger than that of the daughter nucleus and emitted electron. How could this be? The problem was solved in 1959 when Cowans and Reine found the elusive particle and made the energies add up.

4.1 Fuels and tasks that use energy resources

This first teaching sequence will establish the idea that energy is a quantity and its value can be determined. We introduce the idea of attaching numerical values to energy using food labels and then show that it is possible to quantify the amount of energy transferred to perform some tasks by working mechanically.

Students should know that fuel and oxygen are required for humans to perform tasks that involve mechanical working. They will be able to discuss systems (such as fuel plus oxygen) and to describe the way in which those systems store energy and know that energy is measured in joules. They will be confident that it is 'energy resources' that are used up rather than 'energy'.

Ideas students have and potential pitfalls

Many students have a strong conception of energy as a substance. Furthermore, they may think that energy is an ingredient, that food contains energy and that this ingredient 'makes things happen' or 'allows the body to work'.

Additionally, although students can state that energy is conserved, they can also hold the contradictory idea that it is 'produced' and subsequently 'used up' to perform a task.

To counter both of these pitfalls, it helps to avoid references to energy being 'released', 'absorbed' or 'carried'. Certainly avoid 'produced' and 'used'. Instead, refer to energy being stored by systems and being transferred between systems. In effect, energy does not exist on its own, it only has meaning if it is associated with a system.

 Science literacy

Energy has a similar role to momentum in the physics lexicon: they are both conserved quantities. When representing or describing energy changes, it is worth asking yourself 'Would I use this phrasing or diagram for a momentum analysis?'

For example, in a collision, you might say that momentum has been 'transferred' from a moving car to a stationary car. But probably not that momentum is 'released' or 'absorbed' or 'created' or 'used' in the collision.

Using fuels to do jobs

A good place to start with energy is to consider fuels. You can show that tasks which require a fuel involve both a force *and* movement. If either is missing, then no fuel is required. Use the following two steps to lead up to that conclusion:

Step 1. Movement but no force

If there is movement but no force, then we do not need a fuel.

Ask students whether a fuel or food is required to:

→ run across a field; skate freely across ice
→ fire a rocket into space; for the rocket to drift forever beyond the force of gravity
→ accelerate a racing car; skidding on an oil slick.

In each pair, the first example requires a fuel (because there is a force) and the second does not (because there is no force). You could use some video clips or photos to illustrate fuels being used.

Step 2. Force but no movement

If there is force but no movement, then (again) we do not need a fuel. For example, lifting a book onto a shelf requires a fuel to be used up. However, the shelf can hold the book (stationary) without any fuel.

Give more pairs of examples (and possibly use photographs). In these pairs, one of them is moving (and requires a fuel) and the other is not:

→ leaving a car parked outside; driving from Manchester to Birmingham
→ Tower Bridge supporting the roadway; lifting the platform on Tower Bridge
→ the Blackpool Tower supporting the viewing platform; the lift carrying three people up the tower.

It is better to avoid examples that include people, because human bodies are complicated: while the bookshelf requires no fuel, a person holding the book above their head would.

Using a fuel to move

You can use a steam engine to demonstrate that, when there is both a force and movement, a fuel is used up. The steam engine may seem a little old fashioned, however it still has currency: boiling water to make something move is still the basis for some types of power station. Furthermore, it illustrates the principle that we can build machines to do jobs for us. If you do not have a steam engine, you could use a battery-driven motor to lift the weight. The experiment is described on IOPSPark (See Resources at the end of the chapter).

Test the demonstration beforehand to determine how much weight the steam engine can lift. It is more impressive to lift a large weight slowly than a small weight quickly. Show the steam engine lifting the weight up to the desk. To perform this task, the fuel was burnt in oxygen and the fuel had to be used up.

Then engage the brake on the steam engine and leave the weight hanging; remove the burner to show that, once the weight is stationary, no more fuel is required. Lead the students towards the idea that an energy resource is required only when there is movement.

Emphasise that it is not 'energy' that is used up but an 'energy resource' (in this case a fuel or a battery). Once the fuel and oxygen have been turned into carbon dioxide and water, we cannot get them to do anything useful. Always try to discourage references to 'energy being used up' and gently shift students towards identifying the resource that has actually been used up: a fuel, food, a battery or possibly the Sun.

Food as a fuel

Food is a familiar energy resource. And it gets used up. During a day, a person will perform a number of tasks because they eat some food and breathe some oxygen. The body is an amazing machine that combines the food's sugars with the oxygen in a controlled way to keep the person warm and to allow the muscles to operate. The oxygen is essential in this discussion, without it the food would not let us do any tasks.

Introducing systems

It helps to refer to systems and to define all the parts of the system. In this case, the energy is initially stored by a system comprising food plus oxygen.

By the end of a day, the energy is stored by the surroundings (which are now at a slightly higher temperature). The surroundings are a different system from the initial system. Therefore, we often say that the energy has been 'transferred' from the food + oxygen system to the surroundings.

Systems help to avoid the suggestion that energy is possessed by or deposited in objects as in: 'a bar of chocolate *contains* 200 calories'. This phrase suggests that energy is an ingredient. It is more helpful to say that the energy is 'stored' by the system comprising food and oxygen.

Introducing 'transfer'

In many events, the amount of energy associated with one system will decrease and the amount associated with another system will increase. A good way of describing this change is to say that the energy has been 'transferred' from one system to another.

It is worth trying to reserve the word 'transfer' for energy that is being stored in different places. If you are using the stores approach, try to avoid saying 'energy is transferred from gravitational to kinetic energy' or 'energy is transferred from a gravitational store to a kinetic store'. To avoid using 'transfer' in this context you can say 'the gravitational store has emptied a little and the kinetic store has filled up a little' or 'the energy has been *shifted* from the gravitational store to the kinetic store'.

Calorific values

Remind students of an activity in which they burnt some fuels (including foods) to raise the temperature of some water. Different foods raised the temperature by different amounts. This is the basis of calorimetry: the technique of burning a fuel in oxygen to determine how much energy was stored by the fuel + oxygen system. This amount is sometimes called the calorific value.

Suggest that students compare the calorific values of different foods and food types (fat, sugar, protein, carbohydrate and fibre). Provide them with some food labels, ensuring that the foods are rich in different food types. They can plot a bar chart to show the different calorific values per 100g. The x-axis is the food name and food type, and the y-axis is 'amount of energy stored chemically by food plus oxygen'.

Energy as a quantity

The exercise above helps to reinforce the idea that energy is a quantity. You can help further by assigning values measured in joules to any mention of energy with phrases like 'the amount of energy stored is 20 joules'.

Introducing stores

The calorific value of a foodstuff is the 'energy stored chemically by the food plus oxygen system'. This phrase can require a lot of decoding by young learners. It is neater and less burdensome to refer to an imaginary 'chemical store' associated with this system. This is not a real store but a shorthand way of describing how the system stores energy. Stores are a way of introducing, with simple, visual representations, the various different ways that a system can store energy.

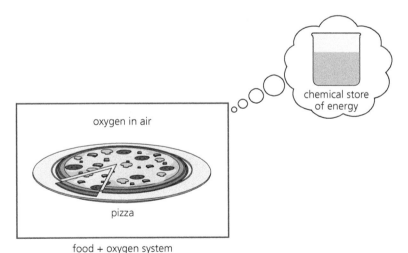

Figure 4.1 It can help to refer to an imaginary chemical store that is associated with the fuel + oxygen system.

Once you have established this terminology, you can then simply refer to the 'chemical store' with occasional reminders that it is associated with the food plus oxygen system. Further up the school, students will start to do calculations and can refer to 'the energy stored chemically'.

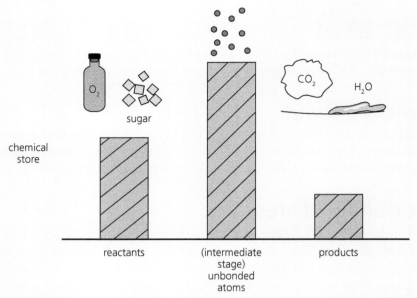

Figure 4.2 The reactants store more energy chemically than the products. Note that energy is stored by the chemical reactants and not by chemical bonds; indeed, it requires effort to break those bonds.

> ## π   Maths
>
> The calorie is the unit of energy used in nutrition; the stated calorific value of a chocolate bar is '230 calories'; confusingly, the actual value is 230 kilocalories but the prefix is usually dropped. In physics calculations, the energy stored chemically by the chocolate bar and oxygen is 1.2 MJ; 1 kcal is equivalent to 4.18 kJ.

Comparing resources and tasks

There are plenty of data on the amounts of major energy resources used in the UK and around the world. In early secondary school students can be encouraged to compare the amount of energy stored in different resources with the amount needed to perform different tasks. Information around some energy values for foods and the energy cost for travelling different distances by different means can be found on IOPSpark (see Resources at the end of this chapter).

Lifting apples to introduce the idea of working mechanically

At the beginning of this section, we introduced the idea that some tasks require effort. These tasks involve both a force and movement. In this demonstration, you will quantify the amount of effort through the term 'work' and introduce a formula for the amount of energy transferred by 'working'.

KEY ACTIVITIES

You will need four small apples, a metre rule and a newton meter. Before the lesson, choose an apple that weighs 1 N (if necessary, remove or add some weight to this apple). You only need to do this for one of the apples. Dispose of the apples after the lesson so that they are not eaten.

Make a point of weighing the apple and of measuring out 1 m height (if necessary, add some books to a bench to make up the height). Now lift the apple from the floor to the 1 m mark. Say that 'Lifting the apple involves both a force and movement and requires me to do work'. State that the amount of work you have done is 1 joule (1 J). You could ask a few students to try lifting the apple to get a sense of what 1 J feels like.

Next lift two apples through 1 m. Ask students to think how much work you have done to lift twice as many apples. Ensure that all students consider an answer. Help them to reason their way to the answer of 2 J.

Then repeat with three and four apples (3 J and 4 J). Ask how much work it would take to lift 45 apples through 1 m; and so on.

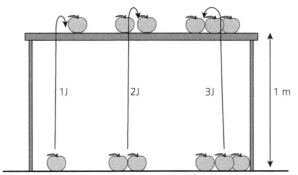

Figure 4.3 The energy transferred by working is proportional to the force.

You should draw out the idea that the energy transferred by mechanical working is proportional to the force. Doubling the force doubles the amount of mechanical working; tripling the force triples it; and so on.

Now lift the original apple through 2 m. Again, ask the students how much energy has been transferred by working. Help them reason their way to 2 J. As before, give them various quick calculations for lifting the apple through 3 m, 4 m, 6 m and 12 m. Lead up to the idea that the energy transferred by mechanical working is proportional to the distance.

Next, ask how much energy would be transferred if you lifted three apples through 2 m. Help them reason their way to 6 J.

Finally, give them the relationship for the energy transferred by working (or work) as:

$$\text{energy transferred by working (J)} = \text{force (N)} \times \text{distance (m)}$$

$$W = F \times d$$

Force is measured in newtons, the distance in metres and the work in joules.

Give them lots of practice in multiplying force by distance to determine the energy transferred by mechanical working. Try to phrase the questions in a way that brings out the reasoning behind the relationship. This activity will help students build an idea of the size of one joule of work (see Resources at the end of this chapter).

Introducing the term 'gravitational store'

Remind students that, in order to lift the apple, the amount of energy in the chemical store has decreased. This energy is now stored by the system comprising the apple, the Earth and gravity.

This system stores energy because the objects have been pulled apart against the force of gravity. We say that the system is storing energy gravitationally. As with the term 'chemical store', you can use the shorthand: 'energy in a gravitational store'. As before, this is not a literal store but a way of representing the energy stored by the system.

The diagram below uses bar charts to show the changes in the energy in the chemical and gravitational stores before and after the apple has been lifted.

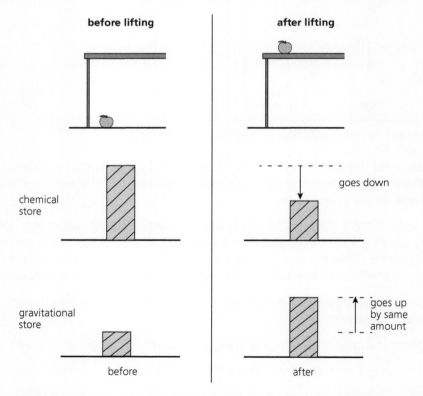

Figure 4.4 You can represent the amount of energy in each store using bar charts. You might prefer to put the bars side by side. However, stacking the bars hints at the idea that the total amount of energy is constant.

Introducing working as a pathway

Like stores, pathways are also placeholders for future calculations. In this case, the pathway is 'working mechanically'. The pathway takes the system from one point in time to another.

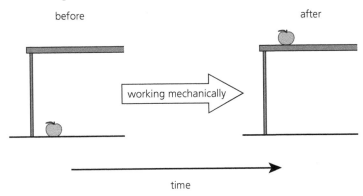

Figure 4.5 Working mechanically

It is worth taking care to not be too literal about the representation of pathways (or stores). It is not the case that energy flows along pathways; such a representation would reinforce the idea that energy is a substance. Instead, describe the pathways as the route that the system takes. The pathway results in energy being stored differently and in a different place, but it is not a pipeline for energy.

Transferring energy mechanically (machines)

In this section, we will look at some of the ways in which systems can store energy mechanically. This is a good way to gently introduce students to these important ideas and techniques: the conservation of energy; making predictions using an energy analysis and the utility of start and end points.

Students should be able to identify these ways in which a system stores energy: gravitationally, elastically and kinetically. By age 16, they should be able to use formulae to evaluate how much energy is stored in each case.

They should know that energy is a conserved quantity and, as such, allows us to perform illuminating calculations. By age 16, they should be able to set up and perform some of those calculations.

111

Ideas students have and potential pitfalls

Even in mechanical situations, students may think that a raised object, such as a book, possesses or contains energy. Phrases like 'the book fell because it had more gravitational energy' reinforce this idea and also reinforce the misleading impression that 'energy makes things happen'.

Therefore, continue to emphasise that it is *systems* that store energy; and discourage references to energy as the capacity to drive or cause activity. In particular, try to avoid explaining away physical mechanisms by using an energy framework as an explanatory tool.

Teaching procedures
Big pendulum

A memorable way to introduce the idea of energy conservation is to use a big pendulum. The bigger the pendulum, the more striking this will be. You can suspend a bob from a beam in your laboratory or, even better, a high-ceilinged room that has a sturdy and accessible fixing point. A heavier bob (like a bowling ball) makes it more impressive, and videos of this can be found online. It is important that the bob is spherical because irregularly shaped objects might rotate in flight (and strike the demonstrator). You should run this as a demonstration and try it beforehand to ensure it is safe.

Stand with your back to a wall and lift the bob. With the string taught, allow the bob to touch your chin. Invite the students to predict what will happen when you let the pendulum swing. You can build up some drama saying that you are willing to take this risk for their education. Then let the bob go (make sure you drop it rather than push it) and keep absolutely still. Try not to flinch but certainly do not lean forwards. The longer the string, the closer it will get to your chin. There are some good videos online of this demonstration (see Resources at the end of the chapter).

You can now have a rich discussion that will lead up to the principle of conservation of energy.

Discussion

You will be relieved that the pendulum did not strike your chin; but it would be strange if it had done. If it had swung higher, then we would have 'got something for nothing'. Instead, the pendulum returns to its original height. This is the beginnings of a conservation law: the height afterwards is the same as the height at the beginning, that is to say height is conserved.

However, this conservation law only works at the ends of the swing (when the bob is not moving). As the pendulum drops, it speeds up so maybe the height and speed combine to give a new conserved quantity.

This more general quantity is energy; the total amount of energy stored by the system depends on both the bob's height and also its speed. The system can store energy in two ways; and we can write an equation that includes a term for each of these ways:

total energy = energy stored gravitationally + energy stored kinetically

This 'total energy' is conserved throughout the swing. If the energy stored gravitationally goes down, the energy stored kinetically goes up and vice versa. There is an animation of the energy analysis on IOPSpark (see Resources at the end of the chapter)

Later in this chapter, we will discuss dissipation in terms of energy and of particles. If your students notice that the pendulum swings slightly short of its starting point, you could briefly touch on it here.

Using the stores approach

At this point, you can reintroduce the idea of stores. Here, the system comprises the Earth, the bob and gravity. There is both a kinetic store and a gravitational store associated with this system. Remember, these are imaginary stores that we are using as placeholders for future calculations.

Lifting the pendulum results in a gravitational store being filled a little. When the pendulum falls, the gravitational store empties and the kinetic store fills. You can use the word 'shift' for energy being stored in different imaginary stores so as to reserve 'transfer' for changes in location (page 106).

Beware of explaining away

It is all too easy to use energy-labelling procedures to provide a scientific-sounding narrative that 'explains away' the underlying causes of a phenomenon. In this case, it is common to see 'explanations' like 'the pendulum speeds up because gravitational energy is converted to kinetic energy'. This sentence is frustrating: it appears to give an explanation but actually provides no insight and masks the fuller explanation based on forces (which is given below).

Introducing a three-part discussion

To avoid 'explaining away' using energy, it helps to provide explanations based on processes and mechanisms; and to keep these explanations separate from the energy analysis. This can be achieved by consciously structuring the discussion in three parts:

1 description (of the phenomenon)
2 explanations (based on mechanisms and processes)
3 analysis (based on energy ideas).

Using the pendulum as an example, we have:

→ Description: The swinging mass returns to its original height.
→ Explanation: The force of gravity is pulling the bob downwards. When you let it go, it speeds up as it falls towards the bottom of the swing. As it rises up the other side, gravity is still pulling it downwards so its speed decreases until it stops.
→ Energy analysis: The energy stored gravitationally depends on height. Given that energy is conserved, the energy stored gravitationally at the extremes is the same each time. And therefore the mass reaches the same height.

The role of energy analysis

The explanation and analysis perform very different roles and are both important. The explanation refers to underlying mechanisms and processes. The analysis involves predictions based on calculations. Even associating the word 'analysis' with energy helps to emphasise energy's role as a tool for calculations.

Falling objects

Energy calculations are particularly helpful in analysing motion in a gravitational field (either falling or rising). There are many standard examples; we will look at dropping a soft ball from a window.

Introducing snapshots, start points and end points

The analysis is simplified by taking two snapshots in time. The points for these two snapshots are a matter of choice depending on what you are trying to predict (speed, bounce height or temperature rise, for example). Usually, the first is before an event and the second at the end: the 'start point' and the 'end point'. The fact that energy is conserved means that the total energy is always the same at each snapshot. Adding up the stores at each snapshot will always give the same total. In this experiment, you can drop a soft ball out of a second floor window (ensuring nobody is underneath). You can then record the drop using a phone or video camera.

We will choose the snapshots as follows:

→ Start point: ball in person's hand.
→ End point: just before it lands (because we are interested in the speed).

At the start point, the ball is stationary but raised up. So the energy is stored gravitationally; at the end point, the ball is moving so the energy is now stored kinetically. In the stores approach, you can say that a gravitational store has been emptied a little and a kinetic store has been filled by the same amount.

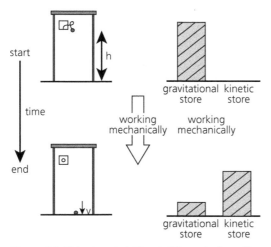

Figure 4.6 This chart is laid out differently from Figure 4.4; you can choose which layout you prefer.

> It can help to use more concrete visualisations, such as liquid in beakers or Lego bricks, to represent the amount of energy in stores and to emphasise conservation by showing the total amount is unchanged. This technique is discussed on IOPSpark (see Resources at the end of the chapter).
>
> Care should be taken when using such representations so that they do not reinforce ideas about energy as a substance.

Making the analysis quantitative

From age 14, energy analysis becomes quantitative; and freefalling objects are a standard calculation in examinations. Using the energy analysis above, we can say that:

increase in energy stored kinetically = decrease in energy stored gravitationally

We have formulae for each of those terms, so we can write:

$$\frac{1}{2}mv^2 = mgh$$

The mass appears on both sides. From this, you can argue that the final velocity does not depend on mass. This confirms an experiment Galileo was said to have carried out: dropping balls of different masses from the tower of Pisa. The fact that speed does not depend on mass is more apparent when the equation is rearranged to make the speed the subject:

$$v = \sqrt{2gh}$$

Once it is rearranged, this equation (and the energy analysis) enables us to quickly determine the object's maximum velocity.

Maths

Some students will find rearranging this equation challenging; the ASE book *The Language of Mathematics in Science* is an excellent guide for teaching these skills, but it is particularly important that the same approach is used for rearranging equations as is used by the maths department.

Also, notice that v is the *maximum* velocity; this is because we assumed that there was no friction. In reality, through friction, some energy will be dissipated, meaning that the actual velocity will be less (see Section 4.3, page 122).

Activity to verify the energy relationship

Drop a soft ball (such as a tennis ball) out of a window. Measure the height of the drop and use Tracker video analysis tool (see Resources at the end of this chapter) to determine its velocity at the bottom. You can confirm that the velocity matches the value predicted by the energy analysis. Reinforce the effectiveness of energy analysis in making the prediction.

Alternatively, there is a standard activity, described on IOPSpark, with a trolley that gives students the opportunity to confirm that the loss in energy stored gravitationally by a falling mass pulling a trolley corresponds to the increase in energy stored kinetically by the moving trolley (and mass) (see Resources at the end of this chapter).

Uneven tracks

The prediction from an energy analysis works whatever route a falling object takes. So, for example, it also works for rollercoasters, skateboards and cyclists freewheeling down a hill. We do not need to know the shape of the track, the energy analysis still provides a prediction of the maximum speed.

Storing energy elastically

You can use a variety of jumping toys to introduce the idea that energy can be stored elastically. Some use a spring, others are simply a rubber dome that can be turned inside out.

Turn the rubber dome inside out and place the toy on a hard surface:

→ Description: After a moment, the dome will 'flip' and leap into the air. As ever, it helps to distinguish the explanation from the energy analysis.
→ Explanation: The rubber is in tension but slowly creeps back to its original shape. At a critical point, it snaps back into shape. In doing so, the top of the toy pushes down on the desk and there is an upwards force on the toy, launching it into the air.

→ Energy analysis: Choose a start point when the cap has been inverted and an end point at the top of its flight.

  → Start point: Energy is stored elastically.

  → End point: Energy is stored gravitationally.

You could make this quantitative by measuring the height of the flight and, using the mass of the toy, determine how much energy was stored elastically at the start.

Practice with stores

At this point, we have introduced four ways in which energy can be stored: chemically, gravitationally, elastically and kinetically. If you are following our recommended approach, you have four stores at your disposal: chemical, gravitational, elastic and kinetic. To complete our set of mechanical stores, we can add a vibrational store: this is associated with systems that store energy due to a vibration or oscillation. Examples include a mass on a spring, a twanged ruler and a vibrating tuning fork.

> Note that waves are best not thought of as vibrational stores. They are continuous processes and are therefore pathways (see page 101). For example, sound waves and water waves transfer energy by working mechanically. It is particularly unhelpful to refer to sound as a form or store of energy; it is a process by which energy is transferred from one place to another. The energy generally ends up in a thermal store of the surroundings when the sound is absorbed.

KEY ACTIVITIES

It is time for some hands-on activities. You can do a carousel of activities of mechanical changes. In each case, get students to analyse the situation in a similar way to the three-part approach (page 113).

Ask students to focus on the start and end point. This will help avoid the unhelpful temptation to mirror the physical explanation with a complicated chain of stores. (See Resources at the end of this chapter for a discussion of chains on IOPSpark)

They should also draw charts of each situation. You could provide a framework or table to help them with this task. It is important to choose your examples carefully (to draw out the important ideas). Some good ones are:

- elastic bands fired upwards and horizontally; wear eye protection
- elastic band cars (on the flat and going up a ramp)
- a spring suspended from a clamp-stand
- a twanged ruler
- trolleys with rubber bands across the runway
- bouncing balls (which we investigate in the next section).

Ask students to consider different start and end points (for example, a start point might be before a piece of elastic has been stretched or at the point that it is already extended).

Energy stores

It is worth pausing for a moment to consider the language that we have been using. For example, we have not used adjectives to describe energy such as 'gravitational energy', 'elastic energy' or 'kinetic energy'. These adjectival descriptions imply, misleadingly, that energy comes in different types. Instead, we have described the way in which energy is stored: 'energy stored gravitationally' which emphasises the idea that the quantity that is stored is energy: just energy.

Furthermore, when referring to stores, we always refer to the quantity stored as energy, for example, 'a gravitational store' or 'gravitational store of energy' is preferable to saying a 'gravitational energy store'.

4.3 Raising the temperature by working

The purpose of this section is to show that thermal effects are also encompassed in ideas about energy. Specifically, in a situation in which a moving object comes to rest, where it might appear that energy is 'lost', it is not: some part of the system will have got hotter and the energy is now stored thermally.

Science in context

The term 'energy' was first used by Thomas Young in the 19th century and began to replace 'vis viva', the term coined in Newton's time meaning 'living force'. Up until the early 1800s, vis viva described what we think of as energy stored by mechanical systems; while caloric described what we would think of as energy stored thermally. So energy was a unifying concept. It encompasses both mechanical and thermal phenomena.

In this section, the new idea is that we can raise the temperature of an object by working it. Students should know that a hot object stores more energy due to the random movement of its particles and that this is the same energy that is stored in mechanical situations. It is now stored thermally.

They will learn that most activities run down. In energy terms this means that, although the total amount of energy remains the same, the energy has been dissipated and is stored in a way that is less useable.

Ideas students have and potential pitfalls

Students are likely to view 'heat' as a substance that is either a distinct form or a special form of energy.

This unhelpful view is reinforced by many explanations that use 'heat' as though it is different from energy; as in 'the heat stored by the surroundings'. It is more helpful to refer to 'energy stored thermally'. This reinforces a view of energy as the unifying quantity across mechanical and thermal situations, that is to say *the quantity associated with an increased temperature is still energy; just energy.*

Introducing the thermal store

If you are using 'stores and pathways', you can refer to a 'thermal store of energy'. This is an imaginary store associated with an object whose temperature can change. Remind students of the big pendulum and the observation that it didn't quite reach your chin. In this section, they will consider why it stopped short. At first, it might appear that energy is not conserved. However, of course, it is.

A unifying model

When discussing thermal situations, it is good practice to *develop explanations based on particles*. For example, it is more informative to say 'a hot object stores energy because its particles are moving around vigorously' than to say 'it stores heat'. The latter implies that heat is a substance, distinct from energy. It is best to avoid the notion of heat altogether. The particle model of matter is dealt with in more detail in Chapter 5 Matter.

Nothing lasts for ever

Allow a toy car to run across a desk from a small ramp. Set the ramp height so that the car comes to rest before the end of the desk. Ask the following questions to initiate separate discussions about the mechanisms and energy analysis.

1 What caused the car to slow down?
   → Explanation: The friction between the axles and bearings is a force that opposes the motion of the car. Therefore, it slows down. Furthermore, friction makes the particles in those surfaces knock against each other and vibrate more vigorously. Consequently, the axle and bearing will get ever so slightly warmer.
   → Over time, those slightly warmer components will raise the temperature of the surroundings because vibrating particles collide with air particles, making them move faster.
2 What happened to the energy?
   → Energy analysis: To account for the energy that is no longer stored mechanically, you can say that the energy is now stored thermally by the surroundings.

Choose a start point at the *bottom* of the ramp and an end point when the car comes to rest. If you are using the stores representation, a kinetic store has emptied and a thermal store has filled a little.

> Note that if you choose the start point at the *top* of the ramp, the initial store would be a gravitational store.

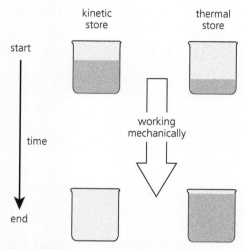

Figure 4.7 The amount of energy in the thermal store increases by the same amount as the decrease in energy in the kinetic store.

Rollercoasters and skateboarders

In this activity, students use a car on some tracks to investigate a skateboarder or rollercoaster. For the skateboarder, set the track up in a U-shape. For the rollercoaster, set up a ramp with a hump.

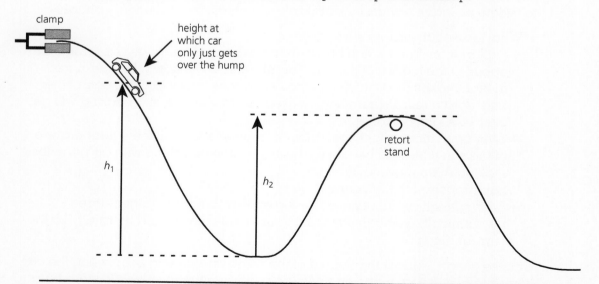

Figure 4.8 A 'rollercoaster' showing h_1 and h_2

Students set up the track using clamp stands (you could have a demo version to illustrate the set up). They set the height of the first ramp to about 65 cm and the height of the hump (h_2) to just under 50 cm. They let the car go from different heights until it only just gets over the hump. They measure the height that they let it go (h_1) and put h_1 in a table with h_2.

They then lower the hump by about 5 cm and find the new value of h_1. They can collect six results and plot a graph of h_2 against h_1.

It should be a straight line through the origin with a gradient that is likely to be around 0.8, showing that the energy stored gravitationally drops to about 80% of its starting value. As ever, it helps to separate the explanation from the energy analysis. You can explain the slowing down and temperature rise in terms of friction between surfaces that makes the particles vibrate more.

Now think about the energy analysis. Choose a start point where the car is let go and an end point at the top of the first hump. The energy is stored gravitationally in each case. However, at the end point, some energy is also stored thermally (by the axle, bearings and surroundings). The hump is always lower than the start height because some energy is stored thermally at the end. Figure 4.9 illustrates why the amount of energy stored gravitationally must be lower.

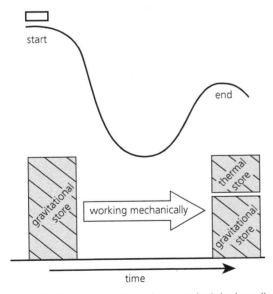

Figure 4.9 In this example, we have stacked the bars directly above each other. This reinforces the idea that the total energy is constant.

Introducing dissipation

Dissipation results in activities running down and energy resources being used up. And, in both cases, the change cannot be reversed. In energy terms, this is usually because friction has resulted in a temperature rise of the surroundings. This rise in temperature is very small and it is not possible to get the slightly tepid surroundings to do anything useful (such as lift the car higher up the ramp).

You can illustrate this by filming the rollercoaster car going over ever decreasing humps. If you show the film backwards, it is clearly reversed: we would never expect the tepid surroundings to spontaneously make the car go over higher humps. You can show other examples of videos that are clearly in reverse: the pendulum swings getting smaller (or a child on a swing), sliding a book across a desk, braking cars, bouncing balls and skidding bicycles. Discuss how your students know the film is running backwards. The answer is that dissipation runs only one way in time; it is not reversible.

> Note that in all of these processes, energy is still conserved. It is neither lost nor destroyed. It is stored in a different way (thermally).

Observing temperature rises

In the following activities, students will investigate examples in which friction or mechanical working result in observable temperature rises.

In each case, the process can be discussed in terms of particles. Specifically, 'the temperature rises because the particles have been made to move faster by working mechanically'.

Hammering metal

You will need some 15 mm copper pipe, a hammer and a strong wooden board (to protect the lab bench). Wear eye protection. Ask the students to feel the temperature of the copper before and after hammering (making sure they wash their hands afterwards). It will be warmer at the end. You could show this with an infrared thermometer.

At the start point, your body is storing energy chemically. At the end, the copper is storing more energy thermally. The energy has been transferred by mechanical working.

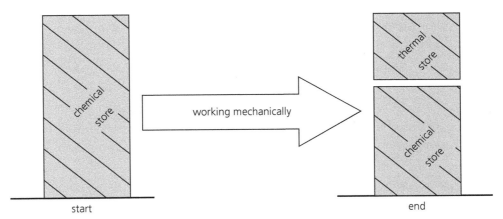

Figure 4.10 The temperature is raised by mechanical working.

Teaching points

Work towards a physics-based description of the processes, noting that:

→ It is very easy to say that 'hammering the copper produces heat'. Beware of doing so. This suggests that heat is different from energy and has been 'created by doing work'. It is more consistent with the rest of physics to say: 'hammering the copper makes its particles vibrate more vigorously; the result is that the copper is storing more energy thermally'.
→ It is also easy to say 'hammering the copper heats it up'. Again, try not to. It is better to say that hammering the copper 'raises its temperature' because the temperature rise was brought about by working rather than heating.

The two points above show that it is possible to avoid using the word 'heat' altogether in a scientific context. And doing so is helpful, because it prevents confusion with the vernacular use of the word.

Raising the temperature

We have used the phrase 'raising the temperature' rather than 'heating' because these phenomena are different and it is helpful to keep them distinct:

→ 'Heating' is a process by which energy is transferred due to a temperature difference. It is only one way of raising the temperature. As we have seen, it is also possible to raise the temperature of something by working it rather than heating it.
→ 'Raising the temperature' is only one possible result of heating. It is possible to 'heat' something without raising its temperature, for example, the temperature of boiling water remains constant even though the water is being heated, because the energy is stored due to a change in state (rather than a rise in temperature).

There is more on the particle model of matter in Chapter 5 Matter.

Other examples

Try some other situations in which mechanical working causes a temperature rise. Get students to discuss the phenomena and listen for terms like 'heat', 'heating', 'temperature rise' and 'energy' being used appropriately.

KEY ACTIVITIES

You could set these activities up as a carousel. In each case, students should use the three-part approach (description, explanation and analysis), taking care to include energy in the analysis only:

1 Bicycle pump
   When you compress the air in a bicycle pump, it gets warm; the temperature rises because particles colliding with the advancing plunger bounce off at a higher speed. You can measure the temperature rise with an infrared thermometer.
2 Fire piston
   You can buy a fire piston to show how hot the air gets. It gets so hot that it ignites some cotton wool inside the syringe. The ignition illustrates how hot the air gets and is the principle of a diesel engine. Avoid including the combustion in the energy analysis.
3 Paper clips
   Repeatedly bend a paper clip until it breaks. Then feel the temperature of the point at which it broke.
4 Rubbing hands together
   Rub your hands together and note how they feel. Emphasise that rubbing them together 'raises the temperature' at the surface.
5 Electric drill in wood
   Wearing eye protection, use a cordless drill to drill into a block of wood that is firmly clamped; the drill bit gets hot. Use an infrared thermometer to show the temperature rise.
6 Modelling clay
   Repeatedly compress modelling clay to raise its temperature.
7 Boiling water by friction
   Using a piece of cord to raise the temperature of a small cylinder of water by friction.
8 Smoothie maker
   You can use a smoothie maker to turn a few pieces of fruit (e.g. apples) into a smoothie. The smoothie is noticeably warm (especially if you run it for half a minute or so). Use a coffee grinder as an alternative.

Efficiency

Efficiency is an extremely important idea. The more energy that is dissipated, the less efficient a system. So, in the earlier rollercoaster example, each hump was about 80% efficient. The efficiency tells us what proportion of the energy is stored in a useful way after an event:

$$\text{efficiency} = \frac{\text{energy stored usefully after an event (J)}}{\text{energy stored usefully before an event (J)}} \times 100\%$$

Squash balls

When you bounce a ball (such as a squash ball), it will not return to its original height. The system (Earth, ball and gravity) is storing less energy after the bounce than before the bounce. Both the explanation and the energy analysis are similar to those for the rollercoaster. The temperature of the squash ball rises a little in each bounce; students can confirm this by squeezing the ball 20 times and note that its temperature rises.

Get students to measure the bounce height of a squash ball for different release heights and make a table of the bounce height (h_2) against the release height (h_1).

Using the relationship below, they can calculate the efficiency in each case and find the average:

$$\text{efficiency} = \frac{mgh_2}{mgh_1} \times 100\%$$

This experiment could be extended to comparing a squash ball with a table-tennis ball and other balls. In each case, ask them to draw bar charts of the start and end points.

The table-tennis ball bounces higher. This is because it is compressed less in the bounce; therefore less work is done on the ball's material and the air inside, so less energy is dissipated.

4.4 Transferring energy by heating

Students will now explore a more familiar mechanism for raising the temperature: heating. Heating is a well defined idea in the sciences: it is the process by which energy is transferred due to a temperature difference. The mechanisms underlying the process are described convincingly by ideas relating to particle interactions, waves and radiation.

Students should know that it is possible to transfer energy to an object by heating it (using another body at a higher temperature); and that heating can take place by contact (conduction and convection) or at a distance (radiation). They will be able to describe these mechanisms in terms of particles and radiation.

They should be able to distinguish temperature from energy and be able to reason that the amount of additional energy stored after a temperature rise depends on the change in temperature, the mass of an object and its material. By age 16, they should also be able to perform calculations involving specific heat capacity and specific latent heat.

Ideas students have and potential pitfalls

Students often have difficulty distinguishing the quantities of temperature and energy. This arises, in part, through the everyday use of 'heat' to mean temperature (for example: 'turn the oven heat up to 200°C').

Students are likely to have a conception of heat as a substance. This can arise through phrases like 'the heat stored in a cup of tea'; or 'the tea lost its heat to the surroundings'. Therefore, try to avoid such phrases.

 Science literacy

It will help to avoid to avoid and discourage using the word 'heat' at all in this topic. Instead, it is more helpful consistently to refer to:

- the quantity that is stored as energy
- the measure of hotness as 'temperature'
- the process by which energy is transferred as 'heating'.

Heating to raise the temperature

In Section 4.3, students rubbed their hands together to raise their temperature by working. Ask them if there is another way that they could raise the temperature and try to elicit the answer 'by heating' or 'by putting them in contact with something hotter'.

You could demonstrate this using a beaker of warm water and, with care, ask them to put their hands around it. Body temperature is about 37°C and the beaker is at a higher temperature (~50°C). Energy is transferred from the hotter beaker to their cooler hands. Call this effect 'heating' or 'transferring energy by heating'.

Raising the temperature of water and equilibrium

Students will need an immersion heater (see Safety note below), a 12 V power supply, a 500 ml beaker of water, a thermometer and a stop clock. Ask them to make a table of temperature against time as the immersion heater raises the temperature of the water. They take the temperature of the water and record this against a time of zero in the table. They put the immersion heater in the water and switch it on; they start the clock as they switch on the immersion heater. They should take the temperature of the water every minute until it is levelling off. They can put the values for temperature and time in the table and plot a graph.

To begin with, the graph goes up steadily. However, as the water gets hotter, the rate at which the temperature increases will slow down until, eventually, the water reaches an equilibrium temperature. You can refer to the two processes of transferring energy:

→ by electrical working to raise the temperature of the immersion heater
→ by heating to transfer energy from the hot immersion heater to the water.

You can call these pathways. As discussed in Section 4.1, page 111, they do not represent pipelines along which energy flows. They are ways of representing and discussing continuous processes. In this case, the processes are concurrent; and therefore the pathways are shown in parallel in Figure 4.11.

> Note that, in the energy analysis, there is no need to refer to the energy stored thermally by the immersion heater. There is no sense in which the energy transferred to the water had to pass through or be stored by the heater, the transfer is a continuous process: heating.

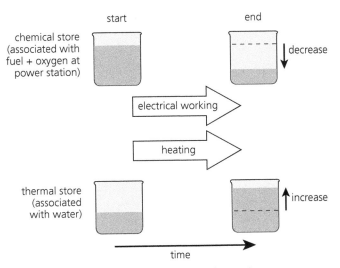

Figure 4.11 Energy analysis for immersion heater in water

> Safety note: It is important to use immersion heaters that are designed to go into water. Some are not, and they can cause steam explosions. The book ASE (2020) *Safeguards in the School Laboratory 12th ed.* has more details (see Resources at the end of this chapter).

Thermal capacity

Students can try heating different amounts of water and measuring the temperature after 3 minutes. The energy transferred by heating is the same each time because it is the same heater left on for the same time.

They will find that as the volume goes up, the rise in temperature decreases. In fact, the rise in temperature should be inversely proportional to the mass: doubling the mass will halve the temperature rise and tripling the mass will reduce it to a third. Taken to its limit, putting the immersion heater in a swimming pool for three minutes would have a very small effect (this idea is important for discussing the small temperature rise when energy is dissipated).

We can reason this inverse relationship in terms of the energy transferred. A fixed amount of energy can result in a large mass having a small temperature rise or a small mass having a large temperature rise. If one goes up the other goes down to compensate.

A larger mass of water has a larger capacity for storing energy thermally. We say it has a bigger 'heat capacity'. The experiment illustrates that the heat capacity of an object is proportional to its mass.

Different materials

You can now introduce the idea that different materials have different heat capacities. For example, it takes less effort to raise the temperature of 1 kg of aluminium than it does to raise the temperature of 1 kg of water. Aluminium has a smaller capacity for storing energy or a smaller 'specific heat capacity'. The word 'specific' means 'for a kilogram' and ensures the comparisons between materials are fair. The specific heat capacity of a material is the energy that has to be transferred to raise the temperature of 1 kg of that material by 1 °C. It is given the symbol c and defined by the equation:

energy transferred by heating (J) = mass (kg) × specific heat capacity (J/kg °C) × change in temperature (°C)

$$E = mc\theta$$

Science in context

Water has a particularly high specific heat capacity. This is why you should always be careful when you put tomatoes in a toasted sandwich. The water in the tomatoes will give a worse burn than, say, egg. The tomatoes are at the same temperature as the egg but storing more energy; therefore, they can raise the temperature of your tongue more than the egg.

Table 4.3 Chart of different specific heat capacities

Substance	Specific heat capacity J/kg °C
Water	4200
Wood	1700
Air	1000
Aluminium	900
Steel	450
Copper	390
Lead	130

You can determine the specific heat capacity of aluminium using an immersion heater and aluminium block. This experiment is described on IOPSpark (see Resources at the end of this chapter).

Melting and boiling

Energy has to be transferred to change the phase of a material. And, importantly, at a phase change, the temperature does not change. In effect, 100 g of water at 0°C stores more energy (thermally) than the same amount of ice at 0°C.

You can show a cube of ice melting on a warm surface. The surface is at a higher temperature than the ice and transfers energy to the ice (by heating). As the temperature of the ice rises, the particles in its lattice vibrate more vigorously, until they are vibrating so much that the bonds between them break, and the particles form a liquid.

At that point, the temperature stops rising. The reason that the water stores more energy is because the particles are arranged differently rather than vibrating more vigorously. Energy was transferred to the ice to break the bonds. We still refer to this as energy stored thermally (or energy stored in a thermal store). In other words, a thermal store covers energy stored due to both the random motion of particles and their arrangement.

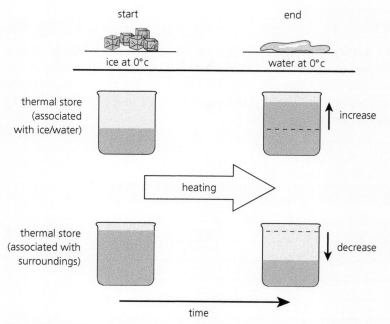

Figure 4.12 Even though they are at the same temperature, the energy stored thermally by water is more than the energy stored thermally by the ice.

The amount of energy transferred to change the phase of 1 kg is called the specific latent heat. The specific latent heat of fusion is the energy transferred to turn 1 kg of the substance from a solid to a liquid. The specific latent heat of vaporisation is the energy that has to be transferred to turn 1 kg from a liquid to a gas. Specific latent heat is given the symbol L and is defined by the equation:

energy transferred by heating (J) = mass (kg) × specific latent heat (J/kg)

$$E = mL$$

Measuring specific latent heat

You can determine the specific latent heat of vaporisation of water by boiling a kettle of water and using the power rating of the kettle.

This demonstration provides opportunities for good discussions about safety and experimental design. The first question is how much water to put in the kettle. If there is too much it will boil over, which is a safety concern but will also harm the results (water is lost without being boiled away). If there is too little water, it may not cover the element or it may boil away completely. Also, the students will notice that it is difficult to take a very precise reading from the balance while the kettle is boiling (it fluctuates due to the movements of the kettle). Finally, there is a question of how leaving it on for longer will improve the result, because any reading errors have a smaller relative effect on the change in mass.

KEY ACTIVITIES

For this demonstration, you will need a small plastic travel kettle with a removable lid; a power rating of 0.7–1.0 kW is suitable to avoid the scalding splashes that you get with higher power kettles (you will need to know its power rating which should be marked on it). Use a kettle that has a thermal cut-out (most do), and remove the lid so that it does not switch off automatically. Put about 400 g of water in the kettle (so it is about a third full) and put the kettle on the top pan balance, making sure that the kettle will not topple. There will be boiling water so don't let the students get too close and keep the demonstration behind a screen; you should wear eye protection. We suggest using a webcam to display the stop clock and balance readings on a data projector.

Switch on the kettle and bring it to boiling point. Once it is boiling, the students will be able to see that the mass starts to drop. Take a reading on the balance and start the stop clock while leaving the kettle boiling. After about a minute (or when the mass is significantly lower), stop the clock and take a reading for the mass. Alternatively, students could plot real time data while the experiment runs.

The energy transferred by electrical working and heating in the kettle is given by:

$$\text{energy transferred (J)} = \text{power (W)} \times \text{time (s)}$$

$$E = Pt$$

We also know that:

$$\text{energy transferred (J)} = \text{mass of water boiled away (kg)} \times \text{latent heat (J/kg)}$$

Therefore:

$$\text{power (W)} \times \text{time (s)} = \text{mass of water boiled away (kg)} \times \text{latent heat (J/kg)}$$

$$\text{latent heat (J/kg)} = \frac{\text{power (W)} \times \text{time (s)}}{\text{mass of water boiled away (kg)}}$$

$$L = \frac{Pt}{m}$$

The specific latent heat of vaporisation is big compared with the specific heat capacity as breaking bonds takes a lot of effort. It is for this reason that scalds from steam are so much more serious than scalds from the same amount of hot water (though they are also nasty).

You can measure the specific latent heat of fusion of ice by melting ice in a funnel with an immersion heater, as described on IOPSpark (see Resources at the end of the chapter).

Heating

Conduction

Conduction is the mechanism by which energy is transferred within and between systems that are in contact:

→ Between surfaces: Energy is transferred between two touching surfaces by the vibration of particles. The particles in the hot surface are vibrating more vigorously than those in the cooler one and, on average, they make the less active particles vibrate more.

→ In an object: Particle motion also contributes to conduction through materials. It is notable that the best conductors are metals. They are not slightly better, they are enormously better. Copper has a thermal conductivity that is about 3000 times bigger than an insulator, like wood. That is why you would use copper to make the base of a saucepan but wood to make the handle.

It is no coincidence that good thermal conductors are also good electrical conductors. In both cases, their conductivity is a result of free electrons in the metal lattice. When the temperature is raised at one end of a metal rod, the electrons begin to move around at high speeds; some of them move along the rod, colliding with ions on their way, making those ions vibrate. A faster moving electron reaches further down a rod much more quickly than the metal ions pass on vibrations.

Many insulators also trap pockets of air which further reduces the rate at which energy is transferred. You could mention thermos flasks, which have a layer of vacuum or partial vacuum (see Resources at the end of this chapter for links to thermal conductivity on IOPSpark).

It always helps to develop explanations based on the particle model of matter. The two paragraphs above do this. These explanations give a deeper understanding and avoid explaining away the mechanisms with phrases like 'heat flows from the beaker to your hands'.

Feeling cold

Good conductors feel colder than insulators even at the same temperature. For example, the metal of a bicycle handlebar feels colder than the plastic grip.

The explanation requires ideas of both conductivity and heat capacity. Your hands are at a higher temperature than the handlebar and the grip. Therefore, when you touch them, energy is transferred (by heating). The surface of the plastic grip quickly reaches the same temperature as your hand so the process stops. Furthermore, the plastic is an insulator so your hand only has to raise the temperature of a thin layer near the surface.

However, when you touch the metal handlebar, your hand has to raise the temperature of the whole handlebar because the metal is a good conductor.

The handlebar has a much larger thermal capacity than the thin layer of plastic, therefore, your hand has to keep transferring energy for longer and it feels colder.

Convection

Strictly speaking, convection is a mechanical process (in which matter moves around) rather than a thermal one. Most fluids expand if their temperature rises; and therefore their density decreases. As such, a warmer fluid floats above a cooler one. A hot air balloon uses this effect. You can demonstrate the principle of a hot air balloon using an empty tea bag and lighting it at the top.

However, if the fluid is not constrained, the warmer fluid will flow (or float) upwards and the cooler fluid will replace it, forming a current called a 'convection current'. A good example is hot air rising above a radiator or a hot road in summer. You can demonstrate convection currents using two gas jars filled with cool and warm water that have been differently coloured using food dye. Use a card to cover one of the jars and invert it over the other one. If the warm water is on top and you remove the card, nothing happens. If the cool water is on top, the warm water will float upwards and the cool water will sink In both cases above, the convection current is in the fluid (air or water); the teabag and dye are merely indicators of the moving air.

Radiation

All objects emit electromagnetic radiation (see Resources at the end of this chapter). However, hotter ones (like an electric bar fire) radiate at a higher power and the radiation has, on average, a higher frequency.

On average, a hot body will transfer energy to a cooler one by radiation, even if they are not in contact. There is a net transfer from hot to cold, because the cooler one is exposed to higher intensity radiation than the hot one.

Dull surfaces radiate at a higher power than shiny ones (all other things being equal). Students can confirm this using beakers of water. One beaker is wrapped in shiny foil and the other is painted black. The beakers start at the same temperature. Students can measure the temperature every minute for ten minutes and plot a graph of temperature against time.

The hot beakers emit waves in the infrared region of the electromagnetic spectrum. As they radiate, the energy that they store decreases and their temperature drops.

Different surfaces absorbing

You can show how different coloured surfaces absorb infrared differently using gloves or socks (as long as they fit tightly). Get students to put their hands behind their backs. A partner puts a white glove on one hand and a black glove on the other one (without saying which is which). The gloved student then stands with their back to an infrared lamp (or sunshine on a summer's day) and has to identify which hand has which glove.

This can be extended to a demonstration with coins stuck to the back of metal sheets with wax or petroleum jelly. One sheet is polished and one is painted black. Place the sheets an equal distance from a heater or a Bunsen flame. Ask students to predict which coin will fall off first and to explain their prediction. This experiment is described on IOPSpark (see Resources at the end of the chapter).

How to reduce the rate of cooling

Ask students if we can slow the rate at which a cup of tea cools. They are likely to come up with the idea of insulation. Set up an activity to compare different materials. You can relate this to thermal insulation of clothes or in the walls of houses.

 Science literacy

Try to use phrases that emphasise the process of heating; such as 'the beaker transfers energy to the surroundings by heating'; this is more helpful than 'heat is transferred to the surroundings'.

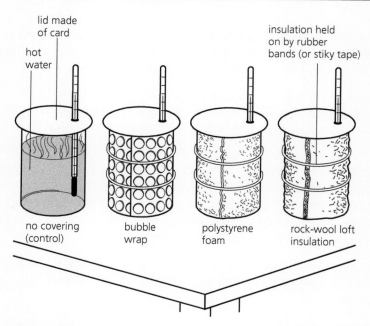

Figure 4.13 Beakers with insulation

Each group sets up four beakers, three wrapped with different materials and one without any insulation. It is worth setting these up on a tray to catch any spills. You can go round the lab with a kettle of water (at about 65 °C) and add some water to each beaker. The students start the clock as the temperature passes through 60 °C. They then measure the temperature every minute as the water cools. It is best to put a lid on each beaker to reduce evaporation.

They can put their results in a table and include a column that shows the temperature drop each minute. This last column is the rate at which the water is cooling in °C per minute. Ask them to compare the rate of cooling at the start (when the water is hot) and at the end (when the water is merely warm). The bigger the difference in temperature, the faster the cooling. You can discuss this difference in terms of particles: when the particles are vibrating more vigorously (on the surface of the hotter beaker), they will transfer energy to the surroundings at a higher rate. Draw out the idea that it is the temperature difference that drives the change: the higher the temperature difference, the higher the rate at which energy is transferred from the hot water to the surroundings.

You will develop the important ideas of rates in the next sequence on power.

Science in context

You can ask students which material they would use to keep a cool drink cold. This helps them to realise that the material is not itself warm; instead, as an insulator, it is preventing energy being transferred by heating.

4.5 Power, efficiency and the electrical grid

In this section, you will introduce students to the system of generating and supplying electricity and what an energy analysis can tell us about our use of resources. Electric circuits enable us to do a job in one place (our home) and use up an energy resource in another place (a power station). Increasingly, that energy resource is renewable; less than 50% of UK electricity is generated from fossil fuels.

Students should know that power is a quantity and learn about the efficiencies of the electricity supply. They will be able to identify the energy resources that are used up and begin to consider some of the choices that we make. Later on, they will perform calculations relating to power and efficiency.

Ideas students have and potential pitfalls

Students may think that the electricity supply is an energy resource or a store of energy and that it is electricity that is used up when running home appliances. To help shift them away from this view, you can identify the actual energy resource in each case (a battery or fuel at the power station).

They may also think that electrical circuits (or the moving charges within the circuit) carry energy from one place to another. This is not a helpful conception.

It is more helpful to refer to circuits as 'working electrically' than 'carrying energy'. Certainly, it is best to discourage use of the term 'electrical energy'.

Electricity is neither a form of energy nor a source of energy: it is a convenient way of transferring energy. In Chapter 3 Electricity and magnetism, there is a discussion about the effectiveness of the rope loop for visualising the workings of electric circuits. It is also a helpful model when discussing the ways in which circuits transfer energy.

Introducing power

A powerful device or person transfers a large amount of energy in a short time. Power is defined by:

$$\text{power (W)} = \frac{\text{energy transferred (J)}}{\text{time taken (s)}}$$

$$P = \frac{E}{t}$$

The relationship shows that power is an example of a rate: energy transferred *per second*.

It is good to discuss rates in general and how rates and accumulation are related. For example, if 60 people walk under a bridge in ten minutes, what is the rate at which they pass the bridge (in people *per minute*); or if a job pays £14 per hour; how much money will be accumulated in five hours? You can practise with lots of examples. Other rates include speed, acceleration and electric current.

Before looking at circuits and electrical supply, you can introduce the idea of power using some mechanical examples.

Science in context

James Watt was an engineer and inventor who improved Newcomen's steam engine; he gave his name to the unit of power and provided an opportunity for one of a very small number of physics jokes: 'Watt is the unit of power?'

Leg power

Students can determine the power of their legs by running up a flight of stairs. This experiment is described on IOPSpark (see Resources at the end of the chapter).

Measure the height of the stairs and find the weight (in newtons) of a selection of students. You will need to be sensitive about your choices. It is likely that the heaviest person (which might be you) will have the highest power because there is usually only a small difference in the times.

Put one person at the top with a stopwatch and get them to shout 'go' and time the run.

For each student, the energy transferred by working, E, is given by:

$$\text{energy (J)} = \text{force (N)} \times \text{distance (m)} = \text{weight (N)} \times \text{height of staircase (m)}$$

$$E = F \times d$$

And power, P, is given by:

$$\text{power (W)} = \frac{\text{energy transferred by working (J)}}{\text{time taken (s)}}$$

$$P = \frac{E}{t}$$

Science in context

An example of instant power analysis is that of endurance cyclists. Telemetry data, including power, from large races such as the Tour de France are often superimposed over video on sites such as YouTube.

Power and continuous processes

At the start of this chapter, we noted that, in some situations, power provides a more revealing analytical tool than energy. A general description of those situations is 'continuous processes'. Electric circuits are a prime example of a process that is continuous.

A simple circuit

Set up a simple circuit with a lamp, switch and battery (the discussion is simpler if you use a battery rather than a power pack). This is the same circuit that would be used in a torch. Switch the lamp on for 10 seconds and ask the students to discuss the mechanisms that result in the bulb lighting:

→ Explanation: There is a continuous loop of electrons in the circuit. The battery drives the electrons round like a chain or a loop of rope (see Chapter 3 Electricity and magnetism, page 67). As the electrons are forced through the filament of the bulb, the electrons interact with ions in the metal, making them vibrate. The vibrations are so vigorous that the temperature rises to about 2500 °C. This is so hot that the filament glows and radiates waves into the room. These waves are absorbed by the surroundings, raising their temperature. After the lamp is switched off, the temperature of the surroundings has gone up.

→ Energy analysis: Now ask them to think about the energy source that has been depleted. They should be able to point to the cell (or battery), which stores energy chemically. Then discuss to what system the energy has been transferred, leading them towards the surroundings.

→ Start point: energy stored chemically by the cell.

→ End point: energy stored thermally by the surroundings.

Introducing electrical working as a pathway

The temperature of the filament has been raised by the whole circuit: the cell drives the continuous loop of electrons through the resistor. If you are using the stores and pathways approach, then the pathway is 'electrical working'. As before, take care not to suggest that energy flows along the pathway: it is the route by which the world has moved from the start point to the end point (see Figure 4.14).

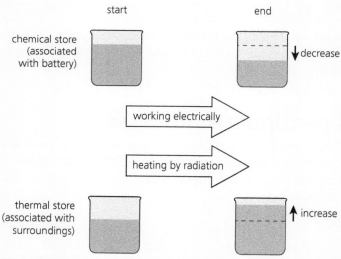

Figure 4.14 Note that the two pathways are shown in parallel. This is to avoid suggesting that energy flows along the pathways.

Circuits and energy

It is worth noting that the circuit neither stores nor carries 'electrical energy'. It has no physical means of doing either. To illustrate this point, in the circuit above, an electron that was initially at the negative terminal of the battery will have moved about 1 mm towards the bulb while the circuit was switched on; so it could not have 'carried energy' to the bulb. It is the existence of the complete loop of electrons that enabled the bulb to light up: as the electron at the battery started moving, so did all the electrons in the circuit. It was the electrons that were already in the filament that made it glow. It is helpful to describe the circuit as a mechanism for doing work electrically rather than a means of 'carrying electrical energy'. Above all, we have avoided suggesting that, somehow, the electrons carry energy from the cell to the lamp. In simple circuits, you should avoid references to 'electrical energy'.

This story is even more important for AC circuits. The current is going back and forth, and an electron at the generator will never leave the generator (it goes back and forth over a very small distance). However, the whole loop is moving back and forth and is therefore still able to do electrical work. It is more helpful to think of circuits as force transmitters (like a rope or chain), rather than energy carriers.

Using mains electricity

You can relate the torch circuit described above to a task that relies on mains electricity, such as boiling a kettle. Assume the electricity source is a gas fired power station so that the energy analysis is the same: a chemical store has been depleted at the power station, with the ultimate effect to raise the temperature of the surroundings in the home. As such, boiling a kettle is entirely dissipative: the only outcome is that energy which had been in a useful store is now in an inaccessible, low temperature thermal store.

Making choices

This analysis might seem to some to be quite dull but is profound. The important idea to take away is that there is a resource cost to doing the tasks we want to do (like having a cup of tea). There are many such tasks: driving to the shops, cooking a meal, mowing the lawn or lighting a house. They all use up resources.

The global resources will not last forever. Therefore, there are decisions to make (for individuals and nations): how many of those tasks can we afford and which ones are most important?

It would certainly help if we reduced consumption. However, we can also:

→ make our systems more efficient
→ use more renewable energy resources.

As ever, these decisions are informed using numbers and an energy analysis.

Generating electricity

You can demonstrate how electricity is generated using a small dynamo attached to a small motor. The Science Enhancement Programme (SEP) energy board (available from Mindsets Online, see Resources at the end of this chapter) is one example of a quick way to set this up, though you can also build a similar circuit yourself.

Prepare the circuit with two connecting leads, leaving one of them unplugged. Ask a student to crank the dynamo. It should be easy (they are only working against a small amount of friction). Now plug in the spare lead so that the fan starts turning. The student should find that they have to push harder on the dynamo.

You can say 'the circuit comprises a complete loop of electrons. Imagine you are pushing them around the circuit – rather like moving a bicycle chain'.

Allow as many students as possible to feel this effect. It takes extra effort to drive the generator when the motor is running. This makes sense from an energy point of view: we would be getting something for nothing if we could run the fan without any extra effort.

Power stations

The circuit described above models a gas power station. Every time someone switches on a fan or a kettle, it requires more gas to be burnt. The demand changes during the day (see Figure 4.15). In order to meet this demand, the operators increase the amount of gas being burnt so as to keep the turbines turning (see Resources at the end of this chapter).

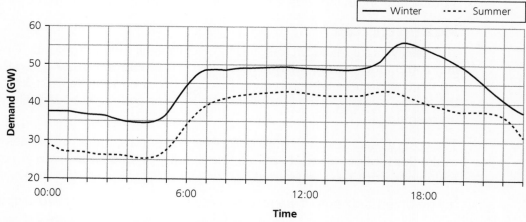

Figure 4.15 The typical demand over a day for a power station

You could set the students a small activity to explain:

→ the increase in demand during the day
→ the increase in demand in winter
→ the specific peak in winter at about 5.30 p.m.

Improving efficiency

The comparative efficiency of electrical appliances, such as filament bulbs and LED bulbs, is better compared by power considerations than energy ones.

This is because neither appliance stores energy, instead they emit radiation, which is a continuous process. We quantify their radiative power in watts.

Lighting appliances radiate waves in the electromagnetic spectrum. By design, they radiate in the visible part of the spectrum. However, traditional incandescent bulbs also radiate a lot in the infrared region. LED bulbs radiate very little in the infrared. Therefore, LEDs provide the same amount of illumination for less power input. This is especially important in battery-driven bulbs such as torches. A Sankey diagram is a good way of showing the power radiated in the different parts of the spectrum. In general, Sankey diagrams show how the power (or any other conserved quantity) is shared between different points of interest (in this case, different parts of the spectrum). The total width of the arrows is constant and the width of each arrow illustrates the proportion of power for that part of the spectrum.

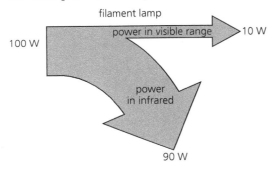

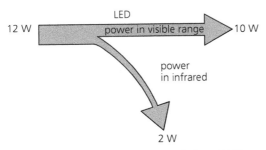

Figure 4.16 Sankey diagram for light bulb and LED

Incandescent lamps are noticeably warm (demonstrating their inefficiency). There are standard experiments for investigating the efficiency of light bulbs and LEDs.

Renewable energy sources

Electricity is often viewed as a clean alternative to fossil fuels for trains, cars and buses. There is some truth in this view, for two reasons. It is certainly the case that power stations tend to be out of town so they do not produce pollution close to large populations. Also, increasingly, energy companies generate electricity using renewables. Some of those are directly driven by the Sun (solar, wind and wave power). In brief, the explanation of wind power might be as follows: the Sun raises the temperature of the atmosphere locally, causing pressure differences that drive winds; those winds turn turbines that are connected to generators that produce electricity; the electrical supply is used to boil a kettle and this ends up raising the temperature of the surroundings.

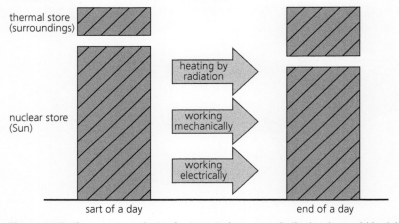

Figure 4.17 The energy analysis of using wind power to boil a kettle would look like this.

The chart below shows the proportion of the UK electricity supply that was provided by different sources in 2019; 48% of the UK's electrical power was provided by fossil fuels and 25% by renewables.

UK electricity generation
Proportion of total electricity generated from different sources in the 12 months ending September 2017

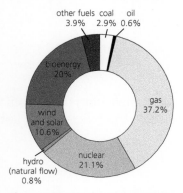

Figure 4.18 Pie chart of electricity generation methods in the UK

Overall, the proportion of global power provided by renewable sources is much lower: about 8.5%. This is because it includes transport and heating, which tend to rely on fossil fuels such as gas, coal and derivatives of crude oil.

Sustainability

Sustainability will be achieved when we no longer have to draw down (and burn) global energy resources; these are mainly fossil fuels but nuclear fuel is also a global resource. The main limit on the available power is the power of the Sun's radiation striking the Earth which is about 1.2 quadrillion watts. This is about 10 000 times bigger than our global needs. The challenge is to harness it.

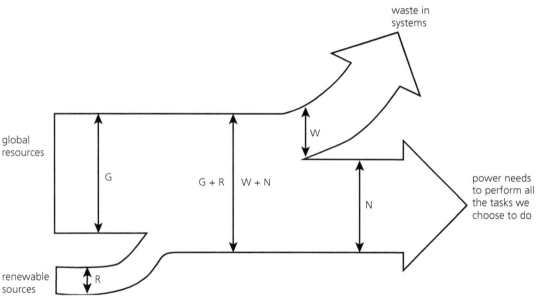

Figure 4.19 Power needs and provision for a home or the world. A sustainable system will exist when G falls to zero and our needs (plus waste) are provided entirely by renewables ($N + W = R$).

In order to meet that challenge, scientists and engineers will continue to find ways of reducing demand, reducing waste and increasing renewable provision. This work is essential for a secure future. Many of these ideas are discussed – with calculations – in David MacKay's excellent and free book *Sustainable Energy – Without the Hot Air* (see Resources at the end of this chapter). Although some of the economic costs have changed over time, it still provides an excellent model for how to make comparative judgements between different choices about energy resources.

Students can use data and examples from the book to calculate, for example, the area of solar panels needed to supply their home; or the area behind a tidal barrage that would power a small town. As well as practising some good problems, they will be left with a positive impression: that physics and energy calculations will play an enormous part in achieving a sustainable future; and so will they.

4.6   Resources

Online resources

Please go to **spark.iop.org/asebook** for a set of curated resources from the IOP Spark website to match this chapter.

Science Enhancement Programme (SEP): www.mindsetsonline.co.uk

Scientific American describes how to build a rubber band powered car: www.scientificamerican.com Tracker tool: https://physlets.org/tracker/

There are many helpful videos online (particularly on YouTube) with demonstrations that you can either use or show to students. For example, the big pendulum can normally be found by searching for conservation of energy and pendulum.

For convection currents, there are multiple examples using liquids and gases. *Do Try This At Home* from the IOP is particularly clear and repeatable in class.

Simulations

PhET simulation 'Energy skate park': https://phet.colorado.edu/

References

ASE (2020) *Safeguards in the School Laboratory 12th ed*. Association for Science Education.

Boohan, R. (2016) *The Language of Mathematics in Science*. Hatfield: Association for Science Education.

MacKay, D. (2008) *Sustainable Energy – Without the Hot Air*.

5 Matter

Alan Denton and James de Winter

Introduction

The 'particle model of matter' is the idea that everything around us is made up of small particles. If we consider their movement and the forces between them, it can help us to understand the properties of solids, liquids and gases and to be able to make predictions about them. Once we are able to think of a simple object like a brick, or a balloon filled with air, as a collection of particles, we can then use this understanding to explain and explore ideas such as density, changes of state, air pressure, floating and sinking, as well as others including electrical conduction (see Section 3.2, page 65), radioactivity (see Section 6.2, page 175) and thermal energy (see Section 4.4, page 126).

In this chapter we will use a basic particle model, in which all the particles of a given substance are the same. In most cases, these particles will be atoms, ions or molecules. For the purposes of our model, we are not going to consider the nature of these particles or the cause of the forces between them in much detail. It will enable us to connect macroscopic, visible behaviours such as thermal expansion and why a sealed balloon stays inflated, to the particle behaviours that can explain these. You will need to judge the extent to which you are precise (atoms, molecules) or less so (particles) in your language, based on the class, what they have previously studied and your own confidence. There is further discussion about the use of appropriate models in the introduction chapter of this book (see Chapter 1 The principles behind secondary physics teaching, page 1).

A teaching sequence

It is unlikely that all of the ideas relating to the behaviour of matter and the particle model will be dealt with in a single set of lessons at secondary level and many of the ideas here will occur in other topics, in particular the content covered in Chapter 4 Energy. However, we feel that there is value in having a dedicated topic in which the nature of matter is taught, and macroscopic behaviours are explained on a sub-microscopic level. Even if your setting does not allow for a separate topic, it is worthwhile considering how an understanding of the particle model of matter builds up across your curriculum.

As students progress through this topic, your descriptions of particles and the forces between them will include more abstract ideas, but you should pick a suitable model of appropriate complexity to teach the phenomena you wish students to understand.

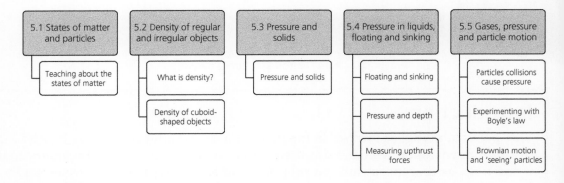

Prior experiences

Ideally, students will reach secondary education with a reasonable understanding of the three basic states of matter and how they behave. They may have heard terms such as 'atoms', 'molecules' and 'compounds' a number of times, although they may not be fluent in differentiating between them. The order of teaching given in the flowchart represents a possible way of teaching, with the later topics including increasingly abstract concepts.

Before students look at how pressure is caused in a liquid or a gas, it is helpful for them to be familiar with forces, velocities and the idea that you need to apply a force to change the velocity of an object. During the teaching of the particle model of matter there are lots of good opportunities to reinforce many of the big ideas from the forces and energy topics.

Teaching and learning challenges

The challenges that students face with understanding the particle model of matter have been extensively researched (see Driver, *Making Sense of Secondary Science*; Taber, *Foundations for Teaching Chemistry*; and ASE, *Teaching Secondary Chemistry* in Resources at the end of the chapter for more details). Being sympathetic to the conceptual hurdles that students may face in this topic can help to inform teaching. The idea that all materials are made up of particles is likely to be second nature to many science teachers and so it can be hard to fully appreciate that some of our students may struggle to develop and become fluent with this world view. Sometimes the word 'microscopic' is incorrectly used to describe these particles when, in fact, they are so small they cannot be seen under a microscope. If needed, the term 'sub-microscopic' is more appropriate.

5.1 States of matter and particles

Prior experiences

Before students reach secondary education, it is likely that they will have learnt about the nature of, and difference between, solids, liquid and gases, which can be explained in terms of the arrangements of particles (for example, their shape and capacity to be poured or not).

The nature of the particle model is such that it is not really something which can be easily worked out from observational data and experiences in school. You should feel confident in presenting this idea as 'a model of the way the world works' rather than feeling you have to explain why. Even the most skilled physicist, while able to describe the nature of matter in detail, is unlikely to be able to answer the question of 'Why is everything made up of particles?'

Teaching about the states of matter

Depending on their prior experiences, an initial section on states of matter and particles may act as a revision or a development of previous learning. As well as becoming familiar with the detail contained in Table 5.1, a key objective here is for students to become fluent in the connections between the description of particle behaviours and interactions, and how they can explain macroscopic (or bulk) behaviours. As a teacher, you may visualise a fully formed particle model of matter and be able to navigate from the bulk to the particle and back again, but this may be a struggle for some students whose particle model is not as well developed.

Table 5.1 shows the main ideas around the arrangement of, and interactions between, the particles of solids, liquid and gases. Without the ability to show these, it is common to use modelling (both physical and virtual). Many teachers ask students to model these three states by *becoming* the particles themselves in a room cleared of furniture: locked together in a solid; *gently moving* around each other in a liquid; and bumping around randomly in a gas. It is important to be precise in your language here as you move between consideration of the bulk material and the particles in the model. It is the material that is boiling, melting, freezing or condensing, not the particles themselves, which for the purposes of this model remain unchanged. Also, some students can imagine or be led to believe that the particles we talk about in the model have the same properties as the material that they make up, for example thinking that a gold particle is solid, shiny and gold coloured.

We deliberately use the phrase 'particles *of* a solid' rather than 'particles *in* a solid' to avoid contributing to the student misconception that substances are made up of particles and other stuff, for example that water is made of water particles inside a continuous liquid.

Table 5.1 Exploring the particle model for the three basic states of matter

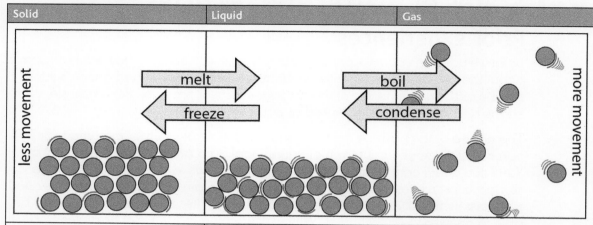

Solid	Liquid	Gas
The particles:	The particles:	The particles:
• *vibrate* around a fixed position • *stay in the same place* compared to each other • are generally *tightly packed* together with the particles touching.	• can *move around* but are still touching • are *less ordered* than in the solid • *fill a container from the bottom up* when pulled down by gravity.	• are *free to move* around • are moving faster than in the liquid • follow random paths as they collide with each other and surfaces.

Using circles to represent particles is sufficient for our model and the phenomena we wish to explain. In other contexts, you may choose to use other shapes such as ovals to emphasise features such as the amount of order and disorder between solids and liquids.

 ## Science literacy

Students should be confident using the words to describe the changes in state: melting, freezing, boiling and condensing. These terms have similar meanings in day-to-day speech and are all examples of 'physical changes'. Some students may have the misconception that 'boiling' means 'very hot' and 'freezing' means 'very cold', rather than being associated with changes in state.

If ice (solid water) is warmed it will melt, and if the liquid water is then heated, it will boil to become a gas, water vapour:

$$\text{ice} \rightarrow \text{water} \rightarrow \text{steam}$$

$$H_2O(s) \rightarrow H_2O(l) \rightarrow H_2O(g)$$

Ice, water and steam have some very different properties and could be considered different materials. However, scientifically, they are different states of the same chemical substance. These changes – ice melting and water boiling – are not chemical changes. A chemical change results in different substances from before.

For example; when iron rusts it reacts with oxygen to become iron oxide, this is a chemical reaction:

$$4Fe(s) + 3O_2(g) \rightarrow 2Fe_2O_3(s)$$

Evaporation is often confused with boiling. 'Evaporation' is a slower process than boiling and it occurs below the temperature at which the liquid boils (the boiling point). It only affects a small percentage of the particles; those that are both at the surface and are moving fast enough to escape. 'Boiling' occurs throughout the liquid once the boiling point has been reached.

The model presented here is a simplified one that, from a physics perspective, helps describe and explain changes in state and temperature. In chemistry lessons and at higher levels of study, a more complex model will provide more detailed insights. We can consider the energy stored thermally in a material (also described as the internal energy of the system) as the sum of the kinetic energy of the particles (related to their individual, random motion) and the potential energy of the particles (relating to their position and interactions with each other).

Science in context

It is worth noting that the boiling point of a substance can change depending on the air pressure: if the pressure is lower, then it is easier for the particles to escape into the gaseous phase, so the boiling point is lower. At the top of Mount Everest, the boiling point of water is 71°C.

'Water vapour' is water in its gaseous form and it cannot be seen. The term 'steam', is often used to describe water in its gaseous form, but is also applied to what is seen coming out of the spout of a kettle or off a pan of boiling water. This is slightly misleading as what you can see there is actually a mixture of water vapour and liquid water droplets that have condensed back from the gaseous phase and are suspended in the air; it is these liquid droplets that are visible. There is often a small space directly above the spout which is hot enough to just contain water vapour, beyond that the vapour begins to cool and condense into droplets.

'Sublimation' is the process in which a solid changes state directly into a gas. Whether it happens or not is a property of the element or compound you are considering, and the pressures involved. It does not happen in most experiments that students are likely to encounter: but one example of sublimation is solid carbon dioxide turning into a gas at normal room temperatures and pressures.

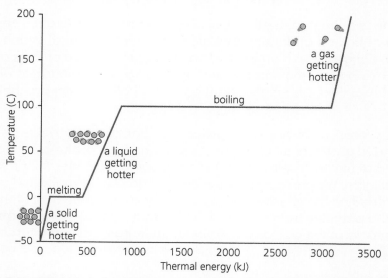

Figure 5.1 A graph showing how the temperature changes for 1 kg of water as it is heated

Figure 5.1 shows an example of how students should be encouraged to annotate graphs to give them more meaning. In this example we have highlighted how the particles are arranged in the different phases, but it could also show which equation to use (specific heat capacity or specific latent heat), or how the interactions and forces between the particles change. The equations that are used to calculate changes of temperature or changes of state are examined in the energy chapter (see Chapter 4 Energy, page 129).

Science in context

Professional physicists may get frustrated that we are limiting ourselves to three states, and it is likely that keen students may want to discuss the others. There are at least two more states of matter that are often considered. 'Plasmas' consist of positive ions and free electrons; they can be found at very high temperatures but also very low pressures, as in the upper atmosphere. 'Bose–Einstein condensates' can be made near absolute zero; they were only created for the first time in 1995 but are now regularly used in experiments in quantum physics.

Careers

Students aged 11–16 years old study matter at a level of atoms and molecules and the smaller protons, neutrons and electrons. At higher levels (16–19 years and university) students will study the Standard Model of particle physics. This is the idea that all known particles and three of the four fundamental forces can be explained by considering a very small number of elementary particles: quarks, leptons and bosons. Students will also explore how these sub-atomic particles interact with each other using quantum mechanics. It is a Pandora's box of the strange and enchanting: the rules of classical mechanics that we use for everyday objects stop working. The fact that quantum mechanics is challenging and frequently counter-intuitive does not make it wrong, and the odd behaviours it predicts, such as the double-slit interference of electrons, have been repeatedly demonstrated.

5.2 Density of regular and irregular objects

Prior experiences

Having established some aspects of the nature and structure of materials, this section moves on to how some of the properties can be described and quantified. Is likely that students will have heard density used as a general descriptive term; however, it is common for them to confuse density with mass, not appreciating that mass is an object property and density a material one. Object properties tell you about a specific object (such as length, height, shape, volume) and material properties (such as density, melting point, specific heat capacity) tell you about a particular material (such as copper, wood or water). This distinction is an important one to make and reinforce.

 Maths

This is a topic in which a lack of mathematical skills can cause problems, because the volume is often calculated from multiple measurements. Classroom examples and questions may also use different units for mass (g or kg), volume (cm³ or m³) and also density (g/cm³ or kg/m³) and so care is needed to support students with these calculations.

What is density?

Although it may seem like an old trick, it can be worth starting this section by asking 'Which weighs more, a kilogram of feathers or a kilogram of lead?' or the follow on question 'If I have a kilogram of feathers and a kilogram of lead, how might they be different?'. In each case, the important idea to draw out of the discussion is that while the mass of something (measured in kilograms) is one description, other information such as the volume a certain mass takes up is also a useful description. Density provides a regular way to compare objects by looking at how the mass and volume of an object are related, and once we have a value for one object, that value will be the same for every object made of the same material.

Density is defined by the following formula:

$$\text{density (kg/m}^3) = \frac{\text{mass (kg)}}{\text{volume (m}^3)}$$

$$\rho = \frac{m}{V}$$

The Greek letter rho (ρ) is used to represent density and it can also be measured in g/cm^3.

Note that upper-case V is used for volume, lower-case v is used for speed and velocity.

Density of cuboid-shaped objects

A classic 'density investigation kit' that a school can buy contains a number of the same sized cuboids, each made of different materials (for example aluminium, brass, copper, steel, lead, stone and plastic). These can be used to perform measurements of mass and volume, and therefore students can use them to do easy calculations to determine the densities. If your school does not have a dedicated kit, then regularly shaped objects for other uses (such as rectangular glass or Perspex blocks for optics) can be used, or your technology department may be able to provide some. These cuboids make it really convincing to students that identically shaped objects can have different masses, because they are made from different materials.

By choosing a regular object, such as a cuboid, it makes the volume calculation very easy (length × width × height); these measurements can all be left in cm. Even with an apparently cubic shape, it is good practice to get students to measure all three sides to be sure. The mass should be calculated by using a regular balance, normally measuring to the nearest 0.1 g.

Density for materials is usually quoted in kg/m^3, but in the classroom it is most likely to be measured in g/cm^3:

$$1\,\text{g/cm}^3 = 1000\,\text{kg/m}^3$$

π Maths

These calculations provide a good opportunity to develop students' confidence in converting between different units, a common source of difficulty. They should also consider the importance of significant figures in relation to their measured and calculated values. More detail on this and related issues around the use of mathematics in physics and science teaching more generally is available in the free publication *The Language of Mathematics in Science*, available from the ASE (see Resources at the end of this chapter).

Science in context

One of the most significant developments in new and exciting materials in recent years has been graphene. Graphene is a form of carbon that is much less dense than steel but can be 100 times stronger, as well as being an excellent thermal and electrical conductor. One of the leaders of research in this field was Professor Mildred Dresselhaus, whose pioneering work earned her the nickname 'the queen of carbon science'.

Once students can confidently calculate the density of simple cubes or cuboids, there are lots of opportunities for other objects that you can direct them to explore. One example is a sheet of paper for which the thickness is hard to measure. Students may need to fold the paper multiple times and take an average to get a more accurate value. Finding the density of irregular objects or liquids can follow. Full details of these and other experiments are available from the IOP in their 'measuring density' collection (see Resources).

Careers

To make very small measurements in situations in which precision is needed, engineers use devices such as Vernier callipers or micrometers as they measure to the nearest 0.1 mm or 0.01 mm. For much more precise measurements, the quantum nature of light can be used to measure distances to the nearest nanometre (0.000 000 001 m) with a process called optical interferometry. Work is ongoing to develop this technique so it can measure distances many times smaller.

Changing density and the expansion of objects with temperature

Until now, we have described the density of an object as if it was a fixed property of a material, but this assumes that nothing else changes. For example, the density of a material can change with temperature. When describing what happens, you should encourage students to make it clear which variables change and which do not.

When the temperature of an object is increased, the particles themselves do not change in mass. What happens is that, on average, they move further apart from each other and so the object expands. As the same mass now occupies a larger volume, the density will decrease.

A fuller explanation of why the particles get further apart with temperature and the associated greater vibration is a complex one. As they gain more energy, they do vibrate more, but the variation of the force between particles and their separation is not a linear relationship. With more energy they could get closer or further apart and can do both, but on average the separation between them increases.

These changes with temperature can be quite small (a few per cent), although the change in state between a liquid and a gas results in a more significant change in density. It is important to stress to students that the change in density happened because the distance between the particles changed and not that the particles had expanded.

Careers

There are many examples in building, infrastructure and vehicle construction in which engineers have had to take into account that objects change when the temperature changes. The clickety-clack noise heard from the wheels of a train happens because the train track is laid as jointed track, with a gap of a few mm between each rail, to allow for the expansion of the track in hot weather and stop the track buckling.

5.3 Pressure and solids

Prior experiences

Having quantified some aspects of materials, this section explores the forces on and within them. Students are likely to have a commonsense understanding of the word *pressure* but in many cases this will be entwined with force, and so pressure will need careful explanation. This is an example of when it is important to be precise with your use of terms and to encourage the same from students.

Treading on a drawing pin in bare feet is likely to be a memorable experience, yet you can push it into a noticeboard the other way around without any pain. If you take a standard house brick and place it on a balance, however you arrange it, up, down, on its side or edge, the balance will always read about $2.5\,\text{kg}$ ($\approx 25\,\text{N}$). If you did the same on your hand, it would feel different for each arrangement and balancing the brick on one corner is likely to hurt. In these cases we would talk about pressure to explain what is happening, and to do so, we need to talk about forces *and* area. Whichever way you arrange the brick, its downwards force (weight) stays the same, but when you change the orientation you can change the contact area and thus pressure it exerts.

Pressure and solids

A simplistic definition of pressure might say that it is a 'measure of how spread out a force is' but a more precise one is as follows:

$$\text{pressure (N/m}^2) = \frac{\text{force (N)}}{\text{area (m}^2)}$$

$$P = \frac{F}{A}$$

Note that upper-case P is used as the symbol for pressure, the lower-case p is used for momentum.

We have some choice in the units we use to describe pressure. Although N/m² is the derived Système international (SI) unit, if we are measuring pressure in class then the areas involved are likely to be much smaller and so using N/cm² will be more appropriate. It is completely fine to measure pressure in N/cm² or even N/mm² but students need to be clear which units they are using: 1 N/cm² is a pressure that is 10 000 times more than 1 N/m². The official SI unit for pressure is the pascal (1 Pa = 1 N/m²).

Science literacy

When referring to stretched or compressed materials, particularly in an engineering context, the term 'stress' is used rather than pressure, but it is still calculated in the same way, dividing the force by the area.

KEY ACTIVITIES

You can organise a simple classroom experiment to be carried out to calculate the pressure under a student's foot. Use 1 cm² squared paper to measure the area of the sole of one shoe and a set of scales to find their weight; be sensitive as some students may not want to discuss their weight (you could do it yourself, for example). Some scales that you can buy for use in physics experiments come with the weight marked in newtons. If using kg scales, students will have to calculate the weight from the mass (for the activity a conversion of 10 N/kg will be suitable). Using the weight and the area, the pressure can be calculated when standing on one or two feet. Even without a ballet dancer in the class, you could estimate the pressure if students were to stand *en pointe* (with a vertical foot, balancing on toes).

The same experiment can be done with a bicycle tyre and there are benefits to teaching in this way. In the foot experiment, the pressure is calculated, but cannot be easily felt or observed – the difference between stilettoes and clown shoes might be clear, but that's about it. With the bicycle tyre, you can both feel the pressure (by squeezing the tyre or by feeling the resistance as you pump it up) and you can measure it easily, using a pump with a pressure gauge built in.

It is possible to show that pressure goes down as the area increases by pressing different sized blocks into a modelling clay pancake with the same force. Or you can vary the force pushing on the same sized blocks to show that pressure increases with force. The size of the indentations gives an indication of the pressure.

As well as numerical calculations, there are some thought experiments that you can ask about to help explore the relationship between pressure, force and area. These might include:

→ Why is it easier to cut vegetables with a sharp knife?
→ Why might high-heeled shoes leave an indentation mark on a wooden floor when flat shoes don't?
→ Why can someone lie on a bed of nails and not get hurt?
→ Why do polar bears and camels have such large paws/pads?

In each case, it is important that you direct students to mention pressure, force and area in their explanations. Saying 'the edge of a sharp knife has a smaller area than a blunt one so the pressure is higher' is not wrong, but a better answer would also note that the force is the same in each case.

5.4 Pressure in liquids, floating and sinking
Prior experiences

Students may well have explored floating and sinking in their primary education, and may have heard the term 'density', but are unlikely to be able to relate them, often considering that just the shape or weight of an object determines whether it will float or sink. They are unlikely to have an appreciation that the upthrust force occurs because the pressure on the bottom of an object is greater than above and that this creates the forces that can make objects float. The idea that liquid pressure is the same in all directions is also a challenge and hard to explain fully unless you direct the students to examine it on a particle level and consider the random motion of particles in all directions. This is discussed in more detail for gas particles in Section 5.5, page 162.

When dealing with floating, sinking and pressure, it is likely that you will meet the following conceptual hurdles:

1 'Light things float, heavy things sink.' Why do some things float? Students may well answer this with a comment such as 'Because they are light enough to float of course! Everyone knows that heavy things sink and light things float.' This is a challenging conceptual hurdle for learners. This intuitive sense of 'lightness' will eventually be understood through the concept of density. Large tree trunks with masses of several hundred kilograms will float, whereas a metal drawing pin with a mass of 3 g is going to sink in water. This is not always obvious to learners but can easily be shown through demonstrations.

2 'How can water push upwards? It is just water, wet and runny.' A second challenge lies in the origin of the upwards force experienced when an object is placed in a fluid, most often a bowl of water. How can water provide an upwards force, called an upthrust? This can be explained by considering pressure changes (this is detailed later in this section).

Floating and sinking

For younger learners, you might want to start this area of student work by eliciting existing ideas and preconceptions. Find a broad selection of objects, some of which will float and some of which will sink. Easy-to-find objects might include a metal paper clip, a drawing pin, a spanner, some plastic cutlery, a large block of wood, a block of polystyrene and a bottle of water. Ask students to weigh the objects and arrange them in order of weight, then encourage them to predict which objects will float and which will sink. Remember to probe the class for the reasons behind their predictions. The predictions should then be tested. It is not uncommon for students to argue that the paper clip will float as it is light. Of course, it sinks! How can this be? If this sort of simple task is done in groups, you will find potential for metacognitive dialogue and you are likely to witness ideas that are challenged and change in real time before your eyes. Make the statement: 'So, if it is not true that heavy things sink and light things float, how can we predict whether an object will float or sink?'

Science in context

If a boat is made of a metal that is denser than water, why does it float? In this chapter we have talked about solid objects made of one material. In the case of a boat you will need to get the students to consider the overall density of the whole boat, which will be a combination of metal, air, people and other cargo. As long as the *overall* density of all of that is less than water, the boat will float.

It is very common for examples related to floating and sinking to involve a solid object placed in a liquid, often because these are easy experiments to set up and observe. This is a good way to introduce these ideas, however it is important to stress to your students that floating and sinking is about relative densities and can also occur with liquids and gases.

A simple and easy-to-set-up demonstration to show that one liquid can float on another involves mixing oil and water. Pretty quickly the students will see two distinct layers, with the oil on top because it is less dense than water. It is common for students and teachers to think that the oil will be denser as it is more 'sticky' or viscous and, while these descriptions are true, you can stress that floating is governed by the relative densities, and not other material properties.

The idea applies to gases as well; a helium balloon floats because it is less dense that air. Convection currents, often taught in the energy topic, are just another example of floating and sinking in which the hotter air is less dense than the cooler air around it and so the hot air rises (floats) above the cold air; this is also how a hot air balloon works.

Pressure and depth

By looking at how pressure varies in a liquid, it is possible to develop a more meaningful understanding of why things float, why submarines have to be very well made and why you should not go swimming with your watch on, unless it is clearly labelled waterproof. It can be useful to start teaching this section with a discussion on students' experiences when swimming underwater, particularly in a deep pool. Some students may have noticed that as they get deeper in the pool, they feel a greater push from the water on their body, caused by the increase in pressure with depth, something they can all experience next time they go swimming.

If you have a pressure sensor or data logger then it is possible to examine this relationship quantitatively, otherwise you will have to use a combination of reason, imagination and compelling oratory to explore this area. You can also explore how pressure changes in air and liquids using the PhET simulation 'Under Pressure'.

The easiest way for students to conceptualise what causes the pressure in a liquid is to get them to imagine that when they are underwater, there is a column of water pushing down on them. As they go deeper, this column of water above them gets taller and the pressure on them increases. This is why all submarines have a maximum depth limit; at greater depths the submarine would be crushed under the pressure.

The equation below shows how the pressure in a liquid depends on the density of the liquid, the height of the column and the gravitational field strength. It may be that your students will not need to use this formula but looking at it shows what quantities determine the pressure in a liquid. This has a logic to it that hopefully students will appreciate, even if they do not measure or feel it:

$$\text{pressure}_{\text{liquid}} \ (\text{N/m}^2) = \text{height of column (m)} \times \text{density of liquid (kg/m}^3) \\ \times \text{gravitational field strength (N/kg)}$$

$$P = h\rho g$$

An important idea to note here is that although we use the idea of a column of liquid pushing *down* to explain the liquid pressure, at a particular depth the pressure is the *same in all directions*, up and sideways, as well as down.

The increase of pressure with depth can be used to explain upthrust (see Section 2.1, page 25). All objects in water will experience a pressure all around them, on all sides. The pressure on the bottom of the object will be greater than the pressure on the top of the object, because the bottom of the object is deeper in the liquid. This difference in pressure means that there will always be an unbalanced force upwards on any object in water: this is upthrust. If the upthrust on an object is bigger than its weight then it will float, if it is less than the weight it sinks. Even when something is sinking, there is still an upthrust force on it, it's just not enough to keep it afloat. Although the examples that students encounter are usually based around water, upthrust acts on objects in all fluids (liquids and gases).

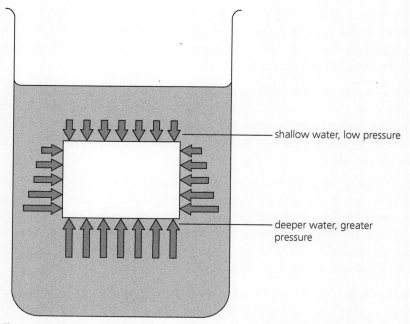

Figure 5.2 The increase in pressure with depth is used to explain upthrust.

Measuring upthrust forces

It is not always easy for students to 'see' the upthrust force when something is immersed in water, although it is possible for them to feel it by submerging a paper cup or air-filled ball into water. The following activity can be used to help show this, as well as promote a discussion about upthrust.

Ask students to hang a metal block securely from a newton meter, get them to note the reading on the scale and then carefully lower the block into a beaker of water. They should note what happens to the reading on the newton meter as the block is slowly immersed in the water

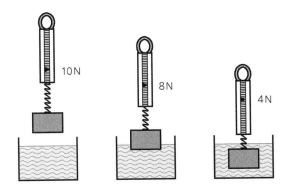

Figure 5.3 Using a newton meter to measure the upthrust with objects that sink

In this example, students can see that there is a buoyant force on objects that sink. It is just that this force is smaller than the weight, which is why these objects sink. The activity can be repeated with different objects including ones that float so students can see that the newton meter reading will drop to 0 N before the block is fully immersed, showing that the upthrust force is equal to the weight and that the newton meter is not providing any upwards support.

At this point, it is possible to ask students to connect ideas about floating, sinking, pressure and depth to provide a more comprehensive explanation of what causes things to float. The difference in density is a way of knowing whether things will float or not, but the upthrust force is caused by the pressure increasing with depth.

 Maths

If something floats, it is possible to work out its density by seeing how much of it sits below the surface. Multiply the fraction below the surface by the density of the thing it is floating in, to give the density of the floating object. Ice floats so that about 8% of it is above the surface, so the density of ice is about 92% of the density of water.

5.5 Gases, pressure and particle motion

Prior experiences

Before students consider the relationships between the pressure, volume and temperature of gases, it is worth finding out what they currently think causes the pressure inside a gas. This is a slightly unusual teaching approach, because in most physics topics we like to start with a physical phenomenon and then start to explain them using models and equations. In this topic we are making a deliberate pedagogical choice to explore it first as a model of particles moving. Once students have a strong mental image of particles moving in a gas, then each successive natural phenomenon you explore with them will support the underlying model *and* can be explained by it.

When we are sitting quietly in a room the air around us appears to be nice and calm and it is simple to imagine that the particles are relatively still. They are not; they are rushing around at random speeds, often of several hundred metres per second. Through careful questioning, you can help students to reconcile their observations that the air in a room appears not to be moving with the scientific understanding that there is continual movement of particles and countless collisions.

Particle collisions cause pressure

It is worth finding out if your students can explain how a gas can cause a pressure using their understanding of the particle model. This will enable you (and them) to ensure that they are familiar with all of the key ideas, before going into more depth. You can do this by asking each student to do a drawing, perhaps on a mini-whiteboard, showing how the particles of air *inside* a balloon stop it collapsing. When all the students have had a chance to do their drawings, you can ask them to explain their diagrams to each other in a small group. Then pick a couple of good examples to share with the class and emphasise the following ideas where you see them:

→ There are lots (and lots) of particles.
→ The particles are very small compared with the space around them.
→ The particles are all moving at random, with a range of speeds *and* in different directions.
→ Each time the particles collide with the rubber, they exert a small force.

When you are discussing air, these particles will mostly be N_2, O_2 and CO_2 molecules, but it is simpler to draw them just as individual particles, because we want the focus to be on their movement.

 Maths

It's not possible or desirable to draw particles at actual size or with the real amount of room between them. Students may be interested to know that in a 1 litre balloon there will actually be about 10^{22} particles.

It is worthwhile being clear to the students about why a constant pressure acts outwards. Even if students do not know at first, you may be able to develop the necessary understanding through detailed questioning. When a particle collides with the ballon side it has an elastic collision: ask them to imagine a particle bouncing off a wall at the same speed. The force to make the particle move away from the rubber has caused an equal but opposite force pushing on the surface that it has hit. With lots of collisions continually happening, this gives a constant outwards force pushing on the rubber. You can demonstrate this by hanging a board up from the ceiling and throwing tennis balls against it, and you can vary the force on the board by throwing the balls harder or more frequently.

You could then ask students to do a very valuable 'thought experiment'. It will enable students to link the macroscopic behaviour of a gas (its volume and pressure) to the behaviour of its particles.

Science in context

Thought experiments can play a powerful part in the scientific process, as they can be the tool that scientists use to generate a hypothesis based on their initial assumptions. They can be used in teaching when a thought experiment is quicker, cheaper or safer than doing the real thing. Einstein used a lot of thought experiments to start to understand physical issues, for example by picturing fast-moving trains shining lights to help develop his theory of special relativity. The paradox of Schrödinger's cat is an example of a famous (in German) *Gedankenexperiment*: an experiment that cannot be practically done, but still gives a useful result or insight.

Tell students to imagine ten particles bouncing around in a fixed container for which you measured the pressure. Ask them to draw diagrams and use their drawings to predict what would happen to the pressure if you alter the set-up.

Starting conditions:

→ 10 particles, fixed volume.

Predict the pressure in the following examples:

→ 20 particles, same volume
→ 10 particles, twice the volume
→ 10 particles, half the volume.

This could be done on a worksheet, but can be done successfully with mini-whiteboards given to pairs of students, in which the area of the whiteboard represents the fixed volume. You can double the volume by placing two whiteboards side by side, or half the volume by drawing a dividing line. The aim of this activity is to get students to explore the relationships between the number of particles, volume and pressure. By asking students to work on mini-whiteboards they can quickly sketch their ideas and adapt them based on peer feedback. This relies on the understanding that students have developed in the discussions about the balloon that a pressure (the force acting over an area) is caused by a large number of collisions. The pressure will increase if there are more collisions or if the force of each collision is larger because the particles are moving faster.

Table 5.2 Results of our thought experiment. Note: particle movement is shown with some cartoon-style movement shading. This is used instead of arrows to avoid confusion with forces.

10 particles in a fixed volume

2 × number of particles in the same volume
2 × number of collisions so 2 × pressure

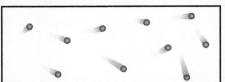

Same number of particles in 2 × volume
½ × number of collisions so ½ × pressure

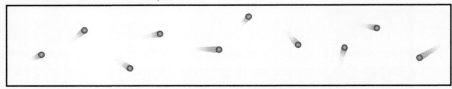

Same number of particles
½ × volume

2 × number of collisions
so 2 × pressure

At first, students may be able to describe qualitative relationships, for example, 'If the volume increases then the pressure decreases'. They should then be encouraged to make predictions about how much each variable will change. This is an example of 'proportional reasoning': where you say how making a change to one variable will affect others (does making X bigger make Y bigger or smaller, and by how much?). In this case, if you double the volume, then the number of collisions on any section of the surface drops by half, so the pressure there has halved.

This gives us our first relationship, which is called Boyle's law. If the temperature of the gas stays constant, and no particles are added or removed, then the pressure in the gas is inversely proportional to the volume:

$$\text{pressure} \propto \frac{1}{\text{volume}}$$

This can also be written:

$$\text{pressure (N/m}^2) \times \text{volume (m}^3) = \text{constant}$$

$$P \times V = k$$

Our second relationship tells us what will happen if we keep the volume of the container and the temperature of the particles fixed:

$$\text{pressure} \propto \text{number of particles}$$

As an extension task, students may be able to predict what would happen if you change the speed of the moving particles:

→ 10 particles, same volume, but twice the average speed.

It is a more complicated relationship because students need to consider both the rate of collisions *and* the force of impact. Although not proved here, students will be able to see that if particles are moving faster (because they are hotter), they will exert a larger pressure:

$$\text{pressure} \propto \text{absolute temperature}$$

Science in context

The usual temperature scale we use is Celsius, which was defined using the freezing and boiling points of water under normal conditions. The lowest possible temperature is −273.15 °C because at this temperature (absolute zero) there is no particle movement. For this reason physics uses an absolute temperature scale (the Kelvin scale), which starts at 0 K. You cannot have a negative absolute temperature.

By starting this topic as a series of linked thought experiments, rather than as a range of practicals, students are reinforcing their understanding of how gases behave in the particle model. Even if students are unable to make all the predictions correctly, they are more likely to make the right connections to theory when they do later experiments.

Technology use

There are other models we can use to demonstrate gas behaviour, including physical simulations with ball bearings bouncing around in a plastic tube. The PhET computer simulation on gas properties (see Resources at the end of this chapter) enables the students to 'see' the particles of a gas as you increase the number of particles, heat the gas up, change the volume and other variables. This could be used as homework to reinforce your thought experiment, as an alternative activity or at the end of the topic as a revision activity. There are lots of nice subtleties in this computer model, such as the small vibrations of the particles even in a cool solid.

Experimenting with Boyle's law

Figure 5.4 shows three ways that the relationship between pressure and volume can be explored for air. Students could first be asked to predict what will happen to the volume of a fixed amount of air if you increase the pressure on it, by sketching either a graph, or a diagram of the particles. Once they have made some predictions, you can investigate them in a number of different ways. You need to make a choice for your student group whether you investigate quantitively (with numbers) or qualitatively (just describing the relationship). There are benefits to each approach, such as the speed of the experiment, how independently students can work, the quality of the results and, of course, the cost and complexity of the kit involved.

Boyle's law:

$$\text{pressure} \propto \frac{1}{\text{volume}}$$

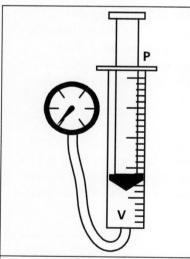
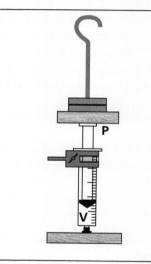
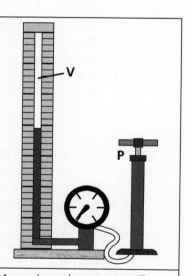

This simple apparatus gives students both a clear 'feel' and numeric indication of how increasing the pressure will decrease the volume of a gas. The results are not usually accurate enough for a convincing quantitative relationship.	The small plastic syringe needs to be sealed at one end and can then be clamped upright. With a block of wood glued, or otherwise attached, you can then add weights on top.	Many science departments will already have a large set of apparatus using a foot pump to increase the pressure. You are measuring the pressure of the air that is trapped.
If you want to examine the numbers, bear in mind that the starting pressure may say 0 *bar* but the standard atmospheric pressure is approximately 1 *bar*, which may need to be added to each pressure reading.	Each weight added increases the pressure, and students can measure the change in volume.	Once two readings have been taken, you could ask students to predict the next ones on mini-whiteboards.
	It balances more easily if you rest the end cap on the table. A 10 ml syringe will move with masses up 1 kg (a weight of up to 10 N), a 50 ml syringe has a bigger area and will need proportionally more.	

Figure 5.4 Three different approaches for varying pressure and measuring volume

If you take readings and plot the relationship, it is conventional to plot *pressure* on the *y*-axis, against *volume* or $\frac{1}{volume}$ on the *x*-axis. If you plot *pressure* against *volume* you should get a curving graph; plot pressure against $\frac{1}{volume}$ for a straight line.

Many teachers also use the 'collapsing can' experiment to demonstrate and talk about the high forces of atmospheric air pressure. It is such a dramatic effect, not just because the pressure decreases in line with the temperature change, but because the steam condenses back to water. If you are doing this experiment it should be reinforced that it's not the partial vacuum inside sucking the can in, but the higher air pressure outside crushing it. More details for this experiment can be found online (see Resources at the end of this chapter).

Science in context

Atmospheric pressure is approximately 100 000 N/m² (weather forecasters usually quote the atmospheric pressure in millibars (mB), 1 B = 100 kN/m²). Students are likely to be surprised by how high this is. If a classroom desk has an area of about 2 m² then you can work out that the force pushing down due to air pressure is 200 000 N, equivalent to a mass of 20 000 kg: the same as several large elephants.

Brownian motion and 'seeing' particles

Throughout this chapter we have used the particle model of matter to help describe and explain how various physics phenomena occur. The strength of this model is that it is consistent with what actually happens and allows us to accurately predict what will happen in a novel range of situations: one of the real powers of modelling in physics. However, as the atoms and molecules are so small, it is impossible for them to be seen with the naked eye or even with a microscope and so there is some element of trust that is needed for students (and teachers) to accept that they are really there. The term 'Brownian motion' is used to describe the random motion of particles suspended in a fluid and provides evidence for the particle model of matter. Even though the atoms and molecules are invisible to us, we can see the effect of them moving as they collide with larger pieces of matter. Some schools may show this phenomenon using a piece of equipment called a smoke cell. It is also possible, although fiddly, to show this under a microscope using milk. Links to these activities are in the Resources at the end of the chapter. Although we cannot directly observe atoms and molecules in motion, we can still infer a lot about their nature from careful study and observation of their interactions. This is a key skill that is used in modern physics research, helping us to study and understand the nature of the Universe: from the gravitational waves given off by black holes merging, to the discovery of the Higgs boson in the Large Hadron Collider.

> **Science in context**
>
> Although more famous for his work on special and general relativity, some of the most important early work from Albert Einstein in physics was the mathematical analysis of the motion of pollen grains in water, first described by botanist Robert Brown. This is called Brownian motion.

 ## 5.6 Resources

Online resources

Please go to **spark.iop.org/asebook** for a set of curated resources from the IOP Spark website to match this chapter.

Simulations

Brownian motion with a smoke cell: https://spark.iop.org

Brownian motion with milk: www.microscopy-uk.org.uk

PhET simulations 'Gas Properties' and 'States of Matter': https://phet.colorado.edu

Stefanelli simulations 'Micrometer' and 'Vernier caliper': www.stefanelli.eng.br

References

ASE (2012) *Teaching Secondary Chemistry* 2nd Ed. UK: Hodder Education.

Boohan, R. (2016) *The Language of Mathematics in Science*. Hatfield: Association for Science Education.

Driver, R., Squires, A., Rushworth, P. and Wood-Robinson, V. (1994) *Making Sense of Secondary Science: Research into Children's Ideas*. New York: Routledge Falmer.

Taber, K. S. (2020) *Foundations for Teaching Chemistry: Chemical Knowledge for Teaching*. Abingdon, Oxon.: Routledge.

6 Atomic physics

Richard Brock, Alex Manning and Kevin Walsh

Introduction

The invisible power of radiation naturally engages students and generates excitement in the classroom. However, the topic can be challenging because nuclear processes are not directly observable, and students can struggle to connect their learning about sub-microscopic phenomena to their macroscopic reality. As was suggested in the introductory chapter, we show how models can be used to clarify difficult concepts about atomic structure and radioactive decay.

Careers

Careers making use of radioactivity cover diverse areas including: archaeology, forensic science, industrial and domestic safety and security, medical diagnostics and treatment, sterilisation in medicine and food production, and various manufacturing processes.

Prior experiences

Students often develop misconceptions about atomic physics through engagement with popular media representations of radiation (Plotz, 2016; see Resources at the end of the chapter). Students tend to associate the term 'radiation' with something unnatural and dangerous, rather than with the transfer of energy in general. When teaching about nuclear radiation, do highlight to students that gamma radiation is part of the sequence of waves on the electromagnetic spectrum. Rather than starting from a discussion of the dangers, for example the Chernobyl disaster, introducing students to natural fission reactors, for example, the one at Oklo in Gabon (Meshik, 2005; see Resources at the end of this chapter), may help to change this belief. Students may also hold the misconception that all electronic devices emit harmful radiation or that, in general, objects exposed to a radioactive source will become radioactive (Plotz, 2016). In addition to the misconceptions above, the nuclear power debate can evoke strong feelings in students, making it a good topic in which to teach about the relationship between science and society (see Section 6.4, page 187).

A teaching sequence

The teaching sequence suggested in this chapter starts with a description of atoms (Section 6.1 Atomic structure, page 170) and follows with a discussion of how the nuclei of atoms change (Section 6.2 What is radioactivity? page 175), how those changes can be modelled (Section 6.3 Half-life, page 184), and finally ends with the uses of radiation (Section 6.4 The applications of radioactive decay, page 185), as outlined below.

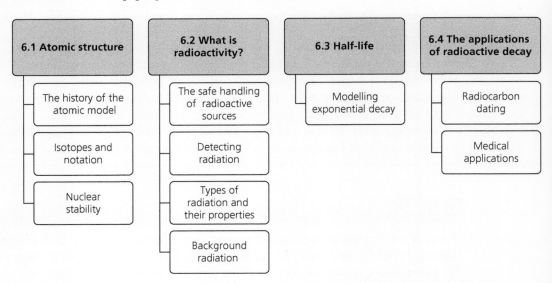

Students are likely to leave primary school with an appreciation of some macroscopic phenomena related to changes of states and separating mixtures, but may not have encountered any formal discussion of the particle model or of the structure of atoms. By the time students are 11–14 years old, learners in many contexts will have encountered the particle model and may have some knowledge of the structure of the atom. During the next stage of schooling (14–16 years old), learners are likely to be introduced to the existence of unstable nuclei and the phenomenon of radioactivity. This teaching will provide a basis for an introduction to any quantum physics they might study post-16 years old. Post-compulsory physics teaching will build on the students' knowledge of radioactivity by introducing the topics of particle physics, quantum theory and the application of radioactive decay to medical physics. Atomic physics can be an inspiring topic for students and enthusiastic learners might be directed to popular books on topics such as particle and quantum physics (see Resources at the end of this chapter).

6.1 Atomic structure

This section provides an opportunity to introduce students to the chronology that, over millennia, has led scientists to their current understanding of atomic structure. Many terms related to nuclear physics have entered the wider current vocabulary (string theory, the Higgs boson and CERN, for example) and young students have a natural curiosity about them. So, while a learner's expectations of deep understanding of such challenging physics must be carefully managed, we can aim to introduce such concepts and set them in an accessible context.

Science in context

You may wish to organise a visit to see the work of physicists at facilities such as the Diamond Light Source in Oxfordshire or the Large Hadron Collider at CERN in Geneva.

The history of the atomic model

Ancient Greek thinkers such as Democritus (around the 4th century BC) used the word that we know as 'atom' to describe something that could not be cut down any further, a basic building block. Another early thinker, Lucretius, made suggestions that we would not agree with today, but many of his descriptions are very similar to what we currently believe. The idea that atoms are in constant motion and undergo collisions bears a strong resemblance to the modern kinetic theory of matter, for instance:

... *as they move, they meet and clash,*

they leap apart at once in different directions.

(Lucretius, 1st century BC)

Other ancient civilisations, particularly in the Middle East, developed similar theories, but for centuries experimental evidence of atoms was elusive (Al-Khalili, 2012; see Resources at the end of this chapter).

While Isaac Newton and Robert Hooke both assumed and used the existence and indivisibility of atoms to explain phenomena (for example, the behaviour of crystals and how light interacts with matter), it was not obvious to historical thinkers (just as it is not obvious to students) that there should be a fundamental building block, an atom, at all.

John Dalton proposed a table of elements based largely on the idea that the elements were observed to react and combine with each other, in neat ratios, to form molecules and this provided support for the existence of atoms. The botanist Robert Brown's 1827 observations of the random motion of very small particles contained in pollen grains in water (Brownian motion) added to the belief that matter was made up of small particles in constant motion.

In 1896, Henri Becquerel discovered the emission of ionising radiation from a uranium salt, and subsequently Marie Curie carried out further explorations of the phenomenon. In 1897, building on work of Wilhelm Röntgen and Sir William Crookes, Sir Joseph John Thomson's discovery that cathode rays were actually streams of small negatively charged particles (later called electrons) provided the first evidence of atomic structure and led to his famous 'plum pudding' model. Two years later, Ernest Rutherford demonstrated that Becquerel's radiation came in different forms, and labelled the first two to be identified alpha and beta radiation.

Careers

When you introduce ionising radiation, you can highlight the wide range of applications of ionising radiation, for example medical tracers that rely on the availability of radioactive sources. Therefore an industry exists centred around the design, manufacture, delivery, storage, maintenance and even the disposal of such sources.

Science in context

Marie Curie noticed that samples of a mineral called pitchblende, which contains uranium ore, were a great deal more radioactive than pure uranium. Further work convinced her that pitchblende did not contain uranium alone, but that there was something else in it. While other scientists doubted her results, Marie worked with her husband Pierre to search for the unknown element. They ground up samples of pitchblende, dissolved them in acid and began to separate the different elements present, using the standard analytical chemistry techniques of the time. Eventually, they extracted a black powder 330 times more radioactive than uranium, which they called polonium. Polonium was a new chemical element, atomic number 84. In addition, they found that the liquid left behind after they had extracted polonium was still extremely radioactive. This was their second discovery, the radioactive element radium.

It was Rutherford's later use of radiation (mainly alpha particles) to probe matter itself that led to the next great development. In what have become known as the Rutherford Scattering Experiments, Hans Geiger and Ernest Marsden, working for Rutherford, fired alpha particles at very thin metal foils (including a gold one, only about 0.4 microns thick). They were looking for how the paths of the energetic particles were affected by passing through the foil: any deflections could provide evidence of the internal structure of the metal atoms. Rutherford was astonished when some alpha particles rebounded from the gold foil, coming back in the direction from which they were fired. Even though the number of particles that rebounded was small (1 in 8000), the discovery shocked Rutherford who years later famously described how it was: '… as if you fired a 15-inch shell at a piece of tissue paper and it came back and hit you'.

After working together on Rutherford's scattering experiment, Geiger and Marsden served on opposing sides of the Western Front during the First World War.

As this result was not expected from Thomson's plum pudding model, Rutherford suggested that the structure of the atom included a small, dense and positively charged region – a nucleus – that was surrounded by the negatively charged and much smaller electrons, a model we still use today. Detailed scrutiny and analysis of the data led to an approximate size of this nucleus: about 1/10 000th of the diameter of the atom. The scattering experiment is often demonstrated using a 'ball bearing and potential hill' apparatus (see Figure 6.1).

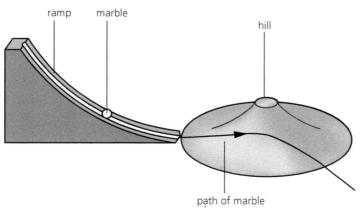

Figure 6.1 An analogy for alpha scattering

A popular analogy to illustrate the relative size of the atom and the nucleus is to imagine the nucleus as a pea in the middle of a large sports stadium. When teaching with models and analogies, it is good practice to be explicit that the comparisons are tools for illustrating ideas, rather than perfectly similar concepts, and to discuss their strengths and weaknesses. For example, in the alpha scattering analogy (see Figure 6.1), a useful discussion might focus on what it would mean for the particle to reach the top of the hill (analogous to fusion, and a good model might include a dip in the top of the hill to show the marble becoming bound by the nuclear strong force). Building on Rutherford's work, Bohr added the idea that electrons cannot move round the nucleus at any distance, but must follow fixed orbitals, and subsequent models conceptualise the atom as having a dense nucleus surrounded by a hazy probability cloud of electrons. The convergence of historical models of the atom to the current description is a useful context in which to discuss the nature and evolution of scientific models over time.

 Technology use

In addition to the physical model of alpha scattering, an online simulation (see Resources at the end of this chapter for the link to the PhET website) is an excellent way of enabling students to reproduce the experiment (the PhET version also includes a plum pudding model).

Isotopes and notation

Having described atomic structure to the students, the next step is to encourage them to consider variations in this structure. A nucleon is a particle in the nucleus, that is, a proton or a neutron. The following numbers are used to describe nuclei:

→ Mass number: the total number of nucleons in the nucleus. It usually has the symbol A.
→ Atomic number: the total number of protons in the nucleus. It usually has the symbol Z.
→ Neutron number: the total number of neutrons in the nucleus. It usually has the symbol N.

This means:

$$Z + N = A$$

It is worth reminding students (who may have already studied some of this in chemistry) that since atoms are neutral, Z is also the number of electrons surrounding the nucleus in the atom. When electrons are lost or gained from an atom, it is no longer neutral and becomes charged; this particle is known as an ion. As electrons are negatively charged, when electrons are lost, a positive ion is formed; when electrons are gained, a negative ion is formed. Therefore, in the case of ions, the atomic number (Z) represents the number of protons but not the number of electrons. For both ions and atoms, the atomic number, Z, identifies the element. It is possible to have different nuclei of the same element that contain the same number of protons but different numbers of neutrons. These are called isotopes and those that are unstable (and thus radioactive) are called radioisotopes. Some examples, the isotopes of hydrogen and carbon, are summarised in Table 6.1.

Table 6.1 Common isotopes of hydrogen and carbon

Isotope	Atomic number (Z)	Neutron number (N)
Hydrogen		
^{1}H	1	0
^{2}H	1	1
^{3}H	1	2
Carbon		
^{11}C	6	5
^{12}C	6	6
^{13}C	6	7
^{14}C	6	8

It is useful to give students the opportunity to practise calculating the number of neutrons or protons in a range of different isotopes. A possible way of doing this is through a card sort activity or worksheet.

Nuclear stability

In light nuclei, the number of neutrons tends to be equal to the number of protons. As the number of protons increases, extra neutrons are needed to keep the nucleus stable (neutrons prevent the nucleus from breaking apart due to the repulsive force that acts between positively charged protons). However, as nuclei get bigger, increasing numbers of neutrons are needed to bind the nucleus and, in larger nuclei, there are more neutrons than protons. The exact relationship between the ratio of the nucleons is not straightforward.

The number of protons and neutrons in a nucleus is critical to its stability. The disintegration and emission of radiation can alter these numbers and sometimes (but not always) produce a more stable nucleus, see the nuclear decay equations in Section 6.2, page 182.

Technology use

The PhET 'Build an Atom' simulation can be a useful model here (see Resources at the end of this chapter).

Numbers of protons and neutrons are not the only determinant of stability. Some unstable nuclei, after a nuclear transition, release energy through the emission of gamma radiation that does not result in a change to the number of nucleons. A useful analogy is a beaker of glass marbles. A little shake of the beaker will cause the marbles to settle and adopt an arrangement that results in a reduction of the (gravitational) potential energy of the collection of marbles, while their total number remains unchanged.

6.2 What is radioactivity?

The nuclei of isotopes that are unstable produce emissions in a process known as radioactive decay. These emissions can be harmful and teachers using radioactive sources need to take some precautions.

The safe handling of radioactive sources

While there are some specific safety considerations that you should consider when teaching lessons using radioactive sources, if appropriate precautions are taken, the risks are low. Don't be put off using radioactive sources and try not to strengthen the misconception that all radiation is dangerous. Introducing everyday sources of radioactivity, for example, smoke detectors, a piece of granite rock and some foods (for example, bananas), can emphasise this point. Seeing radioactive sources and hearing the characteristic chirp of the Geiger counter is a powerful learning experience that can enthuse students about learning physics (details of how to carry out this demonstration can be found on page 179). It is not possible to cover all safety considerations in depth in this section. *L93 Managing Ionising Radiations and Radioactive Substances in Schools and Colleges*, produced by CLEAPSS and available at the link given in the Resources at the end of this chapter, is essential further reading. In addition to the CLEAPSS guidance, further information is available from the ASE Topics in Safety website. Schools in Scotland should refer to the Scottish Schools Education Research Centre (SSERC) guidance (also see Resources).

Before starting to use radioactive sources, you should find out who is responsible for radiation protection in your context. In the UK, each school should have a Radiation Protection Supervisor (RPS) who is advised by an external Radiation Protection Adviser (RPA). Check with the RPS if there is any specific training your school requires you to complete before using the sources. It is the RPS's responsibility to ensure that the safety practices outlined here are being followed, considering any circumstances that may render individuals more vulnerable to radiation, such as pregnancy or illness. Radioactive sources should be stored in a locked steel storage cabinet labelled with the radioactive warning symbol. Your school should have a procedure in place to record the usage of sources in lessons. You or a technician should fill in a log with the date and time a source is used so that its location can be tracked, and the sources should be signed back in when returned. It is good practice to refer to an existing risk assessment (or consult the RPS if none exists) before using the sources and the CLEAPSS document L93 lists specific risk assessment information for different sources. Typical sources found in schools are listed in Table 6.2. Such sources should only be obtained from reputable educational suppliers. In Scotland, when purchasing sources, permission must be obtained from SSERC. In other parts of the UK, schools should refer to CLEAPSS documents PS078 and L93 (which can be found on the CLEAPSS website, see Resources at the end of the chapter).

Careers

Raising awareness of working safely with radiation is an opportunity to introduce associated careers. In any company or institution where radiation is being used, there is a need to monitor and assess the radiation levels and the effects they are having on personnel and the environment. Radiation Protection (RP) is the name given to this area of work and RP advisers, officers and supervisors will be employed wherever such assessment is legally required.

Table 6.2 Typical radioactive sources found in schools

Source	Type of radiation emitted	Half-life
Americium-241	Alpha and gamma	430 years
Strontium-90	Beta	29 years
Cobalt-60	Beta and gamma	5 years
Radium-226	Alpha and gamma (with beta radiation emitted from decay chain products)	1600 years

When using sources, it is good practice to place warning signs on your laboratory doors to indicate that radioactive sources are in use. Radioactive sources are typically mounted in a metal case with a wire gauze over one end.

Handle the sources with a tool, such as forceps or tongs (alternatively, Isotrak sources have an inbuilt aluminium handle) that keep the source at least 10 cm away from your hands and only remove the sources from their cases for the minimum time necessary. Plan, prior to the lesson, how to arrange students so that you avoid pointing the sources directly at them during a demonstration. Students under 16 should not handle the sources themselves, although CLEAPSS suggests that students under 16 may use cloud chambers providing that the sources remain sealed in the chambers during the lesson.

 Technology use

A good video describing the safe handling of radioactive sources was produced by the Institute of Physics for Teachers TV (see Resources at the end of the chapter for a link).

Detecting radiation

One reason students find learning about radiation challenging is that the emissions are not directly visible. Therefore, demonstrating detectors and explaining how they allow radiation to be studied is an important aspect of teaching the topic. All of the detectors described here make use of the fact that the types of radiation that are the focus of this chapter are ionising; that is, they cause atoms to gain or lose electrons to become ions. The detectors described below measure the count rate, the number of ionising events detected by the device in a given time (usually per second). This count rate will be less than the number of disintegrations that occur per second in the source, the activity measured in becquerels (Bq), because detectors imperfectly record decays (for example, because the counter does not entirely surround the source and so cannot capture all the radiation emitted.

Spark counter

Perhaps, the simplest form of radiation detector is the spark counter. The detector can be used to demonstrate the ionising power of alpha sources (the ionising power of beta and gamma sources tend to be too low to be detectable with a spark counter). When an alpha particle passes through the air, gas molecules are ionised, causing air that is normally an insulator to become an electrical conductor. The spark counter works by setting up a potential difference across some air so that when ionising radiation passes through the detector, air molecules are ionised and a cascade of charged particles produces a visible and audible spark.

The spark counter's positive terminal should be connected to the positive terminal (the one with the resistor) of an extra high tension (EHT) supply and the negative terminal connected to the EHT's earth connection. Turn up the voltage on the supply until sparks are produced and then turn it down slightly to the point at which spontaneous sparking stops (typically around 4500 V). Introducing a downwards facing alpha source to the gauze with forceps should cause sparks to appear (darkening the room will increase their visibility considerably). The number of sparks produced in a given time will give an indication of the source's activity. The detector can be used to show the penetrating power of the alpha particles by moving the source towards and away from the detector. You could also angle the source away from the detector, showing the sparks stop, and try inserting a sheet of paper between the source and the detector to act as a barrier to observe a reduction in the number of sparks.

> Safety note: Do be careful not to touch the exposed metal grid once it is connected to the EHT.

Cloud chamber

While the spark chamber provides a visual and audible representation of the activity of sources, it doesn't provide much information on the radiation's path of travel. Cloud chambers (see Figure 6.2) can provide an impressive visual demonstration of the tracks of radioactive particles. The detector contains a compartment with an atmosphere in which alcohol vapour is super-cooled by dry ice (solid carbon dioxide) so that it is just on the point of condensing. When ionising radiation travels through the air, the alcohol vapour condenses around the area of ionisation creating a visible track. You can draw an analogy here to the vapour trails (contrails) formed by aeroplanes, when water vapour in the jet engine exhaust is condensed by the very low temperature of the high-altitude atmosphere.

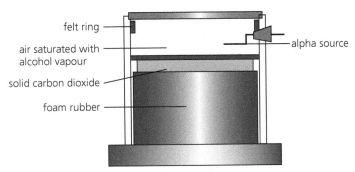

Figure 6.2 A cloud chamber detector

To set up the chamber, soak the felt ring at the top of the chamber with alcohol and fill the base with dry ice. Insert the source into the chamber and switch on the chamber's light source. You may find that rubbing the lid of the chamber with a cloth (which transfers a static charge) makes the tracks easier to see. It can also help to level the chamber with a rubber wedge. It is worth emphasising that the chamber allows the passage of individual particles to be visualised.

Do practise the set-up process beforehand (it requires some patience to get it right) and video record your efforts so you can show students if need be. A personally produced video clip is always better than one taken from the internet. The cloud chamber can be used to demonstrate the range (distance of travel) of alpha and beta particles, the random nature of emission and the presence of background radiation; you will occasionally see a cosmic ray track passing across the chamber. Some cloud chamber models also allow you to introduce a piece of tin or aluminium foil to act as a barrier. The foil will absorb alpha particles and their tracks will terminate at the metal, showing their low penetrating power.

> Safety note: Do follow the CLEAPSS guidance on using dry ice (which can be found on the CLEAPSS website, see Resources at the end of the chapter); use a plastic scoop to transfer the dry ice. Thick gloves or tongs can be used to avoid contact with bare skin.

Science in context

Charles Thomson Rees Wilson, credited with the invention of the cloud chamber, was inspired by observations he made while studying atmospheric phenomena on the top of the mountain Ben Nevis.

Geiger–Müller (GM) tube

Many students are likely to be familiar with the Geiger–Müller (GM) tube from its depiction in popular media. This detector consists of a tube filled with a mixture of inert gases and sealed with a thin window that allows radiation to enter. When ionising radiation enters the tube, ions are created in the gas. These accelerate to the electrodes, creating an avalanche of charged particles that produces a current between the anode and cathode and which the counter registers. The GM tube is the easiest of the detectors to use and the visual display of count rate can be further enhanced by using the built-in loudspeaker (if available) or by connecting an external speaker, so pupils can hear the count rate.

The GM tube can be used to:

→ measure background radiation (see page 183)
→ compare the count rates measured from different sources
→ show the range of different forms of radiation by moving the detector further from the source
→ show the penetrating power of different emissions by placing different materials, such as paper and aluminium sheets, between the source and detector and observing the change in count rate (see Figure 6.3).

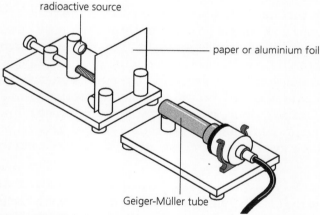

Figure 6.3 A GM tube being used to demonstrate the properties of radiation

KEY ACTIVITIES

You can demonstrate the charged nature of beta decay by using a beta source (for example, strontium-90) and a GM tube counter. Place a strong horseshoe magnet, or a set of magnets from a motor kit, close to a source sited behind a slit (a video can be found on the Institute of Physics website, see Resources at the end of the chapter).

Charged particles are deflected by magnetic fields and, by moving the GM tube, it is possible to show that the beta radiation travels in a curved path.

Types of radiation and their properties

The three types of radiation that you are likely to introduce in physics teaching are shown in Table 6.3 below.

Table 6.3 Properties of three types of radiation

Type of radiation	Symbol	Composition	Charge	Ability to penetrate	Ionising power
Alpha	$^{4}_{2}\alpha$	A helium nucleus, two protons and two neutrons	+2	Low, blocked by a few centimetres of air or a sheet of paper	High
Beta minus	$^{0}_{-1}\beta$	A high energy electron	−1	Medium, blocked by a few millimetres of aluminium	Medium
Gamma	$^{0}_{0}\gamma$	Electromagnetic radiation	0	High, attenuated by a few centimetres of lead	Low

It is important to relate the properties of the types of radiation to their composition, noting that alpha is the least penetrating but (indeed, because) it is the most ionising. Similarly, gamma is the most penetrating but (and, again, because) it is the least ionising.

The different properties of the types of radiation can be demonstrated using the GM tube and a set of sources (or a simulation if these are not available). You might begin by demonstrating how a source's detected count rate, using for example americium-241 which emits alpha and gamma radiation, falls when a piece of paper is placed between source and detector (note that because of the short range of alpha radiation, the source needs to placed right next to the counter). You can contrast this with the limited change in reading experienced when a piece of paper is placed between a beta source (for example, strontium-90) and the detector. Finally, you can demonstrate that in order to reduce the measured count rate of a gamma source such as radium-226 to close to the background count rate, several centimetres of lead shielding is required. In each case, you might ask students to predict what will happen and then explain the observation.

Note that students may develop a range of misconceptions including the idea that atoms disappear in radioactive decay, rather than the nucleus changing, and that beta minus decay is the emission of a valence electron, rather than one from the nucleus.

Below are a number of diagnostic questions that can be used throughout the teaching sequence to help clarify students' thinking:

1 How much positive charge does the nucleus contain?
   → The equivalent amount to the total negative charge of the electrons, in order to cancel out the negative charge and produce a neutral atom overall.
2 Is the nucleus a single positive lump of positive charge or can the nucleus be broken down further?
   → It can be broken down further into protons and neutrons. Rutherford discovered this in 1920.
3 Why doesn't repulsion between protons in the nucleus cause it to break apart?
   → Rutherford suggested other particles should be present in the nucleus that would prevent this from happening. James Chadwick discovered these particles – neutrons – in 1932.
4 Beta particles were later identified as being high energy electrons. The Rutherford model has no electrons in the nucleus, so where do beta particles come from?
   → Neutrons can decay into a proton and an electron.
5 What determines the stability of a nucleus?
   → Stability depends on the numbers of protons and neutrons in the nucleus.

Science in context

In addition to alpha, beta and gamma radiation, J. J. Thomson proposed delta radiation, high energy electrons produced by the passage of another particle, for example, an alpha particle.

Nuclear decay equations

Having considered the radiation emitted from nuclei, you could direct students to then explore how nuclei change as a result of such emissions. Decay equations describe how the nucleus changes when the different types of radiation are emitted. Decay equations show the mass number of an isotope (the top number) and the atomic number (the bottom number), which both must add to the same total on each side of the equation. For example, in the alpha decay of radon:

$$^{219}_{86}\text{Rn} \rightarrow \, ^{215}_{84}\text{Po} + \, ^{4}_{2}\text{He}$$

The mass number of the left-hand side is 219 and on the right-hand side $215 + 4$ is also 219. Similarly, for the atomic number, $86 = 84 + 2$. The same principle applies in the examples of beta and gamma decay below:

$$^{14}_{6}\text{C} \rightarrow \, ^{14}_{7}\text{N} + \, ^{0}_{-1}\beta$$

$$^{137}_{56}\text{Ba} \rightarrow \, ^{137}_{56}\text{Ba} + \, ^{0}_{0}\gamma$$

As gamma radiation does not involve the emission of any nuclear particle, the mass and atomic numbers remain unchanged. The nucleus resulting from a decay may not itself be stable and may also decay. For example:

$$^{238}_{92}U \rightarrow {}^{4}_{2}He + {}^{234}_{90}Th$$

The thorium isotope then decays with the emission of beta radiation:

$$^{234}_{90}Th \rightarrow {}^{0}_{-1}\beta + {}^{234}_{91}Pa$$

This process of interlinked decays is known as a decay chain.

Background radiation

Radiation is present in the environment even when no artificial sources are present. Such radiation is referred to as background radiation and its main source is the naturally occurring radioactive gas radon. As indicated above, you can use a GM tube or a cloud chamber, in the absence of artificial sources, to demonstrate the presence of background radiation. It is worth leaving a GM tube measuring during a lesson to highlight the continual presence of background radiation. It is good practice, before conducting any investigations that involve measuring the activity of sources, for example the demonstrations of penetrating power described above, to measure the background activity several times, determine an average count rate and remove this value from all readings. It is also a valuable activity to record the background count in different locations around the school and/or the local community.

 # Half-life

The nuclei of some atoms are unstable and decay, emitting radiation. This process is random (it is not possible to predict which nucleus in a sample will decay next) and spontaneous (it occurs without an external stimulus). The activity of a source is defined as the number of decays that occur per second and has units of becquerels, Bq. As the number of radioactive nuclei left in a sample decreases, providing the resulting nuclei are stable, the activity of the sample falls as fewer radioactive nuclei remain. This is an example of exponential change, a type of change in which the rate of change of a quantity is proportional to the quantity present at that time. While it is impossible to anticipate when any individual nucleus will decay, for a sample containing many atoms, how the activity will decrease with time can be predicted. The time taken for the activity to halve is constant; this is called the half-life. The half-lives of a number of different isotopes and examples of their uses are shown in Table 6.4. Further details of such applications can be found in Section 6.4, page 185.

Table 6.4 Some radionuclides, their half-lives and uses

Isotope	Half-life	Use
Carbon-14	5700 years	Carbon dating
Cobalt-60	5.3 years	Radiotherapy
Strontium-90	29 years	Thickness control

Half-life is the average time taken for the number of radioactive nuclei in a sample to fall to half its original value (see Figure 6.4).

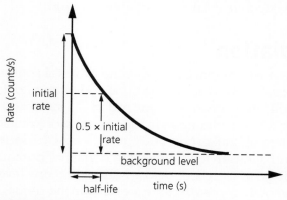

Figure 6.4 An illustration of the concept of half-life

Students can find the concept of half-life challenging and may come to believe that it refers to the time taken for an atom to split in half, or that it refers to half the time it takes a nucleus to decay. It is worth emphasising the definition of this key term carefully and revisiting it within the teaching sequence. It is possible to measure the half-life of radioactive isotopes in the classroom.

Modelling exponential decay

As argued in the introductory chapter, the power and beauty of physics as a discipline is linked to the observation that similar patterns can underlie diverse phenomena in the Universe. One such pattern is the exponential relationship that can be observed in a wide range of situations including cooling curves, the damping of oscillations, population and investment growth and, of course, radioactive decay. Radioactive decay can be modelled in a number of ways, and it is worth discussing the strengths and limitations of each model.

The popcorn model

Cook some popcorn kernels in a covered pan and ask students whether it is possible to predict which kernel will pop first – draw an analogy to the randomness of radioactive decay. Ask the students to listen to the rate of popping (the 'activity') and point out that the rate is high (after the pan has warmed up) when there are many unpopped kernels, but then decreases over time. The model can be critiqued as the non-uniform energy distribution means that the popping won't be entirely random.

The coins, sweets or dice model

Students can be given a number of small objects (for example, coins, dice, counters, or small sweets/confectionery that are marked to distinguish the sides) and told a condition for when they decay (for example, landing heads up, landing with the 'mark' uppermost, landing on a six). Take care if using counters or coins in the simulation as students may acquire the misconception that the likelihood of decay of the nucleus is always 50:50. Using dice can allow you to vary the decay rate (for example, decay only occurs when a six, or an odd number, is rolled).

The students first count the number of objects they have and record the number in a table (for example, 100 coins), then throw the objects and remove any that meet the decay condition (for example, landing heads up), counting and recording the remaining number and then throwing again. The process is repeated until all the objects have 'decayed'. Students can then plot a decay curve of number of objects remaining against the number of throws and calculate a 'half-life'. Note that because 'decay' happens in turns, rather than continuously, the graphs produced by these activities differ slightly from decay graphs for isotopes.

Technology use

Some pieces of apparatus are available that allow you to measure the half-life of isotopes in the school laboratory: a radon-220 generator, a caesium-137/barium-137 elution source, and a protactinium generator. For further details on these options, see CLEAPSS document L93 (listed in Resources at the end of this chapter).

6.4 The applications of radioactive decay

While we have included this discussion of the applications of radioactive decay at the end of the chapter, we recommend that you interleave the material with the content. For example, when discussing the penetrating power of types of radiation, you might discuss how medical technicians choose radioactive tracers with penetrating power appropriate for different uses within the body.

Radiocarbon dating

Careers

Carbon dating is used in archaeology to measure the age of materials.

The constant half-life of radioactive isotopes means that measurement of the amount of isotope remaining in a sample of material can be used to determine its age. For example, living things absorb carbon, either through photosynthesis in the case of plants or by eating plants in the case of animals. The majority of the carbon absorbed is stable carbon-12 (C-12), but a small proportion is the radioactive isotope carbon-14 (C-14), formed by the interaction of atmospheric nitrogen with cosmic rays (see Table 6.1). While an organism is alive, the ratio of C-12 to C-14 remains constant as new carbon is continually being absorbed from the environment. After the organism dies, the C-14 decays with a half-life of 5700 years and is not replaced, therefore affecting the ratio of the two isotopes. This change in ratio can be used to determine the age of the sample. While this method is generally quite reliable, it is interesting to note that radiocarbon measurements can sometimes be difficult to interpret: whales and seals that have died recently have been incorrectly radiocarbon dated as hundreds of years old because they have absorbed C-14 that dissolved in the ocean and has remained undisturbed, continually decaying, before being taken up by the animals. A similar approach to radiocarbon dating can be used to date rocks, and so determine the age of the Earth, by measuring the levels of uranium isotopes and lead present in rocks.

Medical applications

Ionising radiation can be used to both treat and diagnose diseases. Emphasising the therapeutic and diagnostic power of radiation can help to change students' beliefs that radiation is inherently harmful. One diagnostic application is radioactive tracers: radioactive isotopes that are introduced into the body so that their passage can be monitored from outside the body. For example, iodine-131 is a radioisotope that can be used to estimate the production of growth hormone in the thyroid gland. Low dosages of isotopes are used so that tissue does not get damaged. Radiation can also be used to treat disease. Perhaps the best known example is radiotherapy, in which ionising radiation is used to destroy tumours. It is likely that some students will have personal connections to someone who has experienced radiotherapy and its benefits and side effects. Do be sensitive to this and draw on your knowledge of individual students to guide how to approach teaching the topic. Some good resources for teaching about the uses of radiation in medicine can be found on the Institute of Physics website (see Resources at the end of the chapter).

Nuclear power

Although, in the early 1930s, Ernest Rutherford had described the possibility of generating energy from nuclei as 'moonshine' (McCracken and Stott, 2013), physicists soon developed ways to safely release and harness nuclear energy. Fission is the process in which atomic nuclei break into smaller parts, referred to as daughter nuclei. The process can be spontaneous, as in radioactive decay, or induced, as in a nuclear reactor. In induced fission in a reactor, the absorption of a neutron causes a nucleus to break, or fission, into daughter nuclei, releasing additional neutrons and energy. If, on average, the fission releases more neutrons than were originally absorbed, the neutrons can cause other nuclei to fission, releasing further neutrons in a process known as a chain reaction (see Figure 6.5).

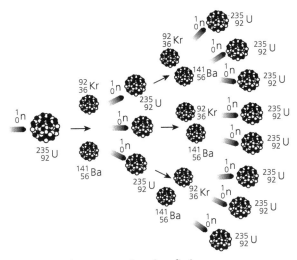

Figure 6.5 The process of nuclear fission

The process of nuclear fission can be simulated by using a physical model made of matchsticks. A grid of matchsticks can be inserted into a modelling clay base to represent the uranium-235 nuclei in a sample of nuclear fuel in a reactor. When one of the matches is lit with a splint, the energy from that ignition will cause adjacent matches to combust leading to a chain reaction. It may help to tilt the base slightly to help ignition. It can be useful to highlight analogies between energy and the neutrons, and the burnt matchstick heads and daughter nuclei.

> Safety note: Carry out this demonstration in a fume cupboard as it produces a lot of smoke.

Science in context

An engaging activity following the teaching of fission is a debate on the issues surrounding the use of nuclear power. This can be a class debate or smaller discussion, allowing students to engage with socio-scientific ideas related to a current controversial issue. An excellent resource to structure such debates is the IDEAS pack (see Resources at the end of the chapter).

Careers

The nuclear power debate will increase awareness of a range of careers within the industry. Nuclear power stations are obvious employers making use of those with physics knowledge. The designing, building, operating, developing and maintaining of such installations all require nuclear physicists and engineers.

In contrast to fission, which occurs when large nuclei break apart, energy can also be released when two or more light nuclei join together in a process known as nuclear fusion. Fusion of hydrogen nuclei into helium is responsible for the energy generation in the Sun and other main sequence stars. As nuclei are positively charged, it takes high temperatures and pressures to cause fusion to occur and the challenges of reaching, containing and sustaining these conditions mean that commercial fusion power stations remain some years away from realisation. An approach to modelling the process of nuclear fusion is a fusion forces roller coaster (see Resources at the end of this chapter).

> ### Careers
>
> There is a wide range of careers for nuclear physicists. In the UK, the National Health Service is a major employer of physicists. The Institute of Physics and Engineering in Medicine (IPEM) is the professional organisation representing the workforce of all physicists, engineers and technologists with roles delivering healthcare. Manufacturers of radioisotopes, including companies such as Alliance Medical, employ physicists in this field.
>
> Other options are careers in radiation protection, UK Atomic Energy and the UK's Atomic Weapons Establishment.

 ## Resources
6.5

Online resources

Please go to **spark.iop.org/asebook** for a set of curated resources from the IOP Spark website to match this chapter.

Safety

The Association for Science Education. Search "Topics in Safety 19 – Ionising Radiations": www.ase.org.uk

The CLEAPSS website has information on using dry ice, choosing new radioactive sources, and for safety advice on managing ionising radiation and radioactive substances. Search "Use of Dry Ice SRA030", "PS078 Choosing new radioactive sources for school use: advice for science departments" and "L93 Managing Ionising Radiations and Radioactive Substances in Schools and Colleges": http://science.cleapss.org.uk

Scottish Schools Education Research Centre. Search "Health and safety: Radioactivity": www.sserc.org.uk

The STEM Learning website has information on the safe handling of radioactive sources. Search "Demonstrating Physics: Radioactivity": www.stem.org.uk

Other resources

Beta radiation - deflection in a magnetic field. Search "Teaching Radioactivity: Beta radiation - deflection in a magnetic field": www.youtube.com

Nuclear Power Debate. Search "IDEAS Resources" (see, activity 2, generating energy): www.stem.org.uk

Careers

The British Nuclear Medicine Society is a membership organisation for those working in nuclear medicine: https://www.bnms.org.uk

Companies such as Alliance Medical employ physicists for the manufacture of radioisotopes: https://www.alliancemedical.co.uk

The Institute of Physics and Engineering in Medicine (IPEM) is the professional organisation representing the workforce of physicists, engineers and technologists with roles delivering healthcare: https://www.ipem.ac.uk

The National Health Service is a major employer of physicists in the UK: https://www.healthcareers.nhs.uk

The National Skills Academy Nuclear (NSAN) is a membership organisation for those working in the nuclear industry: https://www.nsan.co.uk

The UK Atomic Energy Authority is a government organisation focused on nuclear power. Search "UKAEA": https://www.gov.uk

Simulations

Fusion forces roller coaster: www.youtube.com

Rutherford scattering: https://phet.colorado.edu

Spark counter: http://practicalphysics.org

Cloud chamber: https://spark.iop.org

Protactinium generator: http://practicalphysics.org

References

Al-Khalili, J. (2010) *Pathfinders: The Golden Age of Arabic Science.* London: Penguin.

Lucretius (2007) *The Nature of Things.* (R. Jenkyns trans.) London: Penguin.

McCracken, G. and Stott, P. (2013) *Fusion: The Energy of the Future.* Waltham, MA: Academic Press.

Meshik, A. P. (2005) The workings of an ancient nuclear reactor. *Scientific American*, 293 (5), 83–91.

Plotz, T. (2016) Students' conceptions of radiation and what to do about them. *Physics Education*, 52 (1), 014004.

Further reading

Carroll, S. (2012) *The Particle at the End of the Universe: The Hunt for the Higgs and the Discovery of a New World.* London: Oneworld Publications.

Gribbin, J. (2012) *In Search of Schrödinger's Cat: Updated Edition.* London: Penguin.

Irvine, M. (2011) *Nuclear Power: A Very Short Introduction.* Oxford: Oxford University Press.

Jorgensen, T. J. (2016) *Strange Glow. The Story of Radiation.* Princeton, NJ: Princeton University Press.

Pearce, F. (2018) *Fallout: A Journey Through the Nuclear Age, From the Atom Bomb to Radioactive Waste.* London: Portobello Books.

Tuniz, C. (2012) *Radioactivity: A Very Short Introduction.* Oxford: Oxford University Press.

Carol Davenport

Introduction

Waves are a helpful model to describe how energy can be transferred from one place or object to another without there being a physical connection between them. We can use a simple model of 'source–transfer–absorber' to describe this energy transfer, which can be used for all types of wave. One reason that it is important to understand waves and their behaviour is that they carry information, with different waves being used in different ways by animals (including humans), plants and electronic sensors.

Compare the use of ultrasound to image the inside of the human body with the destructive power of an earthquake. Imagine the vast scales over which gravitational waves carry information across the Universe about the destruction of black holes and then compare that with the unimaginably small scale of electrons in a scanning electron microscope. All these phenomena can be described using the same idea: waves.

The properties that we observe with one type of wave can also be observed in other types of waves, for example, superposition of both water waves and sound waves produces standing waves; reflection of both light waves and sound waves (sonar) produces an 'image' of an object.

Prior experiences

Between the ages of 5 and 11, students are likely to have considered sound and light as separate phenomena and not as two examples of waves. Students will have explored sources of sound and different ways of making sound, and linked these to vibrations. They may have investigated changing the loudness and pitch of a sound through the use of musical instruments. They can probably describe how sound travels to the ear, and how hearing sounds can be affected by different factors, such as age or how close the sound source is.

Science in context

Exploration of sound provides students with the opportunity to develop scientific skills, for example observing patterns between the volume of a sound and the strength (amplitude) of the vibration that caused it, or how changing the physical characteristics of the sound source can alter the pitch of a sound.

Light is often introduced later than sound. Students may have experienced that they need light in order to see, and may have been taken into a light-proof room to experience total darkness for themselves. Students will have explored how shadows are formed, and how the straight-line path of light can explain the shape of shadows. They may have investigated how light is reflected from different surfaces, including curved or rough surfaces. Students may know that white light is a mixture of different colours of light, and that using coloured filters can affect the apparent colour of an object.

A teaching sequence

One possible teaching sequence is to begin with familiar examples of waves that younger students (11–14 years old) will be able to explore for themselves and then bring in the use of analogies to describe wave properties as the students become comfortable with the properties of the different types of waves (Section 7.3, page 208). These properties can then be extended to bring in numerical calculations (Section 7.4, page 212) across different scales; microscopic and macroscopic. Older students (14–16 years old) can be introduced to refraction of waves and the speed of light in different media, beginning with the refraction of light, but extending the idea to refraction of seismic waves and its use in Earth science. During this stage, students should be able to use diagrams to represent and describe the properties of waves. Finally, students should explore the electromagnetic spectrum and its uses, and how physicists' understanding of light, and the models used to describe it, have changed over time.

Careers

Students who study physics post-16 years will continue to develop their understanding of waves through superposition of waves as it applies to sound in musical instruments, through stationary waves on strings and in air, and to light through diffraction in spectrometers and in, for example, telescopes or ultrasound in medicine. Beyond this, an understanding of waves is used in quantum physics, for example to model the orbit of electrons, and in opto-electronics. An understanding of waves is important for a range of possible future careers and students may find themselves making use of waves in careers as diverse as acoustic designer, radiographer, geospatial technician or seismologist.

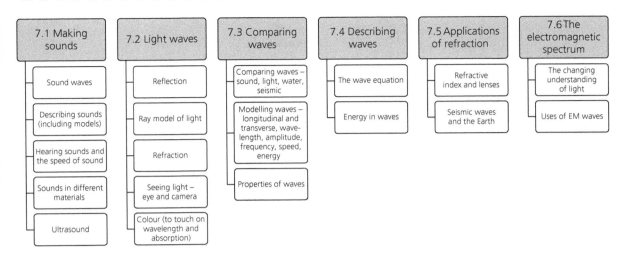

7.1 Making sounds	7.2 Light waves	7.3 Comparing waves	7.4 Describing waves	7.5 Applications of refraction	7.6 The electromagnetic spectrum
Sound waves	Reflection	Comparing waves – sound, light, water, seismic	The wave equation	Refractive index and lenses	The changing understanding of light
Describing sounds (including models)	Ray model of light	Modelling waves – longitudinal and transverse, wavelength, amplitude, frequency, speed, energy	Energy in waves	Seismic waves and the Earth	Uses of EM waves
Hearing sounds and the speed of sound	Refraction	Properties of waves			
Sounds in different materials	Seeing light – eye and camera				
Ultrasound	Colour (to touch on wavelength and absorption)				

Sound waves

Any teaching about sound will need to be done with sensitivity to those students whose hearing is impaired. If there is a hearing impaired student in the teaching group, it would be a good idea to find out how the student would like the situation to be handled. While some students may be happy to be involved in hearing experiments with their friends, others may not.

Making sounds

Students will be familiar with sounds, and how they are made, particularly if they have played a musical instrument. The challenge for the teacher is to move the students on to develop a confident grasp of the vibration concept. Young students notice the vibration of a cymbal but, even at the age of 16, some students may have difficulty with the idea of transferring the vibration of the object to air.

You could begin with revision of earlier experiences, such as providing a range of musical instruments or simple sound makers and ask students to describe the sounds and discuss with them their use of words such as 'low' and 'high'. This will allow you to emphasise the vocabulary that you want students to use: pitch, loudness and frequency. Students can also use instruments such as guitars or boomwhackers to explore how the pitch of sound can be changed.

Ask students to describe the instruments that they are familiar with from home, or that are used in the music they listen to. You could also introduce a broader range of instruments from different cultures. It could be worth collaborating with your music department for this.

You can demonstrate how a source of sound vibrates using a tuning fork in water or by putting polystyrene beads onto a loudspeaker cone. Placing a candle flame in front of a loudspeaker that is broadcasting a slow drum beat can also be used to show the idea of vibration, or there are slowed down videos of vibrations causing sounds. The Institute of Physics resource 'Seeing sound' describes other useful activities to help students to visualise the vibrations that lead to sound (see Resources at the end of this chapter).

Describing sounds

It is a good idea to begin by asking students to model the motion of a sound wave using a metal slinky. Moving the slinky backwards and forwards parallel to the length of the slinky will show the longitudinal motion of the air particles, and the direction of travel of the sound wave. You can also model the sound wave by asking the students to stand shoulder-to-shoulder in a line next to each other to form a 'student sound wave' (Whalley, 2003). These two activities introduce the idea of the sound moving through a medium with the particles of the medium oscillating about a fixed point, rather than moving along with the sound. They also provide the opportunity for students to 'compare and contrast' the two models of sound.

Once students are comfortable with the motion of a sound wave, it is useful to introduce the idea of a 'slink-o-scope' which translates the longitudinal motion of a slinky into a transverse 'trace' (see Resources at the end of this chapter).

At this point a simple explanation of sound can be introduced: a vibration acting as the 'source' of the sound, which travels through a 'medium' until it is reaches another object ('receiver').

You can introduce students to using oscilloscope traces to represent sounds – but making sure not to refer to the trace as 'the sound wave'. It is useful to use an oscilloscope and a microphone because it allows students to make the link between the size of a vibration (amplitude) and the loudness of the sound, and the number of vibrations (frequency) and the pitch (Figure 7.1). The common way of showing sound waves in popular culture is by using an image of a transverse wave, and so students may have a misconception that sound waves are transverse waves. This misconception can be inadvertently reinforced when an oscilloscope (either in the lab or online) is used to show the loudness (amplitude) and pitch (frequency) of different sounds. Using the slink-o-scope can help to allay this misconception.

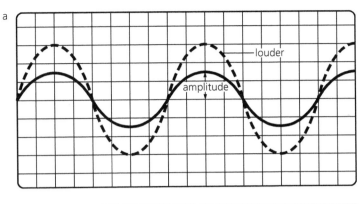

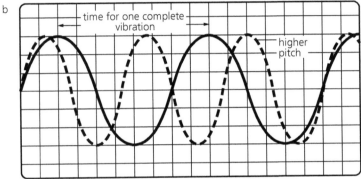

Figure 7.1 Oscilloscope displays of different sounds: a) the louder the sound, the greater the amplitude of the vibration or sound; b) the higher the pitch, the greater the number of vibrations per second (the frequency)

Hearing sounds

The next stage is to appreciate that sound is vibrations which are received by the ear. A scale model of the ear is useful for appreciating the relative sizes of the parts and how they are interconnected, and the passage of vibrations from the outer ear canal, through the tiny bones of the middle ear into the inner ear, which stimulate nerve impulses. This should lead to an appreciation that the ear is a delicate organ and can suffer impairments. It is estimated that about a quarter of young people listen to music that is loud enough to damage their hearing.

Technology use

You could use an online signal generator (or audio signal generator) to check the frequency range of the class's hearing – ask them all to indicate when they can no longer hear the sound as the frequency is increased. The teacher will probably be first, as this is age dependent! The range of hearing for an adult is typically from 20 Hz to 20 000 Hz (20 kHz). Some students may hear as high as 30 kHz. The unit for frequency is hertz (Hz), the number of vibrations per second.

195

Great care needs to be taken to identify any students or adults who are hearing impaired and those who have hearing aids or cochlear implants as they may be very badly affected by activities involving different intensities and frequencies of sound. When a loudspeaker is driven by a signal generator, the amplitude (and thus volume) should be kept low and the sound generated only for a short time, particularly for infrasound (<20 Hz). Various sound frequencies, including those beyond the upper threshold of hearing, have been known to cause unpleasant effects, even nausea, in some individuals.

Science in context

You could introduce the 'mosquito' acoustic deterrent device which was invented to prevent teenagers congregating in outdoor spaces around shops or in public spaces. It plays a high pitch tone which can be heard by teenagers, but not generally by those who are over 25. Encourage your students to consider the ethical issues that the use of this device poses.

Careers

The topic of hearing, and hearing loss, is an opportunity to introduce careers that require an understanding of both physics and biology, particularly healthcare careers such as audiologist and speech therapist. You could also discuss sound engineering as a career.

Sounds in different materials

The difference between sound travelling in a gas (air) and a solid can be demonstrated by giving students a piece of string and asking them to hold it in tension between their teeth and hand, and then to pluck it to make a sound. The students will be able to hear the sound clearly, but the person next to them will not. They may link this to 'string telephones' that they may have investigated when they were younger.

You can also get them to listen to a gently struck coat hanger or slinky which is hung from a string in contact with the outer ear (see Figure 7.2). The effect is of a surprisingly loud and full sound. To hear sounds travelling in liquids students could be reminded of the plumbing gurgles you can often hear if you submerge your head in the bath!

These demonstrations show that vibrations are transmitted more efficiently in a solid than in air.

Science in context

The effect of different materials on sound transmission can be linked to the idea of noise reduction. Students could carry out an investigation into the effectiveness of different materials at reducing sound, by placing a buzzer inside a box and using a decibel meter to measure the sound with different insulation materials.

Students can also be introduced to the reflection of sound waves and the idea that different surfaces will reflect and absorb sound waves differently. You can draw a parallel with the behaviour of light, and students will recall that light may be reflected, scattered or absorbed by different surfaces. Sound is reflected more effectively from hard surfaces, which is why many people enjoy singing in the shower where their voices sound much better.

The speed of sound

The discussion of waves travelling through different media can be an opportunity to introduce the speed of sound. Students may think that sound will travel faster through air because it is 'thinner' and therefore easier for the sound to travel through. To address this misconception, you should revisit the 'student sound wave' model (see page 194) and use it to show the difference between sound transmission in a solid (where the students/particles are close together and connected) and in a gas (where the students/particles are much further apart and are independent of each other).

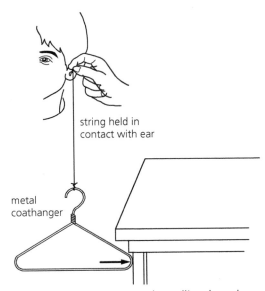

string held in contact with ear

metal coathanger

Figure 7.2 Listening to sound travelling through a solid

Measuring the speed of sound in air can provide a challenge to students' skills. It is possible to carry out an investigation on the school field, with a suitable visible sound source (such as the clapping together of two blocks of wood) and with consideration for variables such as the wind. Alternatively, students could achieve an echo of a clap from the wall of a building. They should clap immediately every time they hear the echo (so that claps are synchronised with the echoes) and measure the time for a series of claps and echoes. The value of the speed of sound is about 330 m/s, depending on temperature. In practice, expect values within ±20% of this. With older students, you could measure the speed of sound using data-logging equipment or an oscilloscope (see Resources at the end of this chapter).

Ultrasound

Ultrasound can be used to introduce students to reflection as a property of waves. Most students will probably be aware of the medical use of ultrasound during pregnancy to observe the developing fetus. Ultrasound has other medical imaging uses because it is inexpensive and non-invasive, for example it is used widely for investigating the presence of gallstones in the liver.

The ultrasound probe is both a transmitter and receiver of waves. Reflections from interfaces between different tissues arrive at the receiver after a time delay that depends on the depth of the interface. This information allows an image to be built up. Imaging of soft tissues is particularly good. Note that although students may have seen such images on television, they often assume that the waves used are electromagnetic rather than sound.

Careers

The use of ultrasound technology provides more examples of careers in which an understanding of both biology and physics is helpful, such as medical physicist, ultrasound technician and sonographer.

7.2 Light waves

Careful thought will be required to adapt work about light for students who are partially sighted – the Royal National Institute of Blind People (RNIB) has useful advice for science teachers who have visually impaired students in their classes (see Resources at the end of this chapter). In addition, about one in 12 males and one in 100 females are 'colour blind', although it would be more accurate to say that they are colour deficient and have difficulty in distinguishing some colours. It is rare to find anyone who cannot see colour at all. Red/green confusion is the most common condition and can sometimes be helped by looking through a red filter.

The idea that we see because our eyes give out something, rather than receive light, is a common misconception in younger students. When students are asked to draw their explanation of how the eye works, using arrows to show how light travels, some are likely to draw light rays coming from the eyes (Osborne et al., 1990). This 'active eye' idea is encouraged by comic-book ideas of, for example, X-ray vision. Some secondary students will still hold this view.

Some students may not have experienced complete darkness, and so think that it is possible to see reflective objects when there is no (obvious) source of light present. If you don't have a suitable room available, this misconception can be addressed by putting a shiny, reflective object into a box which is lightproof, apart from a small hole. Students can then use the hole to look into the box and will see nothing.

In primary school, most students will have distinguished luminous from non-luminous objects, but you might wish to review this using electric lamps (filament, LED and fluorescent), flames and the Sun. Students may be less sure of the status of the Moon, fluorescent substances, mirrors and shiny materials, as they may confuse reflection with generation of light, so it is worth emphasising the difference between a source and a reflector of light.

> The light from data projectors and high intensity LEDs is very bright and can cause eye damage. Students should not stare into the beams from such devices. The Sun must never be viewed directly, even during a solar eclipse. A safe way to view the Sun is via an image projected on to a suitable screen.

Out of this discussion two important points may arise: that light cannot be seen in transit and that it appears to take no time to travel. This is the opportunity to show beams of (laser) light shining through dust (which can be made from talcum powder) or similar. However, what is actually being seen is the scattering of light off the particles in its path, not the beam of light itself. The straight-line travel of light can also be observed in this situation. Reference could be made to 'sunbeams', which are only visible when there is mist or dust to show them up. This effect is simulated at music events using smoke machines.

The speed of light is nearly 300 000 kilometres per second (3×10^8 m/s), so it appears to travel instantaneously over terrestrial distances. However in the vastness of the Universe the delay can be significant. The light reflected from the Moon takes 1.5 seconds to reach us, whereas light from the Sun takes about 8.3 minutes. From the nearest star the light has travelled for over 4 years to reach Earth, and from the farthest point of the Universe it has taken over 13 billion years – the age of the Universe itself. This means that looking into space is looking back in time. When we look at a star in the night sky, we are seeing it as it was when the light left the star – perhaps millions of years ago. This idea may not help students get a feel for the speed of light, but many will be interested in the idea of seeing past events.

Science in context

If students have studied sound recently, comparison with the speed of sound can be made, with examples such as thunder and lightning, and the use of a starting pistol for races. To calculate the distance of a thunderstorm, count the number of seconds for the gap between lightning flash and thunderclap and divide by 3 (for kilometres) or by 5 (for miles).

Reflection from a surface

Many students will know that when light interacts with materials it can be reflected, absorbed or transmitted. However, they may not realise that many materials cause a combination of these effects. For example, ordinary window glass reflects as well as transmits light, as students will realise if they look out of a lighted room into the night. This can be demonstrated with a safety screen in a darkened laboratory.

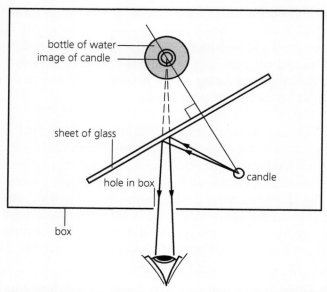

Figure 7.3 'Pepper's Ghost' is an optical illusion that uses the fact that glass both reflects and transmits light. Using a candle produces a realistic 'ghost' flame.

Students need to realise that it is not just mirrors or smooth surfaces that reflect light. The difference is that these surfaces give 'regular' reflection and can produce images. Almost all non-luminous objects are visible by reflected light, but this is 'diffuse' reflection. The model of bouncing a ball off a wall can be used to explain the difference. If the wall is smooth, we can predict the way the ball will rebound. If the wall is rough, the ball will bounce unpredictably in one of many directions (is scattered). Matt surfaces are microscopically rough, so light reflects off (scatters) in all directions. Consequently no image is formed.

Science in context

When light travels through a medium such as air or glass, it will meet dust particles and other imperfections such as variations in density. These reflect and scatter the light. High in the atmosphere blue light is scattered the most, which is why most of the sky is blue. Similarly, unscattered light directly from the Sun makes it appear yellow. At sunset and sunrise, because the Sun is lower in the sky, there is much more scattering of the light by the atmosphere and it now appears red, which is scattered the least, while the rest of the sky is less blue.

Many students will be confident from earlier study about using mirrors to investigate the reflection of light and will be familiar with the idea that the angle of incidence is equal to the angle of reflection (if not with those terms). However, they may not have used protractors to measure the exact angles, and so students could investigate reflection with a ray box and plane mirror on paper (see Figure 7.4). You can then demonstrate how to draw a ray representation of the law of reflection, using the normal to the plane surface (see Figure 7.5).

Students have to learn that we consider angles *relative to the normal*, the line drawn at right angles to the surface; it is not obvious why we do this when considering a plane surface, but for a curved or irregular surface it makes more sense.

Students can then try to apply this law to the reflections they observe with curved mirrors.

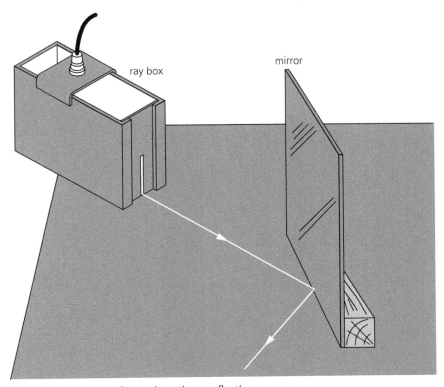

Figure 7.4 Using a ray box to investigate reflection

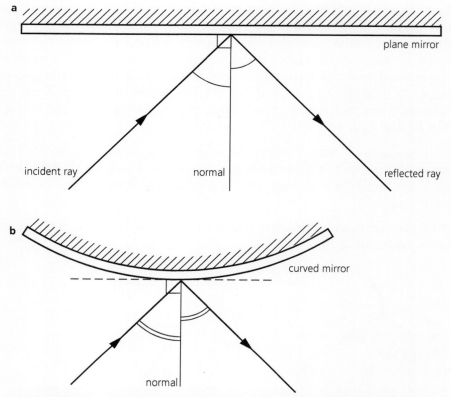

Figure 7.5 The law of reflection: a) reflection at a plane mirror; b) reflection at a curved mirror

Students may be familiar with kaleidoscopes and you could show them one without the casing so that they can see the arrangement of the mirrors for producing the random and changing patterns, Students could then use more than one mirror to explore the number of images that can be formed when the angle between the mirrors is varied.

The image formed by a plane mirror is as far behind the mirror as the object is in front. It is an example of a rather abstract concept – the virtual image. Light *appears* to be coming from a point behind the mirror, when in fact it has bounced off the front of the mirror. Students need to learn to distinguish between our brain's interpretation of what we see (an image behind the mirror) and what is actually happening in terms of light rays. It could help students to think of a virtual image as one you 'cannot put your finger on'. A real image is one you can 'touch'.

You may also encounter the age-old question of why a mirror reverses left to right but not top to bottom. In fact, it would be more correct to say that a mirror reverses back and front. Try writing a word on clear plastic. Hold it up to the mirror and look through it at its reflection. Both words look the same.

The problem is that we normally picture ourselves going round behind the mirror to occupy the space where our reflection is. As we do this, we turn round through 180°, thus reversing left and right (see Resources at the end of this chapter).

Ray model of light

Once students are able to use the concept of light travelling in straight lines, then you can introduce the ray model of light. However, students tend to assume that the rays which they draw are actual objects, rather than a representation and simplification (Ceuppens *et al.*, 2018). It is therefore worth helping students to evaluate the model, particularly by pointing out that light given out by a source is not limited to 'rays' but is radiated in all directions. The model allows us to draw ray diagrams to predict the effects of reflection and refraction, but in doing so loses some of the complexity of the real situation.

Using ray boxes can help students to become more familiar with drawing and thinking about rays of light. However, one note of caution about their use is that although we call them 'ray boxes', what we see are the shadows of the mask and the slits; which happen to have bright areas between them that we call rays. In the reflection and refraction practicals that we do, the beam behaves in a similar way to our ideas about light rays and so we can use this to model the way rays of light are reflected or pass through materials.

Refraction

When light travels from one medium to another, it refracts or changes direction (bends). Using a ray box to demonstrate how light travels through a parallel-sided glass block (see Figure 7.6), you will be able to show that:

→ the change of direction only occurs at an interface between materials of different optical density
→ light which travels perpendicular to an interface is not refracted
→ light 'bends' towards the normal (inwards) when it travels from a less dense to a more dense medium and vice versa.

 Science literacy

The optical density measures the speed of light through a material. A material with a higher refractive index is referred to as more optically dense. Here, the term 'dense' relates to optical density. There is no relationship between optical density and physical density.

An analogy for refraction is the behaviour of a car when it runs off the road onto a softer verge. The front wheel hits the verge first and goes slower than the rest of the car so it swings round towards the verge, increasing the danger of an accident. Another analogy is the turning of a marching band. Those on the inside take smaller steps (shorter wavelength) but with the same frequency, so they move more slowly. The lines of marchers are equivalent to wavefronts.

Careers

There are some interesting applications of TIR (defined below) which allow you to introduce different careers. For example, fibre optics, which rely on TIR, could be linked to communications and telecoms engineering, endoscopes (the viewing devices used for internal examination of the human body and 'keyhole surgery') can be linked to healthcare careers such as surgeon and medical physicist, and the refraction of light in gemstones could be linked to jewellery makers.

KEY ACTIVITIES

Students should explore the relationship between the angle of incidence and the angle of refraction using a glass block. Students often find this practical quite tricky, so it is worth demonstrating the method that they should use first.

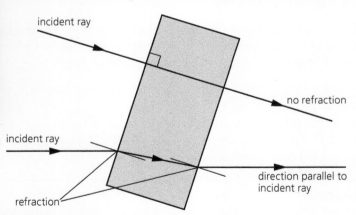

Figure 7.6 A glass block used to show refraction

Students could also explore the refraction of light using a semi-circular block. This will allow them to observe total internal reflection. When light meets an interface with a less optically dense medium, if the angle of incidence is greater than a certain critical value it will be reflected: a phenomenon referred to as 'total internal reflection' (TIR) (see Figure 7.7).

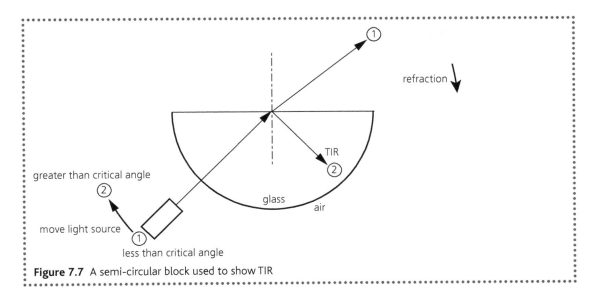

Figure 7.7 A semi-circular block used to show TIR

Seeing light – eye and camera

The eye is often compared to a camera, but many students may not have experienced a shutter camera, and only be familiar with a digital phone camera. Thus they may not easily be able to compare the features of the eye with those of a camera, and so if you can provide an example of an 'old fashioned' camera with a shutter, aperture and lens that would help the comparison. This is an opportunity for the students to evaluate models, for example by comparing the path of rays within a large-scale model of an eye made from a round-bottomed flask, or those within a pinhole camera.

Colour

A prism produces a spectrum from white light (see Figure 7.8). This is a tricky demonstration to set up (see Resources at the end of this chapter). It is best done in a darkened room using a strong source such as a slide projector or a compact light source. A second prism can be used to repeat Newton's experiment to recombine the spectrum to give white light. This is important because it shows the prism is not adding the colour to the light. Ask students to record the sequence of colours, from the least refracted (red) to the most (violet). This difference of refraction for different colours is called dispersion.

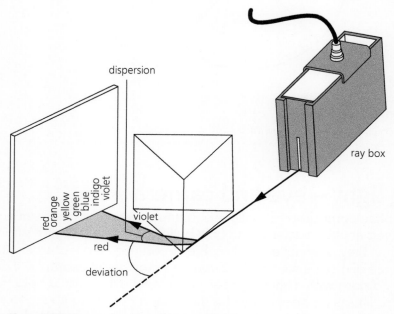

Figure 7.8 Using a prism to produce a spectrum

Students will probably have studied colour mixing using paints when they were younger. This can be a source of confusion because the primary colours for paints (blue, red and yellow) and for light (red, green and blue) are not the same. This is because when we mix light we're combining waves of different frequencies. However, for paint, when we look at a mixture of colours the pigments are absorbing colours from the incident light. So, an object which is painted red is absorbing all of the light apart from the red light – so it looks red (see Resources at the end of this chapter).

It is the interaction of white light with materials that causes us to see particular colours. Coloured opaque objects reflect the colours we see and absorb the rest of the spectrum. Coloured transparent and translucent materials transmit the visible colour and absorb the rest. Some substances produce unusual colour effects. Dyes such as fluorescein or eosin reflect some colours and absorb and then re-emit others (this is fluorescence).

Students can investigate the mixing of coloured lights produced by the filters, using either ray boxes or torches. They will need to record their findings carefully if any pattern is to emerge. Most filters allow through a range of colours, so results may be unconvincing, and this is a good opportunity to discuss how 'real life' is often more complicated than our initial explanation. Filter suppliers often provide details of the transmission characteristics, which students may find interesting.

Most students find the mixing of coloured lights and filters confusing. The effects we see are caused by the fact that we have three colour receptors in the eye. You could start with an explanation of how the eye sees colour. Human colour vision is provided by the cone cells in the retina. These come in three types which respond to red, green and blue. The cone cells need a higher level of illumination than the retinal rod cells, which distinguish black and white. This is why we can only see in shades of grey when there is very little light. Not everyone sees colours the same; most noticeably, some people are said to be 'colour blind' but this would be more accurately termed 'colour deficient'. Students are often fascinated by colour blindness charts (Ishihara tests). Other animals have different colour vision. For example, some birds have four colour receptors.

The red receptors respond to red light and also to orange and yellow. Similarly, the green receptors respond to green and to a lesser extent to yellow and blue. It follows that we can make the other colours by combining different amounts of red, green and blue light, since that is how our eyes see colours. This is why the three primary colours of light are red, green and blue. The secondary colours are cyan (blue and green), magenta (red and blue) and yellow (red and green). Students can investigate the apparent colour of objects, in daylight and artificial light (such as checking the colour of clothes when buying in shops), and the appearance of cars under streetlights. It is worth providing matt silver and white objects, which will reflect all light diffusely and not produce images.

Careers

Careers that require an understanding of colour mixing include theatre set designer, architectural lighting designer and visual artist.

7.3 Comparing waves

Having studied sound and light, students are now in a position to be able to use the big idea of waves as a unifying concept that will allow them to compare and contrast different types of waves. It is also useful to introduce other examples of waves, including water waves and seismic waves.

> ### Science in context
>
> Although water waves can be described as transverse waves, this is a simplified view of them, and they are actually surface waves – a mixture of longitudinal and transverse waves.

> ### Science in context
>
> The work of Hertha Ayrton on water waves at the seashore is a good example of research developing an understanding of one physical phenomenon and the subsequent beneficial applications. Ayrton was a British engineer, mathematician, physicist, inventor and suffragette, and her work in the early 1900s helped model mathematically the ripples left in sand by waves. This understanding subsequently led to techniques to remove poisonous gases from the trenches in World War I. Ayrton worked in many fields and her work on what was known at the time as the 'electric arc lamp', was the precursor to what is now known as the field of plasma physics.

Mechanical waves (sound, seismic and water waves) travel through a medium, while electromagnetic waves travel through a vacuum. It is important to distinguish between the regularity of wave motion and the idea of a wave pulse (see Resources at the end of this chapter). Students need to understand that while energy is transferred by a wave, the medium of transfer is not permanently changed. Waves travel across the sea, but the water remains where it was once the wave has passed. This works in a similar way to when a 'Mexican wave' passes round a sports stadium – the people making the wave do not have to do anything but stand up and sit back down again. In other words, the people move vertically in their seats while the wave moves horizontally around the stadium. This is because waves transfer energy and not mass. Waves also transfer information from one place to another, a useful property that we use extensively in communication and also in space science.

Modelling waves

A 'jelly baby wave machine' demonstrates transverse waves (see Resources). This simple model allows you to show the direction of motion of a transverse wave and the motion of the 'particles' in the medium. The model can be used to identify many properties of waves: amplitude, frequency, speed, reflection and refraction. For example, by removing every other jelly baby after a certain point and noting the difference in movement, pupils can see a model of how waves change at the boundary between materials of different density.

A slinky spring can be used to model a longitudinal wave moving through the air (see Figure 7.9). Small volumes of air are represented by the loops of the spring. Pulse movement can be seen easily with a slinky spring, but the movement of an individual loop is harder to follow. This is because the oscillations are parallel to the direction of travel of the wave.

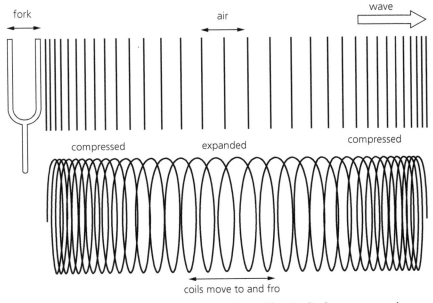

Figure 7.9 Sound waves compared with a mechanical longitudinal wave on a spring

An animation of longitudinal waves is useful here, as are oscilloscope traces produced by sound waves (see Section 7.1, page 195). The oscilloscope plots a graph of voltage against time. The voltage is proportional to the displacement of the air by the sound vibration. So the y-axis represents the displacement of the sound wave. If the time base is set so that a fixed trace is obtained, then the frequency can be calculated. In Figure 7.10, the frequency, f, is two oscillations per second or 2 Hz. Note that Figure 7.10 is a graph of how the displacement of a particular point in the medium changes with *time*. This is what makes a longitudinal sound wave produce a graph showing a transverse variation.

timebase setting = 0.2 s/division

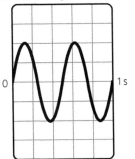

2 waves occupy 5 divisions = 1 s

Figure 7.10 Working out the frequency of a wave from an oscilloscope trace

209

You may need to remind students about the slink-o-scope to ensure that they remember that sound waves are longitudinal.

Transverse waves can also be modelled using ropes by moving one end of the rope up and down to produce transverse pulses. If students keep hold of the rope at both ends, they can observe how the pulse is reflected back. Producing a stream of pulses will develop a stationary pattern, called a standing wave. This shows the main features of a wave. A transverse wave has crests and troughs (see Figure 7.11). The distance from a point on one crest to the same point on the next is the wavelength, λ. A larger flick increases the height or amplitude, a, of the pulse – this is associated with more energy. The rate at which the pulses are generated is the frequency, f; if the frequency is increased then the wavelength decreases (assuming that the wave speed remains constant).

Points to stress:

→ Amplitude, a, is measured from the centre line, not from crest to trough.
→ Wavelength, λ (Greek letter lambda), is the length of one complete wave, measured between, for example, one crest and the next.
→ Frequency, f, depends on how fast the source is oscillating. It is the number of oscillations per second. This is not to be confused with wave speed.
→ Wave speed, v, depends on the medium the wave is travelling through. This cannot be changed by changing the frequency of the source.

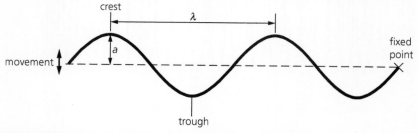

Figure 7.11 Defining amplitude and wavelength of a transverse wave

Properties of waves

The ripple tank is a useful device for showing a range of wave properties (Figure 7.12), although it can be challenging to ensure students see what you are expecting them to observe (see Resources at the end of this chapter). A shallow tank of water is made to ripple with a dipper to produce circular wavefronts or with a bar to produce straight wavefronts. The direction of travel is perpendicular to the wavefront and can be studied from the projected images of the ripples. Students will see a pattern of light and dark lines which are produced by the troughs and crests of the water waves. Single pulses or continuous waves can be produced. In the shallow water of a ripple tank, the water waves can be assumed to consist only of transverse waves. It is useful to demonstrate to students how to use a ripple tank to measure the frequency, wavelength and speed of waves. If possible, students should also try the activity for themselves, perhaps taking measurements of wavelength and frequency from a ripple tank that you have already set up.

 Technology use

If you do not have access to a ripple tank, then there are a number of online simulations that show the same properties, and that can also be used to allow students to 'take measurements' (see Resources at the end of this chapter).

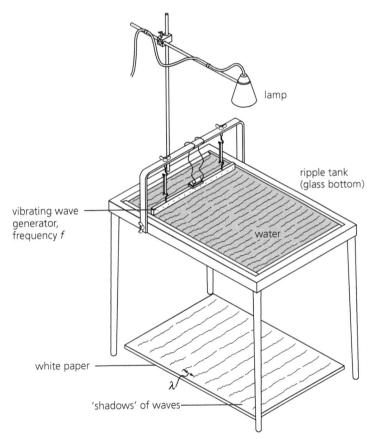

Figure 7.12 One arrangement for showing waves with a ripple tank

Ripple tanks can be used to show reflection and refraction (see Figure 7.13). As you demonstrate these properties using the ripple tank, it is important to remind students that all waves show the same properties as water waves.

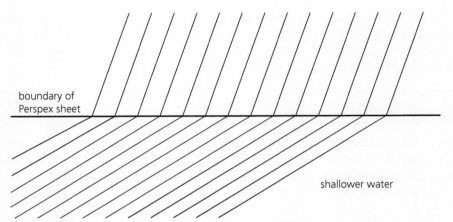

Figure 7.13 Refraction of waves on entering shallower water

7.4 Describing waves

The wave equation

A ripple tank can also be used to demonstrate the important relationship between the wavelength, frequency and speed of a wave, v. Arrange for a straight dipper to produce ripples at a fixed frequency, f. This will be seen to produce equally spaced ripples across the tank Figure 7.12. The distance between the ripples is the wavelength, λ. These move away from the source at a wave speed, v. These quantities could be measured to show that:

$$\text{speed of wave (m/s)} = \text{frequency (/s)} \times \text{wavelength (m)}$$

$$v \text{ (m/s)} = f \text{ (/s)} \times \lambda \text{ (m)}$$

This is sometimes called the wave equation.

The analogy of a runner could be used to explain this idea to students. If the runner takes a fixed length stride, then their speed is the stride length multiplied by the frequency of the strides.

Once students have been introduced to the wave equation, they should be given opportunity to apply the equation to a variety of different situations and waves.

Energy and waves

One of the strengths of the wave model is that it allows us to describe how energy is transferred between objects, or from place to place. This links back to the source–medium–receiver model introduced earlier (see Section 7.1, page 194). When talking about waves, however, it is worth stressing to students that a useful quantity to consider is power, the rate at which energy is transferred. For example, when buying a lightbulb or a set of loudspeakers, it is the power output that will guide your choice.

7.5 Applications of refraction

Refractive index and lenses

Using lenses provides the opportunity to extend students' confidence with the ray model and using ray diagrams to predict the position and nature of images. You should let students handle lenses to distinguish converging lenses from diverging lenses. Converging (convex) lenses are thicker in the centre; they make parallel rays converge. Diverging (concave) lenses are thinner in the middle; they make parallel rays diverge. Students will be familiar with using a magnifying glass, but may not have used a convex lens to produce a real image. You could ask them to produce an image of a window, or filament lamp, on the wall or a screen.

Convergence and divergence of rays can be shown using a ray box and *cylindrically* curved lenses (in contrast to the normal ones which have *spherically* curved faces). It is unlikely that students will be able to see where the light travels through the lens, but they should draw the directions of the rays up to and beyond the lenses. The strength of a lens, its power (measured in dioptres, D), is related to the curvature of the lens surface. It is inversely proportional to the focal length. This is the distance from the lens that a parallel beam of light comes to a focus (Figure 7.14). Students should find the focus of different strength lenses with a ray box and then with spherical lenses and a distant light source. They should represent their observations with a simple ray diagram like Figure 7.14.

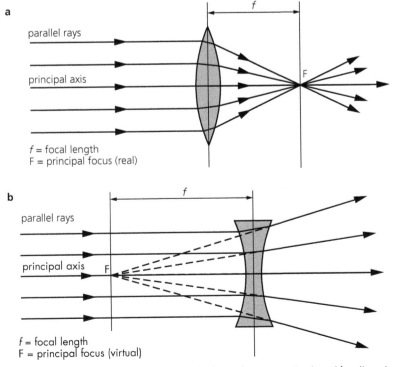

Figure 7.14 Defining the focal length of a lens: a) a converging lens; b) a diverging lens

A model eye can be used to show the effect of spectacle lenses in producing focused images. When a person is long sighted, the eye lens is not strong enough to produce a focused image on the retina, so an additional lens is used. This adds to the convergence. If someone is short sighted, the lens is too strong for the eyeball, so this is corrected with a diverging lens. Check in advance that you have selected the best lenses for this demonstration; those supplied with some kits may not be the best for showing the effects.

You can extend students' understanding of lenses by building a simple telescope using a pair of lenses suitably spaced along a metre rule (Figure 7.15). A relatively weak converging lens acts as the objective lens (focal length about 50 cm, power +2 dioptres, D), with a stronger eyepiece lens with a focal length of about 10 cm (+10 D). Students may need help to see the image. When they do see it, there is a good sense of achievement (see Resources at the end of this chapter).

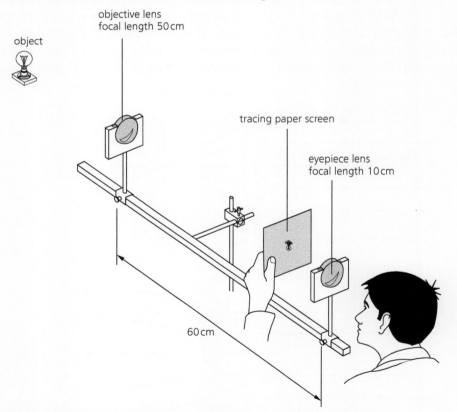

Figure 7.15 A simple telescope; remove the screen to see the final image

Careers

The lenses topic provides the opportunity for discussion of careers that deal with correcting vision including optometrist, dispensing optician and ophthalmologist.

Seismic waves and the structure of the Earth

Disturbances in the Earth's surface are transmitted through the body of the Earth as seismic waves. There are two main types of seismic waves, primary (P-waves) which are longitudinal and secondary (S-waves) which are transverse. P-waves are longitudinal as a result of compression. They can travel through solids and liquids. S-waves are transverse, caused by sideways or shear forces, and so cannot travel through liquids (it might be worth reminding students that water waves travel on the surface). To help your students remember which is which, you can describe P-waves as 'push–pull' and S-waves as 'sideways' waves. S-waves travel more slowly than P-waves. The waves are detected by seismometers situated around the world. The time it takes for the waves to reach the seismometers allows the calculation of the distance away of the earthquake. Measurements from three seismometers are triangulated to locate the source of an earthquake.

Seismic waves are used to find out about the internal structure of the Earth; you could compare this to the ultrasound observation of a developing fetus. Seismic waves are partly reflected and partly refracted at the boundaries between different rocks. The P-waves and S-waves behave differently at the boundary of the Earth's molten core, since S-waves cannot travel through a liquid. This leads to the formation of shadow zones at the surface where no waves are detected.

Careers

The topic of seismic waves and the behaviour of waves through the Earth highlights a range of careers including structural engineer, seismologist, geophysicist, geotechnical engineer and ground investigation engineer.

7.6 The electromagnetic spectrum
The changing understanding of light

Our understanding of the nature of light has changed many times as experimental evidence has suggested different theoretical understandings of the properties observed. The ancient Greeks thought of light as a stream of particles, and this was the prevailing model for many centuries. In the late 17th century, there were a number of competing theories that modelled light as a wave or as a particle. Eventually, in 1803 Thomas Young presented evidence that light was a wave by showing interference of light using a double-slit experiment. Although this model explained many of the properties of light, it could not explain something called the photoelectric effect. This led Albert Einstein to propose in 1905 that some observations of light were best explained if light behaved as discrete particles (called photons).

Today we use a wave model for light of a transverse wave of oscillating electric and magnetic fields, or a particle model of photons, whichever model is appropriate. The nature of light can be challenging for students to understand, and they may find it comforting to know that different models were developed and improved over time. It also helps students to develop an insight into the nature of science. Through a combination of observation, experimentation and theory, our understanding of light has developed through time. At this stage in their education, we would not expect students to fully understand light behaving as both a particle and a wave, or indeed what exactly we mean when we talk about oscillating electric and magnetic fields. However, we can expect them to understand the development of different models of light being used to explain phenomena such as reflection and refraction.

Uses of electromagnetic (EM) waves

Students will have met some of the electromagnetic spectrum but they may not realise that light, gamma waves and infrared radiation are all forms of the same type of wave. Students may consider that infrared is a form of 'heat' rather than a wave, and might also think that radio waves are sound waves. Care will need to be taken to emphasise that the difference between the waves is their frequency, rather than their nature.

Careers

The uses of EM waves provide a good opportunity to highlight a range of careers to students, because each type of EM wave has a variety of uses in different industries and professional roles.

Ultraviolet, X-rays and gamma rays

Use an ultraviolet (UV) lamp to illuminate a range of objects including fluorescent rocks and white cotton. However, remember that ultraviolet radiation (UVR) is hazardous. Excessive exposure to UVR of any wavelength increases the risk of skin cancer. The shorter wavelengths UVB and UVC are more hazardous in this respect and also cause damage to the eyes. Use a screen around the UV lamp, so that students are not exposed to its direct rays (see Resources at the end of this chapter). The light from a UV lamp is likely to be visible as it also emits visible violet light; true ultraviolet is invisible. Fluorescence occurs when a high energy UV photon is absorbed by an atom and a lower energy photon is re-emitted in the visible range. Most detergents contain fluorescers, called 'optical brighteners'. When washed clothes are illuminated by white light, some UV radiation is absorbed and then re-emitted as visible light, causing the 'whiter-than-white' effect beloved of advertisers. Students may have experienced UV lighting at discos and theatre performances and will enjoy fluorescence effects, if blackout can be provided.

All UV radiation may cause skin cancer and short wavelengths may cause eye damage. UV causes chemical changes in the skin resulting in the release of melanin, which gives us a suntan, a natural sunscreen. UV also causes production of vitamin D, so there are some benefits of exposure to sunlight. Students should be able to weigh up the benefits and risks of sunbathing and could look at the effectiveness of the campaigns to reduce sunburn, and therefore cases of skin cancer. You could provide students with UV-sensitive beads that will allow them to experimentally test the effectiveness of different types of suntan lotion.

X-rays were discovered in 1895. The benefits and risks of medical X-rays can be considered or a comparison of X-rays and ultrasound scans can be made. Other uses include scanning luggage at airports. If you have some X-ray radiographs, you could pass these around and explain that this radiation passes through the soft tissues, but not the bones, so can make shadow pictures. Students may know that X-rays are more dangerous than UV.

Gamma rays are emitted by radioactive materials but are otherwise the same as X-rays; they occupy the same region of the electromagnetic spectrum. We cannot say (as some textbooks do) that gamma rays have higher frequencies than X-rays. In fact, the ranges overlap. The distinction between them is in how they are produced. Gamma rays come from radioactive sources, while X-rays are produced by charged particles as they decelerate, for example electrons in an X-ray machine.

You could use a radioactive source and a Geiger counter to demonstrate gamma rays (see Chapter 6 Atomic physics, Section 6.2, page 179). Point out the safety precautions that you are using because gamma rays are dangerous. Schools in England, Wales and Northern Ireland using radioactive sources should follow the guidance in CLEAPSS guide L93. Schools in Scotland should follow the guidance from SSERC (see Resources). When classes include students under the age of 16, work with radioactive sources is confined to teacher demonstrations.

This could be a good time to introduce the idea that electromagnetic radiation can be modelled as packets of energy (called photons) and that the energy of a photon increases from infrared radiation through red to violet, UV, X-rays and gamma rays. Photons of UV, X-rays and gamma rays have enough energy to ionise (remove electrons from) atoms of air and living tissue; these ionising radiations damage or kill living cells. This can cause cancer, skin cancer in the case of UV which is not as penetrating as X-rays and gamma rays.

Careers

Careers in healthcare are an obvious discussion point when teaching about gamma, X-rays and UV radiation. Radiographers will frequently use X-rays to diagnose medical issues, and radiotherapists will use high frequency X-rays to treat patients with cancers. However, you could also discuss careers related to production of suntan lotion: formulation chemists and process engineers.

Infrared (IR) radiation

Our skin can detect infrared radiation; it feels warm or hot. When IR radiation falls on matter, the matter absorbs the energy and its temperature increases. Warm objects give out radiation that depends on their temperature and this is made use of in a thermal camera, which detects IR and produces a visible image. Some digital cameras (including those on mobile phones) can pick up the IR signals from TV remote controls, so you can look at the flashing signal when the channel is changed.

 Technology use

You could use a prism to split white light into colours (see Figure 7.8) and use a thermometer to demonstrate the existence of infrared radiation beyond the visible spectrum (see Resources at the end of this chapter).

Infrared (or visible light) is used for communications, for example in optical fibre internet cables. The IR is amplitude modulated by the electrical signal from the modem. This varying IR beam then travels along optical fibre, with very little loss of power. The light is totally internally reflected in the very thin optical glass fibres. The signals are digital, so they are easily cleaned up to remove noise, before being transformed into an electrical signal at the receiving computer.

The optical fibres are bundled together to give a high message-carrying capacity. The advantages of optical fibres are the increased information-carrying capacity, increased security from interference and reduced size and cost compared with copper wire. In addition, the signals are carried in digital form and can travel further without requiring amplification and noise reduction, resulting in greater cost savings.

Careers

Infrared provides the opportunity to highlight careers in telecommunications: infrastructure developers, communications engineers, electrical engineers and network repair technicians. You could also identify the use of IR cameras in careers in which visibility is limited, including the security services and emergency rescue crews.

Microwaves and radio waves

Students will know that microwaves can be used to heat food, they may know that the radiation makes water molecules vibrate and so the food heats up. Bluetooth® communications also use the same frequency microwaves, but at a very low intensity. You can show this: if one Bluetooth device (such as a phone) is inside a microwave oven, it cannot communicate with another device outside, because the metal mesh in the door blocks the microwaves. Do not switch the oven on! Other mobile phones use microwaves of a slightly different frequency and can still communicate if one is inside the oven. Microwaves are used extensively for communication, including wireless internet and satellite communication. The microwaves are used because they can pass through the ionosphere (a layer of charged particles in the atmosphere that reflects radio waves). They need a line of sight (clear path between the transmitter and receiver), unlike radio waves, which is why so many transmitting/receiving towers are needed.

Radio waves have longer wavelengths/lower frequencies than microwaves, are not readily absorbed and therefore have little effect on matter. It is important for students to realise that radio waves are electromagnetic waves, *not sound* waves. They are used to carry information about the sound and pictures for TV, and this information is decoded by the receiver.

Careers

Microwaves provide the opportunity to highlight careers in the space industry, which isn't just limited to astronauts and satellite designers but includes those who use the information gathered by satellites. Roles include software engineers, spacecraft controllers, astrodynamics engineers, mechanical engineers, satellite assembly technicians and space propulsion engineers.

7.7 Resources

Online resources

Please go to **spark.iop.org/asebook** for a set of curated resources from the IOP Spark website to match this chapter.

AAAS project 2061: http://assessment.aaas.org

BEST: www.stem.org.uk

CLEAPSS guidance document GL127 on use of UV: www.cleapss.org.uk

Institute of Physics IOPSpark: https://spark.iop.org

National Careers Service Job profiles: https://nationalcareers.service.gov.uk

NHS careers: www.healthcareers.nhs.uk

PhET: https://phet.colorado.edu

RNIB teaching science to students with vision impairment: www.rnib.org.uk

STEM's 'Pepper's ghost' trick and 'Sounds Good' activities: www.stem.org.uk

Simulations

Falstad ripple tank: www.falstad.com

Jelly baby wave machine: www.youtube.com

PhET simulations 'Wave Interference' and 'Wave on a String': https://phet.colorado.edu

Slink-o-scope - details on the Institute of Physics IOPSpark webpages and on YouTube

Using a prism to show infrared radiation: www.youtube.com

All other simulations: https://spark.iop.org

References

Ceuppens, S., Deprez, J., Dehaene, W. and De Cock, M. (2018) Tackling misconceptions in geometrical optics. *Physics Education*, 53 (4), 045020.

Osborne, J., Black, P., Smith, M. and Meadows, J. (1990) *Primary SPACE Project Research Report: Light*. Liverpool: Liverpool University Press.

Whalley, M. (2003) My way: using students to model sound. *Physics Education*, 38 (1), 56–57.

Further reading

Auty, G. (2017) The ripple tank: management and observation. *School Science Review*, 98 (364), 65–75.

Zubairy, M. S. (2016) A very brief history of light. In Al-Amri M., El-Gomati M. and Zubairy M. (eds) *Optics in Our Time*. Cham: Springer.

8 Earth in space

Stuart Farmer and Judith Hillier

Introduction

The topic of the Earth in space is the part of the curriculum in which students are likely to be quite interested and enthusiastic. Many will have seen films or TV programmes about space exploration, and some students may be quite knowledgeable about certain aspects. The challenge as a teacher is to nurture and foster this enthusiasm while making sure that they also have a good understanding of the basic concepts about how our Solar System works, and its place in the Universe. As a topic, it offers scope for creativity, and you may well want to explore the possibility of hosting an Astronomy Club, and your school may even wish to offer astronomy as an examination course (see Resources, Roche *et al.*, 2012a, 2012b to support this). Remember that many students have done projects, posters and models about the Solar System throughout primary school, and we would encourage you to focus on developing the depth of students' explanations for these key phenomena, as well as capturing their interest. This will require students to develop mental models of the different celestial bodies and how they move relative to each other: this means that it is a good idea to utilise a range of models, including diagrams, simulations and physical models in the classroom, to help develop their understanding of the sizes and distances involved.

A teaching sequence

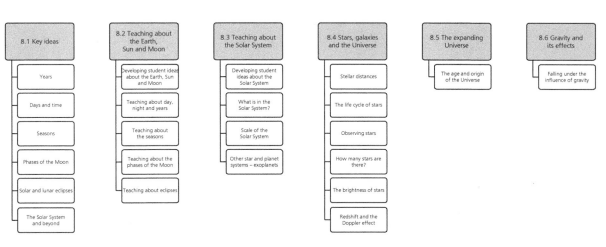

Prior experiences

Before considering how to develop ideas in this topic, it is worth spending some time ensuring that students' understanding of the ideas listed in the 'key ideas' section below is secure. Make sure that you are comfortable with the explanations for them, together with some background information that is likely to be useful when teaching enthusiastic and inquisitive students. Having a question box available in class where students can put any questions they have can be a useful way of gathering their queries and giving you enough time to research the answers.

Astronomers have been observing the stars for centuries and have developed a detailed understanding of how far away stars are and the life cycle of stars. They have also developed models of the Universe that indicate its size, shape, how it started and how it is currently changing. These models use Newton's laws of motion, gravitational attraction and circular motion, as well as special and general relativity. These will be discussed in more detail later.

Throughout this section there are illustrative figures. Due to the very large 'astronomical' distances involved it is impossible to draw all aspects illustrated in any diagram to scale. The use of all such diagrams should be considered with care and with attention drawn to what key aspect any diagram illustrates well, but also when necessary addressing any misconceptions that might unintentionally be introduced.

 ## 8.1 Key Ideas

Years

A year is the time it takes the Earth to make a complete orbit of the Sun. The Earth goes around, or orbits, the Sun in a large elliptical (oval) orbit at an average distance of 150 million km from the Sun. It takes the Earth approximately 365¼ days to orbit the Sun, and it takes light 8 minutes to travel from the Sun to Earth.

> **Science in context**
>
> Since 47 BCE, most of Europe has followed the Julian calendar (introduced by Julius Caesar) where there are 365 days in a year, with every 4th year being a leap year of 366 days. However, this is not quite accurate and so in 1582, Pope Gregory XIII decreed that the last year of a century would only be a leap year if it was divisible by 400; so the year 2000 was a leap year, but the year 2100 will only have 365 days.

Days and time

The Earth also rotates, or spins, on its axis, taking 24 hours to make one full rotation relative to the Sun: this is called a solar day. When we are on the side of the Earth facing the Sun, we experience daytime and when we are facing away from the Sun, we experience night-time. A solar day has been divided into 24 hours since the time of both the ancient Egyptians and the ancient Chinese. The ancient Babylonians divided hours and minutes into 60, and also divided a circle into 360°. The Earth spins 360° in one day, turning 15° in one hour.

Science in context

Historically, local solar time was calculated using a sundial or a sextant, which relies on the Sun being at its highest point in the sky at midday. However, with the industrial revolution and the growth of national transport and communication systems, local solar time became problematic. Greenwich Mean Time was made the legal time in the UK in 1880, and in 1884, the International Meridian Conference adopted Greenwich as the Prime Meridian from which to calculate longitude. Over the next 50 years, different countries have gradually adopted standard hourly time zones, using an offset from Greenwich.

Seasons

Contrary to popular belief, the Earth is not closer to the Sun in summer and further away in winter. The Earth, and all the other planets, orbit the Sun in the same plane, and the Earth is tilted relative to that plane, at an angle of about 23°. This tilt stays the same throughout the year, so that when it is winter in the northern hemisphere, the Earth is in the part of its orbit where the North Pole is tilted away from the Sun and the South Pole is tilted towards the Sun. When it is summer in the northern hemisphere, the Earth has moved round to the part of its orbit where the North Pole is tilted towards the Sun and the South Pole is tilted away from the Sun. The effects of this are threefold: at different times of the year, the Sun appears to be at different heights in the sky, being much higher in summer than in winter. In the northern hemisphere, sunrise and sunset are both further north on the horizon in summer than they are in winter, and consequently, the daytime is longer in summer. In winter, the sunlight is spread out over a wider area, resulting in colder temperatures, whereas it is hotter in summer because the sunlight is more concentrated.

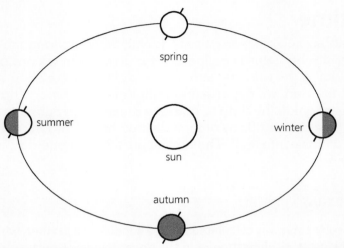

Figure 8.1 Seasons in the northern hemisphere. Day and night are also shown, with only the day side of the Earth visible in the spring position, and night visible in autumn.

Phases of the Moon

The Moon goes around, or orbits, the Earth once every 28 days, which is a lunar month. During this time, it also slowly rotates, or spins, on its axis; as a result the same side of the Moon is always facing the Earth. We have only seen the other side of the Moon via spacecraft. The orbit of the Moon is not in the same plane as the Earth's orbit of the Sun, but is tilted by about 5°. The Moon does not give out light (it is not a source of light), but reflects sunlight. At any one time, approximately half the Moon is in sunlight, and half is in darkness. Because the Moon is orbiting the Earth, the amount of the sunlit half which is visible from Earth changes: sometimes we can see all the half of the Moon which is in sunlight (Full Moon); sometimes we can only see half of the sunlit half (First or Third Quarter); sometimes we are looking at the dark half of the Moon (New Moon). Figure 8.2 shows the Moon as it orbits the Earth, and Table 8.1 shows the phases of the Moon as seen from the Earth.

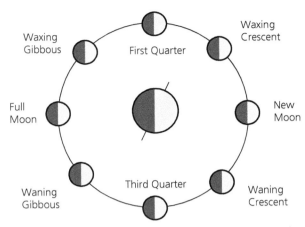

Figure 8.2 Phases of the Moon, showing the Moon as it orbits around the Earth

Table 8.1 Phases of the Moon as seen from Earth

Moon phase	New Moon	Waxing crescent	First quarter	Waxing gibbous	Full Moon	Waning gibbous	Third quarter	Waning crescent
Appearance from Earth	●	◗	◐	◖	○	◖	◐	◗

Solar and lunar eclipses

Eclipses happen when the orbits of the Earth and Moon line up, so that either the Moon blocks the sunlight from reaching the Earth (solar eclipse, see Figure 8.3), or the Earth blocks the sunlight from reaching the Moon (lunar eclipse, see Figure 8.4). We can predict eclipses and the phases of the Moon by calculating the future orbits of the Moon and Earth.

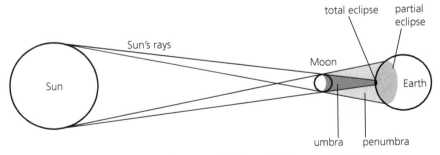

Figure 8.3 A solar eclipse where the Moon blocks sunlight from reaching Earth

Figure 8.4 A lunar eclipse where the Earth blocks sunlight from reaching the Moon

The Solar System and beyond

The Earth is one of a number of objects that orbit the Sun, along with planets and their moons, asteroids, comets and dwarf planets. All of these make up the Solar System, which is about 4.5 billion years old, and is in the outer spiral arm of the Milky Way Galaxy.

The Milky Way contains about 100 billion stars, held together by gravity, in a spiral-shaped disc. The stars in the galaxy are orbiting the centre of the galaxy, and one orbit takes about 250 million years. The Solar System is about 25 000 light years from the black hole which is at the centre of the galaxy.

Science in context

The Hubble Space Telescope and other telescopes have observed lots of other galaxies in the Universe – there may be 100 billion, each with billions of stars. Some galaxies are spiral shaped, others are ovals and some look more like blobs.

It is easy to find multiple online sources that provide a range of information about the objects in the Solar System: size, shape, distance from the Sun, age and what they are made of, for example. As well as using these to allow students to collate, refine and check their own data, you can use multiple sources to explore how accurately we know some of this information. In addition to factual data about objects in the Solar System, it is worth spending some time with simulations modelling the motion of objects in the Solar System. This allows students to develop an understanding the 3-D dynamic nature of the Solar System (and the distances and sizes involved) which is not an easy thing to grasp and takes time. It is also worth finding out about the thousands of artificial satellites or robotic spacecraft that have been launched, as well as the many people who have been involved directly or indirectly in space exploration since the satellite Sputnik became the first artificial object to orbit the Earth in 1957.

Science in context

Voyager 1 was launched in 1977, reached Jupiter in 1979, Saturn in 1980 and in 2012 was the first spacecraft to reach interstellar space, well beyond the edges of the Solar System.

8.2 Teaching about the Earth, Sun and Moon

Students should learn how the Earth, Sun and Moon move relative to each other in time and space. Observations, models and simulations are highly recommended tools in your teaching of this topic.

Prior experiences

Students will have been familiar with the concepts of day and night, days, years, the Sun and the Moon since babyhood. They will have listened to stories, sung songs, and watched TV programmes and films about all of these throughout their childhood, but they may find it difficult to articulate explanations for these phenomena in scientific language. They are also likely to have a number of misconceptions. Lelliott and Rollnick (2010) conducted a review of international research into astronomy education between 1974 and 2008, and this can be summarised as follows:

→ Day and night. Common alternative conceptions include thinking that:
  - the Sun moves around the Earth
  - the Earth orbits the Sun every day
  - day and night are there for the benefit of humans
  - night-time is when something blocks the Sun, for example, clouds or the Moon.
→ Seasons. The vast majority of students and many teachers reference the tilt of the Earth's axis in their explanation, but then evoke the distance theory that the Earth gets colder when it is further away. A lack of clarity in wording and diagrams can contribute to the confusion.
→ Phases of the Moon. Students are usually able to describe the phases of the Moon, but find it difficult to explain, often citing the Earth's shadow as the cause. 2D static diagrams in textbooks often don't help matters. Discussion of eclipses often adds further confusion.
→ Concepts of size and distance. Students often struggle with the concept of scale, sometimes being aware of the relative sizes of the planets and Sun, but usually not the distances in between.

Developing student ideas about the Sun, Earth and Moon

These concepts about day and night, years, seasons, phases of the Moon and eclipses are ones that 11–14-year-old students should be able to access and understand. We would strongly advocate starting with the concepts related to the movement of the Earth relative to the Sun (years, day and night, seasons), and, once students are secure with this, then bringing in the Moon with its phases and eclipses. They can be helped to develop this understanding through careful explanations and narratives, using models and diagrams, as well as using video and animations to actively teach these ideas. Asking students to write scripts for animations or sections of video is useful for helping them use and develop the necessary language and ideas within these concepts, as is suggesting that they write explanations for younger pupils. You may wish to develop your own models, and there are many online simulations to support the teaching and learning of this topic. It can be covered in a fairly short time, perhaps 6 or 7 hours of lesson time, and it is important to remember that students need to be able to explain each concept individually, and also to have a coherent understanding of the Earth–Moon–Sun system as a whole.

Teaching about day and night, and years

A globe of the Earth and a bright torch will be two of the most useful teaching aids for this topic, preferably shown in a room which you can easily darken with blinds. Get one student to hold the globe and another the torch, and then ask them to model the different concepts for the rest of the class. They should find it easy to spin the globe for day and night, and to walk the globe around the torch for years. You could involve the rest of the class by asking them to identify what is represented by a rotation and what is represented by one orbit. See if they understand that the globe should rotate 365 times during one orbit, and ask them about the scale of the model: How big should the Sun be if the Earth is the size of the globe, and how far away is it?

 Science literacy

It is a good idea to take the opportunity to reinforce correct usage of terminology; 'spin' is acceptable for 'rotate', and 'go round' for 'orbit', but you will find students saying 'spin round' and 'rotate round' when they actually mean 'orbit'.

Ask the students some 'What if?' questions: what would happen to day and night if the Earth stopped spinning? What would happen to the length of a year if the Earth moved faster around the Sun, or moved closer to the Sun so the orbit was shorter? You could follow this up by tasking students with writing a short explanation in their own words, accompanied by a diagram. This will give them more practice in using the appropriate terminology correctly and give you a chance to check their understanding at an individual level.

Teaching about the seasons

The reason for the seasons will be challenging for students to explain. It might be useful to take time to discuss with your students the differences they have noticed about the seasons, and try to draw out the points mentioned earlier:

→ the height of the Sun in the sky
→ the positions of sunrise and sunset
→ the number of daylight hours
→ the temperature.

Try to make sure they are aware that the seasons in northern and southern hemispheres occur at different times. Remind them what it feels like to be sat outside in the warm sunshine and then how cold it gets when a cloud covers the Sun. Then, using a globe, get them to observe a torch shining directly at the Equator, close to the globe, followed by the same torch shining on the northern hemisphere when the axis is tilted away from the Sun – spin the Earth while doing this. Point out how the same light is spread over different areas, and then repeat for the axis being tilted towards the Sun. Ask the students what they think will happen to the length of day and to the temperature in the northern hemisphere for these two different situations. You could also model this for students on the board (see Figure 8.5), and if possible, get them to draw a similar diagram on graph paper and calculate the difference in the area over which the sunlight is spread.

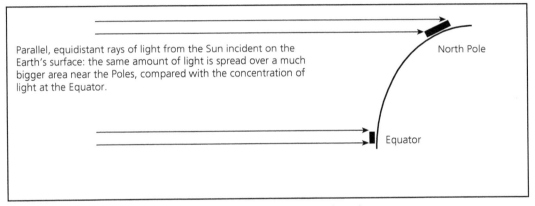

Figure 8.5 Different concentrations of sunlight at the Equator and the Poles

This idea can be demonstrated by shining a light directly at a solar cell connected to a voltmeter, and then varying the angle of incidence of the light falling on the solar cell. The key idea to stress is how the same amount of radiation (visible light and infrared) is spread out over a larger area as the angle between the rays and the surface decreases.

Challenge the students by asking why the explanation is not 'we are closer to the Sun in summer' – they should recognise that the northern and southern hemispheres have 'opposite seasons', but also use a diagram like Figure 8.1 to point out that actually Earth's orbit means that the Earth is closest to the Sun in spring and autumn. Finally, you could get the students to produce their own explanations – written in their own words, or by sorting sentences or labelling diagrams or even making a short video.

Teaching about the phases of the Moon

Once your students seem secure with the movement of the Earth and the Sun, it is time to bring in the Moon. They should have some awareness of how it seems to change shape, but will probably find it helpful if you show them what happens over the course of a month using a time lapse video. Most teachers find that it is important to model the phases of the Moon for students: use a ball which is half black and half white (painting a white ball is easiest) and ask the students to explain why only half the ball is lit up by sunlight at any one time (but remind them that it is not always the same half of the ball which is lit). Making a black paper cover for the half of the ball that is in darkness and which you can rotate around the ball may be useful but considerably more fiddly.

Again, use the ball, globe and torch to model the Earth, Moon and Sun system over the course of a month: start with a New Moon and proceed as the Moon waxes to a Full Moon and then wanes again back to a New Moon. In each case, it is important to be clear about the relative positions of the Sun, Earth and Moon, the path that the light takes and how this affects the appearance of the Moon from the Earth.

 Science literacy

You will need to decide how much terminology you want to introduce to students: crescent, first quarter and gibbous may be accessible for some students, and problematic for others.

Emphasise to the students that, although the Sun always lights up half the Moon, the amount of sunlit Moon visible from the Earth changes. We would recommend that you draw diagrams for them, both of the Moon orbiting the Earth (see Figure 8.2) and the appearance of the Moon from the Earth (see Table 8.1), and get the students to annotate a diagram or draw their own. If you live in a location where it is easy for students to see the night sky, encourage them to make some observations: let them know when the next Full Moon will occur.

Teaching about eclipses

You could start this part by posing the question: what is an eclipse? Usually someone will be able to tell you that it is when the Moon blocks out the Sun. Reply by asking if there is an eclipse every month when we have a New Moon? Hopefully they will know that this does not happen, and you will be able to explain that the orbit of the Moon is at a slight angle relative to the Earth so that usually the Moon, Earth and Sun don't line up to cause an eclipse. But every now and again, in a calculable and predictable fashion, the orbits do line up and either the Moon blocks the Sun (solar eclipse, Figure 8.3) or the Earth blocks the Sun (lunar eclipse, Figure 8.4).

 Technology use

Again, it is a good idea to draw and explain diagrams for your students, which you can then support with simulations that show the dynamic process.

You could get your students to draw their own diagrams or annotate one of yours or write an explanation in their own words. As before, you will need to judge the extent to which your students need to learn the technical vocabulary, such as umbra and penumbra.

 # 8.3 Teaching about the Solar System

Learning about the Solar System provides an opportunity to consider human exploration of space, and to try to understand something of the scale of the Universe.

Prior experiences

While students usually know the names and order of the planets, and some details about them, they are often unclear about planetary motion and the role of gravity. Frequently, there is also confusion about the location of stars relative to the planets, and how the planets are visible. Students and adults can struggle to comprehend the vast distances involved and how much emptiness there is in space. Some will be well aware of the extent to which humans have explored the Solar System, others will be surprised that humans have only walked on the Earth and the Moon. Nearly every student will be interested and engaged by this topic, so try to make the most of this enthusiasm!

Developing student ideas about the Solar System

This topic follows on naturally from learning about the Earth, Sun and Moon system and you may wish to teach the topics one after the other. However, you can teach about day and night in one year, and then, in a subsequent year, do a brief recap before moving onto the Solar System, as having a secure understanding of how one planet and its Moon orbit the Sun will make it easier to grasp how all the other planets and their moons orbit the Sun. We would recommend teaching about the Solar System before moving onto stars, galaxies and the Universe; again, developing an understanding of the size and scale of the Solar System provides a stepping stone for students to start to comprehend the sheer vastness of the Universe.

What is in the Solar System?

This question lends itself nicely to students working independently or in small groups to gather information from books and internet resources about aspects of the Solar System and then presenting it to the rest of the class as models, posters or presentations. It is helpful if you provide guidance as to the amount of detail required, and encourage them to critically evaluate the reliability of their sources, for example NASA can be considered a trustworthy source. We would recommend that you start with the names and order of the planets, then other characteristics such as whether they are rock or gaseous, how their temperature varies with distance from the Sun, and which ones have moons and rings. Developing students' awareness of the history of science is valuable for helping them to understand more about the nature of science. It also helps to move away from the view that physics was done by dead, white, middle-class men – and this is a key message that you, as a teacher of physics, need to get across to your students.

Science in context

Ancient civilisations in Asia, Central America, Europe and the Middle East observed the movements of the Sun, Moon, stars and planets (the ones visible with the naked eye), using these observations to develop clocks and calendars, and to help with navigation. They also named what they could see, so in Europe, we are mostly familiar with the Greek names for constellations.

In the Middle Ages, Islamic scholars, particularly in modern-day Iran, Iraq and Syria, became much more scientific and mathematical in their observations and calculations, refining and developing the work of the Ancient Greeks. Examples include Mariam al-Astrulabi who made highly accurate astrolabes, and Ibn al-Haytham who explained that we see because light enters our eyes and a message is sent to our brains.

It had been thought that the Earth was the centre of the Universe and everything revolved around it, but the increasingly accurate observations showed complicated, looping movements of the planets called retrograde motion. Copernicus proposed that the Sun is the centre of the Solar System, called the heliocentric model. Kepler's laws were the first to correctly describe the movements of the planets and Galileo was the first to use a telescope to make observations, discovering four of

Jupiter's moons. Newton's laws of motion and universal law of gravity helped to refine the heliocentric model of the Solar System and to predict the discovery of other planets, like Neptune.

Astronomers, such as Caroline Herschel, Henrietta Leavitt and Annie Cannon, continued to record their observations of the skies and to share their findings, helped by organisations such as the Royal Astronomical Society (founded in 1820). After World War Two, the Cold War led to the Space Race, with NASA being first to land a human on the Moon in 1969. In the last 50 years, governments and private companies around the world have launched and used a range of satellites and space probes to explore and observe our own planet, the Solar System around us, and as far out into space as we can currently see.

It is important to mention asteroids and comets, and be prepared to answer questions about Pluto and why it is now a dwarf planet (see Resources). Your students may be keen to discuss what it would be like to live on a different planet, and this could be a good opportunity to consider the force of gravitational attraction a human would experience on different objects in the Solar System (for an interactive resource for calculating this, see Resources). There is an opportunity here to link with biological work on the conditions needed for life.

Science in context

Although Venus is further from the Sun than Mercury, its atmosphere is primarily made up of carbon dioxide and this caused a 'runaway greenhouse effect' that means it now has a very high surface temperature.

This is also a valuable opportunity to bring in information about recent space exploration such as China's robotic Moon landing in 2019, the European Space Agency Rosetta probe, which landed on a comet in 2014, and NASA's series of robotic missions to Mars.

Scale of the Solar System

You will probably need to use a range of methods to help your students start to understand how big celestial bodies are and how far apart they are, and develop feelings of awe and wonder at the incredible Universe in which we live. Students will find the large numbers difficult to comprehend, and will also struggle to accept that most of space is just that: cold, empty space. It is impossible to represent everything to scale accurately simultaneously – you will need to use different scales for different sets of objects, and this is modelled explicitly for you below. There is a video on the Harvard website (see Resources), or you can use the information to form a quiz in which you present students with the sizes in the right-hand column, and ask them to match these to the distances in the left-hand column.

> ### 🖳 Technology use
>
> You can also show students some of the excellent simulations to reinforce the size of the distances which are involved and demonstrate how they relate to one another. Being able to manually zoom in and out from the human scale, as well as slowly zooming out from a common size such as a human being or 1 m (use the classic Eames Powers of Ten video), can help students develop a feel for the enormous distances involved. Developing from metres and kilometres to much longer distances, the idea of measuring distances in 'light time' will be needed, building up from light seconds to light years and beyond, for example, (see Resources).

It can be helpful to also ask students to make a model themselves using appropriately sized drawings. You can calculate the scaled sizes and distances yourself, or use an online resource to do it for you. Be warned: you will need a lot of space as a 10 cm Sun is orbited by a 3.2 mm Neptune 425 m away!

The information below can be used as a thought exercise to help students to grasp the scale of the Solar System. Start off by asking them to imagine that the Earth was 5 cm across. If the Earth was 5 cm across ...

Moon size	1.3 cm
Earth–Moon distance	150 cm – stretch your arms out wide
Sun size	5 m – imagine a yellow ball the size of a minivan
Earth–Sun distance	550 m – about six football fields apart
Light travel time	Light travels through space at a constant speed of 300 000 km/s. At this scale, where the Earth is 5 cm across, we've shrunk 300 000 km down to about 1 m. It takes a beam of light a little more than one second to travel from the Moon to the Earth.

Now ask them to zoom out so that the Sun is now 5 cm across. If the Sun was 5 cm across ...

Earth size	A grain of salt, with a dust-speck Moon 2.5 cm away from it
Sun–Earth distance	5.5 m – or ten paces away
Pluto's orbit	2.5 football fields away from the 5 cm Sun
Nearest star to Sun	1500 km
Light travel time	It takes 8 minutes for a beam of light to travel from the Sun to the Earth.

Finally, ask your students to imagine that the entire Solar System is 5 cm in diameter. If the entire Solar System was 5 cm in diameter…

Size of Sun	Microscopic at this scale, a shining speck at the centre
Sun–Earth distance	0.5 mm – Earth orbits very close to the centre of the Solar System
Pluto's orbit	Around the edge of the 5 cm Solar System
Nearest star to Sun	2 football fields away
Nearby star discovered to have orbiting planets	5 football fields away. Two planets have been discovered around the star Epsilon Eridani, which is visible from the southern hemisphere.
Our Milky Way galaxy	Size of Europe. At this scale, our 5 cm Solar System is part of a continent-sized system of 200 billion shining speck stars. These stars, spread 50 km high, are generally separated from each other by more than two football fields.
Light travel time	It takes about 10 h for a beam of light to cross the Solar System and years for light to travel between stars.

Source: https://chandra.harvard.edu/resources/podcasts/2inch/

Other star and planet systems – exoplanets

We now know that the Solar System is not the only star and planets system. The first observation of a planet orbiting a star other than the Sun was confirmed in 1992. Since then thousands of planets have been detected orbiting other stars.

Exoplanets are discovered using a number of methods, one of which, the transit method, can be modelled easily in a school laboratory (see Figure 8.6).

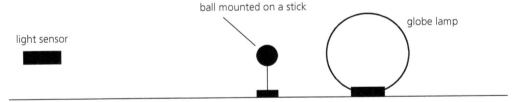

Figure 8.6 Modelling the transit method of detecting exoplanets

Here the ball represents the planet that passes between the observer, represented by the light sensor, and the star, represented by the globe lamp. When the ball is moved slowly across in front of the globe lamp, this models how the observed light level drops when the planet transits in front of the star. The duration and size of the drop in light level allows information about the diameter of the planet, its radius and period of orbit to be determined.

There are a number of activities relating to this and other ideas around exoplanets that can include collecting data from a simulated transit method (see Resources, IOP Exoplanets Activities). Other activities use real data from current research, for example, Perimeter Institute – Figuring Outer Space and Royal Observatory Edinburgh Exoplanets Activity.

235

Careers

One of the strengths of using activities like this is that we can highlight that exoplanet discovery is a current and evolving field in physics research, and one which might be a career path for someone studying physics at higher levels.

Science in context

In 2017, teams using the Spitzer Space Telescope and Very Large Telescope in Chile announced that seven exoplanets had been discovered orbiting the cool red dwarf star TRAPPIST-1, which is situated 39.6 light years from the Sun. Several of these exoplanets are situated in the habitable zone where liquid water could be found and there might be the conditions necessary for life.

8.4 Stars, galaxies and the Universe

No story about the Earth in space would be complete without some discussion of the life cycle of stars, of galaxies, the expansion of the Universe and the Big Bang. Students are fascinated by the current scientific descriptions of a vast, expanding Universe, although it is difficult to convey more than a flavour of the evidence supporting this.

Again, the story that science has to tell students is very dependent on good secondary sources of information and a good collection of images is absolutely essential.

Prior experiences

Students are likely to be familiar with the idea that the Sun is a star, similar to many others seen in the night sky. Likewise, they are likely to be familiar with the term 'Big Bang', but won't have a good scientific understanding of it, perhaps thinking of it as an explosion happening at a point in an already existing space.

Stellar distances

The distance to another star is large, very, very large indeed by human standards. Distances in the Universe are so large that we use distances measured in 'light time': how long it takes light, travelling at 300 000 km per second (emphasise not per hour), to get there. It takes light around 8 minutes to reach us from the Sun and over 4 years to get to us from the next nearest star, Proxima Centauri. Voyager 1, currently the fastest spacecraft that has left the Solar System, is travelling at around 60 000 km/h or 17 km/s. With today's technology it would take over 70 000 years to reach the next nearest star after the Sun. Launched in 1977, Voyager 1 only reached the edge of the Solar System and passed into interstellar space in 2012, 35 years later. It is, as yet, only in science fiction that warp drives are available to allow humans to travel to another star system. Our galaxy, the Milky Way, is approximately 100 000 light years across. The next nearest galaxy, Andromeda, is 2.5 million light years away.

Science in context

As the light from more distant galaxies takes longer to reach the Earth, this means that when we look at stars and galaxies further away from us, we are also looking further back in time. This gives us information about how the Universe has evolved.

π   Maths

For students who are familiar with simple calculations of speed, distance and time, you could provide the distances to some astronomical objects and ask them to calculate the time taken for light and for a spacecraft such as Voyager 1 to travel these distances. Alternatively, students could be given some distances in light time and asked to identify which astronomical objects are a specific distance away from Earth.

The distances to nearby stars can be measured by parallax (see Figure 8.7). This is what causes a nearby star's position to appear to change against the background of the other more distant stars between two times six months apart, for example, between summer and winter. As we know the distance between the two positions of the Earth, and we can measure the angle by which the star has moved, it is simple trigonometry to work out the distance to the star.

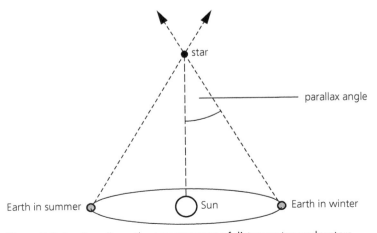

Figure 8.7 Parallax allows the measurement of distances to nearby stars

A simple illustration of parallax can be done by holding up a finger on an outstretched arm and moving your head from side to side and observing how your finger moves compared to the background. A larger scale demonstration can be undertaken outside using one student as the 'star', another student as the 'Sun' and a third as the 'Earth'. Ask the 'Earth' student to move to their summer position and note the angle between the 'star' and a distant object such as a tree. Ask the 'Earth' student to move to their winter position and measure the angle and the distant object again. A scale drawing can be used to calculate the distance from the 'Sun' and 'Earth' system to the 'star'. This can be checked by measuring on the ground and the ideas used here, based on simple geometry, can be applied to much larger distances and larger objects that we are unable to go and check but can still measure with certainty.

 Maths

The use of triangles in calculations was very important in early geometry and astronomy. For example, despite living over 200 years BC, by measuring shadows and using simple geometry, Eratosthenes was able to measure the diameter of the Earth to an accuracy of around 10% of the modern value.

When we refer to the brightness of stars, the terms 'absolute' and 'relative brightness' are often used. Absolute brightness can be used to compare all stars by how much light they give out, whereas relative brightness describes how bright they appear to us from Earth and so is affected by their distance from Earth. Measuring distances to more distant stars uses what astronomers call 'standard candles'. The observed apparent brightness of stars decreases with distance in a predictable way; when the distance doubles, the brightness goes down by a factor of four, three times further away, the brightness goes down by a factor of nine and so on, known as an inverse square relationship. Some stars, called Cepheid variables, vary in brightness cyclically with a period that is related to their absolute brightness and so, by observing these and using what we know about distance and brightness, we can work out how far away they are. In a similar way Type 1A supernovae can be used to determine the distances to even more distant stars, including those in distant galaxies.

Science in context

High quality astronomical observations and measurements can be challenging to collect. The discovery of pulsars in 1967 by Jocelyn Bell Burnell represented a significant breakthrough in the tools available to astronomers. Pulsars are rotating, highly magnetic neutron stars and their regular rotational periods helped provide information for further discoveries, such as the existence of gravitational radiation and the first extrasolar planets.

The life cycle of stars

Stars do not exist in a steady state forever. Stars form when clouds of gas and dust are attracted together due to the mutual gravitational pull of the particles. As the matter falls inwards, it speeds up and becomes hotter. Eventually, the particles are moving quickly enough to glow red hot. As the cloud of gas and dust continues to collapse, the interior reaches a high enough temperature and pressure for nuclear fusion to occur.

Many stars, such as the Sun, remain in a stable state for billions of years. The inward gravitational pull on their matter is balanced by the outward push from the radiation created by the nuclear fusion in their cores.

The stages that a particular star then passes through depend on the initial mass of the star that is formed from the cloud of gas and dust. Light stars form cool, dim stars with a long lifetime. Heavier stars are hotter, brighter, shorter lived and end their lives much more spectacularly.

Once the main hydrogen fuel source of the star is used, helium will begin to fuse into heavier elements. The interior of the star will collapse further under the force of gravity but the outer layers will expand and become cooler and redder. The star will become a red giant. This will occur to the Sun which will eventually expand so much that it will swallow up the Earth.

Science in context

Cecilia Payne-Gaposchkin was an astronomer who, in 1925 as part of her PhD thesis, suggested that the Sun was primarily composed of hydrogen and helium, and that there was a million times more hydrogen than was previously assumed. Her young age and gender may have contributed to the fact that these ideas were not originally accepted by the astronomy community and it took a long time before her significant insight and contributions were fully recognised.

Lighter stars similar in size to the Sun will lose their outer layers and the remaining core will collapse into a white dwarf, a small bright star that will gradually cool down and fade away. Stars heavier than around the equivalent of ten Suns will explode in a supernova event in which the outer layers will be blasted off. The remaining core shrinks under gravity, forming a neutron star. After the supernova, stars heavier than around 25 Suns will result in a black hole so dense that even light cannot escape from its gravitational field.

Science in context

A key figure in the development of our understanding of black holes comes from the work of Subrahmanyan Chandrasekhar, an Indian–American astrophysicist and winner of the Nobel Prize for physics. In his early work he made calculations based on the existence of an object that was unknown at the time but that was later found to be a black hole. This is a great example of how a powerful imagination can help look forwards to important discoveries yet to be made. Over time, Chandrasekhar made many more contributions in this field, in particular a deeper understanding of black holes and the use of X-ray astronomy.

That the Earth has an iron core shows that some of the matter in the Solar System is made up of elements which were formed in previous generations of stars.

The remnants of many exploded stars can be observed as nebulae. A good example is the Crab Nebula, which is the remnant of a supernova event observed and recorded by Chinese astronomers in the year 1054. There are a number of classroom activities available that get students to use real data to explore where a particular star is at in its life cycle, how long it will last and how its mass affects its final fate. One example is the Perimeter Institute, *Figuring Out Space Activity – The Evolution of Stars* (see link in Resources at the end of this chapter).

Observing stars

Since the middle of the 20th century, the development of technology and the ability to launch telescopes into space, our ability to observe space in wavelengths beyond the visible has expanded greatly. Radio telescopes, such as the Lovell telescope at Jodrell Bank, and space telescopes detecting radiations such as X-rays and gamma rays can provide a wide range of additional information about stars and galaxies not available from the visible light observed at the Earth's surface. More recently the discovery of gravitational waves means we have entered an era of 'multimessenger' astronomy where different radiations, electromagnetic, neutrinos and gravitational waves, can be used to gain different information about cosmic events and objects.

How many stars are there?

Until the 1920s it was thought that all the stars of the Milky Way galaxy, in which the Solar System is located, constituted the whole of the Universe.

However, astronomers had observed fuzzy whirlpool-shaped objects. Many thought that these were clouds of gas and dust, either the materials that could form stars in the future or the remnants of past exploded stars, which also can contribute to the gas and dust which forms future stars. However, Edwin Hubble, using the new larger aperture 200-inch diameter Mount Palomar telescope realised they were made up of many individual stars. These objects were other galaxies outside our own galaxy, the Milky Way. Overnight, the Universe had suddenly become much bigger. We now know there are many thousands of millions of galaxies in the Universe:

→ approximate number of stars in a galaxy = 100 000 000 000 (1×10^{11})
→ approximate number of galaxies in the Universe = 100 000 000 000 (1×10^{11})
→ approximate number of stars in the Universe = 10 000 000 000 000 000 000 000 (1×10^{22}).

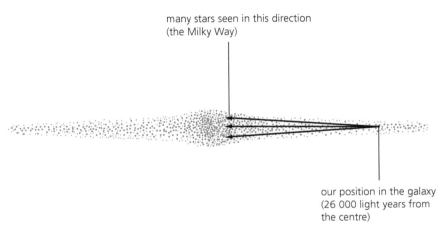

many stars seen in this direction (the Milky Way)

our position in the galaxy (26 000 light years from the centre)

Figure 8.8 Our position in the Milky Way

The brightness of stars

Different stars have different colours, according to their surface temperatures. The temperature of an object is very easy to measure from the spectrum of radiation it emits. The cooler it is, the redder its radiation; the hotter it is the bluer it is. A yellow star like the Sun has a surface temperature of around 6000 °C. Other stars have a surface temperature of 20 000 °C and appear a bluish white. The changing colour with temperature can be demonstrated using a small filament lamp and a variable power pack. As the voltage of the power pack is turned up, the lamp first glows dimly and red, but as it gets hotter it gradually gets brighter and becomes more white as all of the other colours of the spectrum are also emitted. Table 8.2 provides some temperature and colour data for some nearby stars.

Table 8.2 The temperature and colour of some stars

Star	Temperature/°C	Colour
Betelgeuse	3200	red
Alpha Centauri B	5000	orange
Sun	5500	yellow
Sirius	9640	blue-white
Bellatrix	22 000	blue-white

Redshift and the Doppler effect

Light from different stars can be split into the visible spectrum using a prism or grating to help identify what the star is made of. When you shine pure white light into a prism or grating you get a full spectrum, but light from stars does not split equally into all the colours of the visible spectrum, instead you get a characteristic set of coloured lines. These lines, known as the spectrum of the star, allow the elements present in the star to be identified as they each have their own unique patterns. Relatively cheap diffraction grating glasses or homemade spectroscopes made with CDs (see Resources at the end of the chapter for links) can be used to observe different light sources in class and students can see the different spectra. In most schools you should be able to find different ceiling or table lights that have different spectra. Vapour lamps, such as for the elements sodium, neon and mercury, give good clear line spectra for observation in class.

Edwin Hubble looked at the spectra of light coming from some of the stars in the distant galaxies and compared these to light sources here on Earth. He found that, apart from some local galaxies, the spectra from almost all the galaxies have the lines in the expected patterns, but the patterns appear to be shifted towards the red end of the spectrum.

One cause of this redshift is the Doppler effect. If a star is moving away from the observer, its spectrum is shifted towards the red end; if it is moving towards the observer, its spectrum is shifted towards the blue end (see Figure 8.9).

This is an 'apparent effect' which alters the observed colour of the light due to the relative motion of the star and the observer. The colour of the light emitted by the star does not change. The wavelength or frequency of the emitted light remains the same. For a star moving away from us the observed wavelength of the light is longer and its frequency lower.

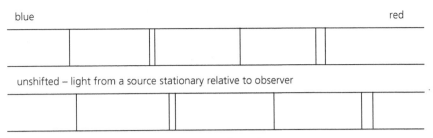

Figure 8.9 Redshifted spectrum

The Doppler effect is a phenomenon that occurs with all waves and can be demonstrated using sound waves more easily than with light waves (see Figure 8.10).

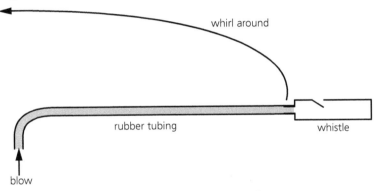

Figure 8.10 Apparatus to demonstrate the Doppler effect

Alternatively, a battery, switch and buzzer can be attached securely to a length of strong string around 2 m long. When switched on they can be whirled around your head. Students seated in front of you will hear the pitch of the sound change as the buzzer moves towards and away from them; a higher frequency when coming towards them, and a lower frequency when travelling away. This can also be observed when a vehicle with a siren passes an observer standing at the side of a road. If your head is at the centre of the circular path of the buzzer you should hear no change in pitch as the buzzer is always the same distance from you.

Light waves behave in a similar way to sound waves but for an object moving away from you, rather than the sound waves having a lower observed frequency and pitch, the light waves are observed as having a lower frequency, longer wavelength and 'redder' colour.

8.5 The expanding Universe

From the redshift data, we can see that almost everything in the Universe is moving away from us; the Universe is expanding. It is natural for students to think that if everything is moving away from us, then we must be at the centre of the Universe. This would suggest our view is a privileged world view. It is easy to use models to show that wherever one is in an expanding Universe, everything seems to be moving away from that point, with the more distant objects moving away faster (see Figure 8.11).

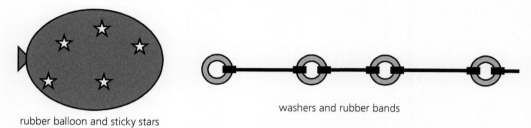

rubber balloon and sticky stars

washers and rubber bands

Figure 8.11 Using a balloon or rubber bands to model that the expansion of the Universe which looks the same from every point within it

It is also natural for students to consider that the galaxies are spreading out by moving through some fixed space; however, most of the expansion of the Universe is because the space between the galaxies is expanding. Although Newton considered there to be a fixed co-ordinate system of space and time against which the movement of objects could be measured, Einstein's Theories of Relativity show that space and time are linked as spacetime and this is not fixed but personal to every different observer. This spacetime is expanding resulting in galaxies moving apart and is called cosmological redshift.

A set of washers and bands as shown in Figure 8.11 can be used to illustrate that no matter where one is in the Universe one will observe more distant galaxies moving away from us faster than galaxies closer to us. This can be a difficult concept for students to appreciate and this hands-on classroom activity can help support their understanding by allowing them to collect data that are consistent with the ideas we wish them to learn. It can also be used to show that we are not in a privileged position and just because we see mostly everything moving away from us, that does not mean we are at the centre of the Universe.

Using a string of around ten washers connected using rubber bands with the same thickness and spring constant, students should lay out the string in a straight line and unstretched. The washers represent galaxies and the rubber bands the space between the galaxies, albeit a simplified model in one dimension. Then choosing at random one of the washers to represent the students' 'home galaxy' they should measure the distances to all of the other washers and note these in a table. The string of washers and bands should then be stretched to double the original lengths. This represents some future time where space has expanded compared with the original arrangement. The end washers should be taped down to ensure this now stretched length is maintained. The distances from the students' 'home galaxy' to all of the others should be measured once more and recorded in their table. When a graph of the new distances is plotted against the original distances a line of best fit should give a straight line through the origin. The further away the galaxy, the further it has travelled in the time between the two sets of measurements. If different groups of students in a class follow the same procedure and choose different 'home galaxies', they should nevertheless all obtain straight lines with the same gradient. This can be used to emphasise that the students, having chosen different 'home galaxies', cannot all be at the centre of the Universe, and indeed this is a meaningless concept in cosmological terms (see Resources for a link to Perimeter Institute – *The Expansion of Space*).

The age and origin of the Universe: what we know and what we don't (yet) know

Using the idea that galaxies appear to be moving away from each other, Hubble was able to work backwards to deduce when the galaxies must have been packed closely together, shortly after the start of the Universe. Today's estimate of the age of the Universe is 13.8 billion years.

Hubble's finding suggests that the Universe started with the Big Bang. There are several independent pieces of supporting evidence for this. In 1965 Penzias and Wilson, while studying microwave radiation from astronomical sources, discovered that wherever they pointed their aerial they picked up microwaves corresponding to a very cool body of 2.7 K (2.7 °C above absolute zero). This radiation is the remnant of the Big Bang explosion, which has expanded and cooled over the age of the Universe. The Big Bang is also supported by other independent evidence such as the relative abundances of hydrogen and helium found in the Universe; the fact that the night sky is dark suggests the Universe has a finite age as light from distant galaxies has not had enough time to reach us yet; this is known as Olbers' paradox.

For some students, these ideas will conflict with ideas they receive from elsewhere, particularly religious ideas about creation. While it is important to respect the right of individuals to hold such views, it should be made clear that the ideas you are putting forward as a science teacher are supported by a considerable body of evidence. Among scientists the interpretation of astronomical data leads to an acceptance of the Big Bang theory.

Recent data indicate that the expansion of the Universe is accelerating. There is no identified mechanism for this, but cosmologists have named it as 'dark energy'. Dark energy should not be confused with dark matter. Measurements of the rotation of galaxies indicate that there is more matter present than can be accounted for by the visible matter that makes up stars, planets and gas clouds. This unidentified, 'unseen' matter has been named 'dark matter'. There is much in astronomy and cosmology for our students to discover in the future.

> ### Science in context
>
> A hypothesis that dark matter existed was first proposed by Lord Kelvin in 1884 based on his estimation of the mass of the Milky Way galaxy. It was difficult to make the precise measurements to confirm this hypothesis and it was not until the 1970s that the research of Vera Rubin and Kent Ford showed that galaxies must contain up to six times as much dark mass as visible mass.

8.6 Gravity and its effects

All students have experienced gravity from a very young age, and probably experimented with it since they were throwing toys out of their prams. This means they are likely to have constructed a number of 'common sense' or 'folk physics' ideas about gravity that do not agree with the accepted scientific explanations.

Students will be familiar with the force due to gravity pulling things downwards to the surface of the Earth. Now they will have to make the transformation from a worldview in which 'down' is a direction between the two horizontal planes of the ground and the sky, to one in which the direction of 'down' is not absolutely fixed but directed towards the centre of the Earth (Figure 8.12).

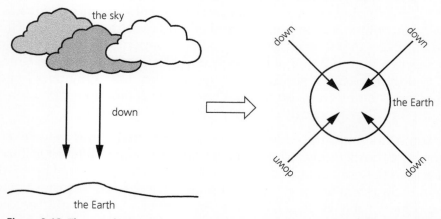

Figure 8.12 The transformation between the commonsense view of 'down' and the scientific concept of 'down'

Rather than the force of gravity being the attractive force between two masses, students may have alternative explanations for the source of the force due to gravity. These are likely to include that it is due to the Earth's atmosphere providing a 'pressing down' force, which leads them to state that there is no gravity on the Moon as it does not have an atmosphere. This may be related to them thinking that there is no gravity in space, influenced by them seeing films in which astronauts float around in space stations. Students might also think that gravity is related to the spinning of the Earth on its axis or to do with the Earth's magnetic field.

Forces occur in several physics topics. There are, therefore, many different ways in which the teaching of gravitational forces can be integrated with other work, and not just in a space-themed topic. There are, however, a number of key ideas that need to be covered, including how things fall, Newtonian gravity and satellite motion.

Falling under the influence of gravity

Do heavier things fall faster?

Students, and indeed many adults, hold the commonsense view that the heavier an object is, the faster it falls. This is true for very light objects with a significant air resistance; they do fall more slowly because the upwards air resistance acting against the direction of movement cancels out some of the downwards gravitational force. However, in the absence of air resistance all objects fall with the same acceleration.

That objects fall at the same rate can be demonstrated using a stone and a tightly scrunched up piece of paper. If asked to predict what will happen, many students will argue for the stone but when dropped together they accelerate at the same rate and hit the ground at the same time. This can be shown in an alternative way with two tennis balls, one of which has been completely filled with water using a syringe and hypodermic needle to make it heavier. When the 'heavy' tennis ball is dropped from the same height simultaneously with a normal tennis ball, students will not be surprised to see they hit the ground at the same time. If the two balls are then passed around the class, students can then compare them and observe they actually had different masses. This cognitive conflict challenges their misconception and creates an opportunity for you to explain the scientific idea that heavy and light objects fall in the same way and, together with the stone and paper example above, help to show that these phenomena are universal.

The fact that it is air resistance, and not the mass, that leads to many students making the wrong predictions can be easily demonstrated by taking two sheets of A4 paper, one flat and one scrunched up, and dropping them from the same height. Here the two objects have the same masses but due to the different surface areas, and therefore different air resistances, they fall at different rates.

The theory-based explanation is that the more massive an object, the more force is needed to accelerate it. If one object is twice as massive as another, the Earth will attract it with twice the pull. However, there is twice the mass to make move, therefore it will accelerate at the same rate as the lighter object. In short, twice as much mass, with twice as much gravitational pull results in the same effect – the same acceleration and the same time to fall to the ground from the same height.

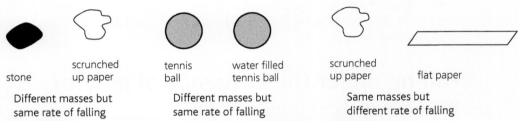

| stone | scrunched up paper | tennis ball | water filled tennis ball | scrunched up paper | flat paper |

Different masses but same rate of falling　　Different masses but same rate of falling　　Same masses but different rate of falling

Figure 8.13 Demonstrating how mass and surface area affect the rate of falling

The 'coin and feather' experiment

The fact that it is the air resistance that makes a difference to the speed of fall of a feather can be shown by doing the classic 'coin and feather' demonstration. A glass tube containing a coin and a feather is connected to a vacuum pump. The tube is first inverted while full of air. The coin reaches the bottom first. Then the air is pumped out. The tube is inverted and both the coin and feather reach the bottom at the same time.

The 'coin and feather' experiment should be done behind a safety screen and wearing safety glasses, because there is a small chance of the tube imploding if there is a fault in the glass. If you do not have this equipment then videos showing Dave Scott, Commander of Apollo 15, dropping a hammer and a feather on the Moon where there is no atmosphere, as well as Brian Cox dropping a bowling ball and feather in a giant vacuum chamber can both be found on the internet (see Resources). Ideas around falling objects, acceleration and air resistance are also covered in Chapter 2 Forces.

Newtonian universal gravitation

The Earth attracts an object near to its surface and generally we describe the object as then accelerating downwards towards the Earth. However, Newton's 3rd law states that the object must also attract the Earth with the same force. We generally do not describe the Earth as accelerating upwards towards the object. That is because the Earth has a huge mass and, therefore, the attractive force acting on this huge mass results in an extremely small (negligible) acceleration. Our observation point is from the surface of the Earth. Therefore, we are only aware of the relative movement of the object accelerating downwards towards the Earth (rather than the Earth towards the object).

There is an opportunity to highlight that gravity is a non-contact force and, similar to electrostatics and magnetism, the concept of a field is very useful in describing how things behave. The gravitational force of attraction acts over very large distances and results in all of the planets, asteroids and comets of the Solar System orbiting the Sun.

Discovering planets and testing theories

Careful observation of the orbits of the inner planets showed they were not quite as predicted by Newton's theory of gravity. This led to predictions that there were gravitational forces due to more distant planets pulling on them and distorting their orbits slightly. As a result, Neptune was discovered. Mercury's orbit is also not quite as Newton's theory of gravity predicts and to account for this another planet, Vulcan, very close to the Sun was predicted. It does not exist but Mercury's orbit was explained when Einstein's General Theory of Relativity, which connects space and time, was shown to make predictions matching the observations which Newton's theory had failed to do.

Satellite motion

The Earth attracts the Moon with the same magnitude of gravitational force with which the Moon attracts the Earth. It is this gravitational force that keeps the Moon in orbit around the Earth. It is because the Moon is moving sideways, or tangentially, around its orbit with sufficient speed that prevents the Moon and Earth collapsing together.

This was one of Newton's great insights, and is often referred to as Newton's Thought Experiment. He considered what would happen if a cannon ball was fired from the top of a very high mountain. The cannon ball would travel a great horizontal distance before it fell and reached the surface of the Earth. If the cannon ball could be fired even faster, it would travel further, but the Earth is a sphere which means its surface curves downwards such that the fast-moving cannon ball would fall over the horizon before hitting the surface of the Earth. If the cannon ball could be fired with a speed of around 8 km/s, and if there was no air resistance, the cannon ball would go so far it would miss the surface of the Earth completely and go into orbit as a satellite (see Figure 8.14).

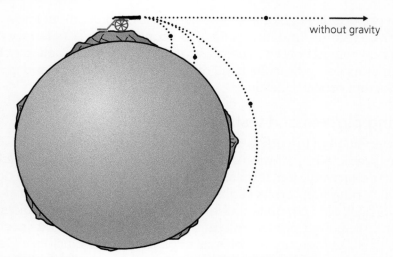

without gravity

Figure 8.14 Newton's thought experiment and satellite motion

The circular motion of the satellite results because along its path there is always a gravitational pull acting on the satellite towards the centre of the Earth. Any circular motion requires a centripetal force pushing or pulling on the object towards the centre of the circle.

The fact that circular motion is not a 'natural' form of motion needs to be explained to the students. From Newton's 1st law we know that objects will remain at rest or travel in a straight line unless acted on by an unbalanced force. In other words, once an object is moving, its 'natural' state is to continue to travel at constant speed in a straight line.

To keep something moving in a circle there needs to be a force acting on it towards the centre of the circle. This can be demonstrated by marking out a large circle, perhaps 5 m in radius, on the grass or a playground outside the school building. Ask one student to stand tangentially on the circle and walk in a straight line – 'natural' movement. Ask another student to walk beside the first and to gently push or pull them in whatever manner is necessary to ensure they follow the circle. This demonstration should make it apparent that they have to be pushed or pulled with a force which is always directed inwards towards the centre of the circle.

An alternative, rainy day, demonstration is to tie a rubber stopper to the end of a piece of string and whirl it around in a circle. You must pull on the string to keep the stopper moving in a circle. Removing this pulling force results in the stopper flying off at a tangent – the 'natural' straight-line motion. Removing the force does not result in the object flying radially outwards from the circle.

Weight and weightlessness

A space station orbiting the Earth is only slightly further from the centre of the Earth than we are on the surface, so gravity is only slightly weaker at the height of the space station. However, students may ask 'Why do people appear weightless when they are in the space station?'

Weight is defined as the force of gravity on the mass of an object. Climb a mountain and you will weigh a little less than at the foot of the mountain. Astronauts in a space station will weigh only a little less than when they are on the surface of the Earth. However, the *sensation* of weight you experience is the reaction force you feel when the ground pushes up on your feet, supporting your weight. If the ground were to suddenly fall away beneath you, you would no longer feel your weight and you will begin to fall. This can be experienced by jumping off a high diving board when you still have a weight pulling you downwards but no longer feel the upwards push of the diving board on your feet.

A similar sensation is experienced when you enter a lift on an upper floor in a tall building and it then accelerates downwards from beneath you. You will experience the sensation of feeling lighter. In this situation you do not wish to feel completely 'weightless' as this would mean the lift was in freefall. However, an astronaut in a space station is in effect in a box, similar to a lift, which is in freefall back towards the Earth but, as in Newton's Thought Experiment, always moving sufficiently fast sideways to keep missing the surface of the Earth. The result is that the astronaut 'floats' relative to the space station as both are falling at the same rate. Loose objects in the space station, such as food or tools, 'float' as well because they are falling at the same rate as the space station and the astronaut.

That objects become 'weightless' in freefall can be demonstrated by hanging a mass, such as an apple, on a newton meter and dropping it. The reading on the newton meter will go to zero. This can be observed more easily by using slow motion photography.

Astronomy and space is likely to be a significant topic of interest for young students ongoing into the future. Dinosaurs and space are often quoted as the two most popular topics for young students, and the dinosaurs are not coming back. There are always going to be new developments in space, whether that be new telescopes providing new data, new space probes visiting planets, asteroids and comets, or new discoveries such as those recently of gravitational waves by the LIGO consortium or the imaging of a black hole by the Event Horizon Telescope team.

There are many possible careers in space-based industries. Although astronauts might be the most prominent 'faces' of the space industry opportunities in that role are relatively limited. There are, however, many roles and careers within the space industry from engineers to medics to communication experts. There are also many opportunities for science, engineering and technology-based jobs related to the satellite industry in which the UK is particularly strong. Solving the problems of operating in the remote and harsh environment of space also has many spin-off benefits in other industries, such as the offshore and subsea energy sector, and many medical applications.

Resources

Online resources

Please go to **spark.iop.org/asebook** for a set of curated resources from the IOP Spark website to match this chapter.

Animations of how long it takes light to travel through the Solar System – Light Speed: Fast, but slow: www.youtube.com

Apollo 15 astronaut Dave Scott dropping a geology hammer and falcon feather on the Moon: https://nssdc.gsfc.nasa.gov

Astronomy Picture of the Day https://apod.nasa.gov

Brian Cox demonstrating the 'coin and feather' experiment in a large vacuum chamber: https://www.youtube.com

Classic Eames Powers of Ten video: www.youtube.com

ESA Education: https://www.esa.int

The Exploratorium describes how to calculate the weight of an object on different planets and how to make your own spectroscope with a CD: https://www.exploratorium.edu

History of Astronomy: https://mathshistory.st-andrews.ac.uk

If the Moon were only 1 pixel: https://joshworth.com

In the sky is an interactive sky map: https://in-the-sky.org

Information about the discovery and status of Pluto as a dwarf planet: https://www.iau.org

The Institute of Physics have a range of resources available at IOP Spark. The Supporting Physics Teaching page – Teaching Earth in Space to students aged 11-14 is particularly relevant: https://spark.iop.org

Interactive scale of the Universe: https://quantumtocosmos.ca

Interactive Time Zone map https://www.timeanddate.com

ISS and other satellites' locations: https://www.heavens-above.com/

Modelling the scale of the Solar System and Universe: https://chandra.harvard.edu

NASA for Educators: https://www.nasa.gov

NASA Scientific Visualization Studio 'Moon Phase and Libration' and 'Understanding Lunar Eclipses': https://svs.gsfc.nasa.gov

The Perimeter Institute for Theoretical Physics website highlights current research, hosts webcasts and lectures and provides free teaching resources aimed at bringing modern physics and cosmology to secondary school classrooms. The Figuring Outer Space compilation of resources contains a series of activities suitable for lower secondary aged students: www.perimeterinstitute.ca

Phase of the Moon, time lapse video: www.youtube.com

Royal Observatory Edinburgh Exoplanets Activity - a series of activities exploring the discovery and nature of exoplanets: https://www.roe.ac.uk

Schoolphysics: https://www.schoolphysics.co.uk

Schools Observatory describes how to make your own diffraction grating and has a 'Solar System in Your Pocket' activity: https://www.schoolsobservatory.org

The stellarium is a free open-source planetarium (computer installed, web based and app versions available): https://stellarium.org

References

Lelliott, A. and Rollnick, M. (2010) Big ideas: a review of astronomy education 1974–2008. *International Journal of Science Education*, 32 (13), 1771–1799.

Further reading

Roche, P., Newsam, A., Roberts, S., Mason, T. and Baruch, J. (2012a) Resources for teaching astronomy in UK schools. *School Science Review*, 93 (344), 53–62.

Roche, P., Roberts, S., Newsam, A. and Barclay, C. (2012b) Teaching astronomy in UK schools. *School Science Review*, 93 (344), 63–68.

Appendix

Quantity	Symbol	Unit
force	F	newton, N
extension (of a spring)	x	metre, m
distance	d	metre, m or light year, ly
displacement	s	metre, m
speed	v	metre per second, m/s
initial velocity	u	metre per second, m/s
velocity, final velocity	v	metre per second, m/s
time	t	second, s
acceleration	a	metre per second every second, m/s^2
momentum	p	kilogram metre per second, kg m/s
moment	M	newton metre, Nm
electric current	I	ampere (amp), A
charge	Q	coulomb, C
potential difference	V	volt, V
resistance	R	ohm, Ω
power	P	watt, W kilowatt, kW
energy	E	joule, J kilowatt-hour, kWh
mass	m	kilogram, kg (also gram, g)
gravitational field strength	g	newton per kilogram, N/kg
height	h	metre, m
specific heat capacity	c	joule per kilogram per degree Celsius, J/kg/°C
temperature	T	degrees Celsius, °C or kelvin, K
change in temperature	$\Delta\theta$	degrees Celsius, °C or kelvin, K
specific latent heat	L	joule per kilogram, J/kg
spring constant	k	newton per metre N/m
amplitude	A	the amplitude of a vibration, e.g. a mass bouncing on a spring
thermal conductivity	k	W/m K
Stefan's constant	σ	W/m^{2}K^4
volume	V	cubic metre, m^3 (also cubic centimetre, cm^3)
density	ρ	kilogram per cubic metre, kg/m^3 (also gram per cubic centimetre g/cm^3)

Quantity	Symbol	Unit
pressure	P	newton per square metre, N/m^2 also newton per square centimetre N/cm^2 pascal, Pa
area	A	square metre, m^2 also square centimetre, cm^2
mass number	A	
atomic number	Z	
neutron number	N	
radioactivity	A	becquerels, Bq
amplitude	a	metre, m
frequency	f	hertz, Hz
wavelength	λ	metre, m
wave speed	v	metre per second, m/s
gravitational field strength at Earth's surface acceleration due to gravity at Earth's surface	g	9.81 newtons per kilogram, N/kg 9.81 metre per second every second, m/s^2

Index

water waves 208, 210-12
Watt, James 136
wave equation 212
wavelength 210, 210-11
waves
    amplitude 210
    comparing 208-12
    describing 212
    energy transfer 191, 208, 212
    frequency 210, 210-11
    longitudinal 195, 210-11, 216
    modelling 208-10

power and 212
prior experiences 191-2
properties 210-12
reflection 211
refraction 211-12, 213-15
seismic 215
teaching sequence 192-3
transverse 194, 208-9, 210
wave speed 210, 210-11
see also light waves; sound waves
weight
    confusion with mass 19, 31

definition 25, 46-7, 251
falling objects 47-9, 251
weightlessness 251
Wilson, Charles Thomson Rees 179
working
    electrical 138-9
    mechanical see mechanical
        working
X-rays 217-18, 218
years 222
Young, Thomas 118, 216